INTERNATIONAL SERIES OF MONOGRAPHS ON
AERONAUTICAL SCIENCES AND SPACE FLIGHT
CHAIRMEN : T. VON KÁRMÁN AND H. DRYDEN

DIVISION II : AERODYNAMICS

VOLUME 1

NATURAL AERODYNAMICS

INTERNATIONAL SERIES OF MONOGRAPHS ON AERONAUTICAL SCIENCES AND SPACE FLIGHT

CHAIRMEN

T. VON KÁRMÁN
Advisory Group for Aeronautical Research and Development, North Atlantic Treaty Organization, Palais de Chaillot, Paris 16, France

H. DRYDEN
National Advisory Committee for Aeronautics, 1512 H Street Northwest, Washington 25, D.C., U.S.A.

HONORARY ADVISORY BOARD

NATURAL
AERODYNAMICS

R. S. SCORER

Reader in Applied Mathematics
Imperial College
London

PERGAMON PRESS
NEW YORK · LONDON
PARIS · LOS ANGELES
1958

PERGAMON PRESS INC.
122 East 55th Street, New York 22, N.Y.
10638 South Wilton Place, Los Angeles 47, California

PERGAMON PRESS LTD.
4 and 5 Fitzroy Square, London W.1

PERGAMON PRESS S.A.R.L.
24 Rue des Écoles, Paris V°

Library of Congress Card Number 57–14447

Printed in Great Britain at The Chapel River Press, Andover, Hants.

PREFACE

THESE chapters began to take shape during extramural courses given in the Department of Meteorology at Imperial College. These lectures were advanced in the sense that they described very largely the results of recent research, yet they were given to audiences composed of aviators, engineers, geographers, meteorologists, mathematicians, and indeed some with no advanced scientific training at all but with an interest in the subject and a mechanical turn of mind. With such a variety of interests in mind the aim has been to develop the basic concepts listed in the chapter headings, all the time taking examples from out of doors air motion as illustrations. Consequently many special topics which could be included in the title have been omitted. For instance, breathing in man and animals could easily occupy a chapter; but however fundamental to life it is not a fundamental hydrodynamical process in terms of which other phenomena can be understood, and it is hoped that readers interested in breathing will be able to pursue their studies more fruitfully by making use of the ideas which are discussed here. The index is intended to guide those enquiring about a particular phenomenon to the fundamental processes which make the phenomenon what it is.

The chief difficulty is the complexity of the subject. The air is so free that it finds a great variety of ways in which to move. The mathematics of any problem in air motion soon become very complicated, and I have therefore tried to show how one can argue what it is necessary to specify in order that there shall exist solutions to the problems posed and to explain qualitatively what the answers are, rather than duplicate the mathematical treatment which may be found in one or more of the very good books available. Yet many of the problems discussed have not yet been satisfactorily solved, and they offer a great opportunity for mathematicians and experimentalists in natural aerodynamical research.

On account of the elementary nature of the treatment it was not thought necessary to give references to original papers, and though a few books are suggested for further reading it is probably best that everyone should explore the literature for himself as far as possible because if he reads this book he is often likely to find the best stimulus in what has not been read by its author.

Though the basic concepts of hydrodynamics are the same whatever the fluid and its surroundings, we are concerned here with air motion in Nature; we find that we have to think rather differently from the mathematician who plays on paper with imaginary 'perfect' fluids or the engineer who makes machines for special tasks. Our study is not purely academic. It is of great use in the control of air pollution for example: we must know our enemy. Natural Aerodynamics can also be a fascinating hobby, especially in these days of steam and smoke which make visible the ever varied and delightful behaviour of the air. Unless we are mathematicians we have to employ a certain amount of ' black-boxery ' in our thinking. We recognise that in certain circumstances the results deduced and stated by experts will follow: we cannot always be concerned with the details of how the black box (in this case the expert's reasoning) converts its intake into its output; but we are satisfied that the detailed design of the black box is within the comprehension of another fairly ordinary person, understand that it is consistent with our general philosophical principles, and that the results of using the box are of a kind we would reasonably expect. Thus a geographer may prefer to slide over the more mathematical parts of Chapter 3 and be content to understand the conclusions, convincing himself that they are at least plausible. He can then make use of the known properties of vorticity to interpret his observations of Nature.

Many readers may have misgivings about Chapter 2, and it can quite well be left out without detriment to the understanding of the other chapters. But it is placed early in the book for two reasons: first it comes logically as an extended example of inertia forces and does not depend upon the concepts developed later, and secondly it seemed desirable to say something about how the wind contrives to blow (though not much about why, for that is the special province of meteorology) before going on to the many consequences of the existence of wind. There are many obscurities which may tax the imagination of engineers versed in fluid mechanics because the full consequences of the earth's rotation are not well known. For example, we all understand that cold air is heavier than warm air and that the pressure is due to the weight of air above. We would therefore ' expect ' that an inrush of cold air into a depression would be the best way to make the pressure rise and fill it up. Yet this is not so; on the contrary such inrushes are a common cause of deepening of depressions and of rejuvenation of their circulations, and it is the arrival of warm air which often makes the pressure rise rapidly and cause the cyclone to disappear! It is interesting that by studying the motion of the troposphere in connections such as this we can *deduce* that active cold fronts must drag the stratosphere downwards while it must often be carried upwards ahead of warm fronts. Such deductions would be impossible if we were satisfied with the simple idea that the pressure is due to the weight of air above: we have in fact to think of the up and down motion of the air above as being governed very largely by what goes on below. Possibly this chapter will be useful to meteorologists because the dynamics of unbalanced flow are not usually given the emphasis due in ordinary textbooks.

The conservative reader may boggle at the digressions from the business of natural aerodynamics into topics with kindred philosophical content. If the reader is of an enquiring turn of mind he will be curious about all of Nature, including ourselves, our behaviour, and our way of thinking. To penetrate the details of appearance and find simpler universal processes is a delight granted to all who study scientifically, and the delight is greater according to the power of the imagination. Those unnecessary paragraphs will, I hope, lead the reader into many further irrelevancies of thought where he will glimpse a little of the beauty of the world of conjecture and become less fierce in his dogmas.

As the subject advances the difficulties increase. If we allow ourselves to pose a problem and then press on regardless of the consequences to an answer, we may find that we have displayed in all its glory our mathematical skill (or someone else's), but only solved a triviality. Often a little more thought can lead us to frame a more meaningful question whose answer is more useful and easier to obtain. Indeed we never know until we have the answer whether a question is worth asking. The ' wouldn't it be nice to know . . .' attitude is unscientific. We have to become gradually acquainted with Nature's ways, and many sophisticated mathematical treatments are pointless because they assume at the beginning that we know what we want to know. Insight into natural dynamics is worth a great many mathematical techniques in pursuing research in which experiments are necessary.

Finally I must acknowledge debts of gratitude. First to the Meteorological Office for enrolling me during the war and presenting me with the impossible task of forecasting the weather. It is a stimulating experience for a scientist, more particularly a mathematician, to have to find within a given time, answers to questions which are always beyond his powers, but which he instinctively feels ought to be within his grasp. Secondly to Sir Geoffrey Taylor, who, however new a problem one takes to him for discussion, always seems to have thought about it long ago and in a few grand remarks brings some order to one's confused thinking. Thirdly to Mr. F. H. Ludlam, a keen observer of Nature, who believes in the poetry of science, and is prepared to consider almost any fantastic suggestion and suggest that almost any accepted theory is fantastic. Fourthly to Professor P. A. Sheppard, an encyclopaedic critic of anything to do with meteorology, a sympathetic listener who gives no quarter in argument, and has a zest for the excitements of reality. Finally to the gliding fraternity among whom there are experts and cranks, whose mad theories about the atmosphere are always based on sound observations of Nature that seem to have eluded everyone else, and who will not believe anything until it has been proved to them without mathematics—good company indeed for any mathematician!

The Pergamon Press have in all matters proceeded expeditiously, avoiding those delays which frustrate so many authors. I would particularly like to thank Mr. W. R. Buchanan, who has converted about 150 pencil sketches and diagrams into excellent drawings. Among these drawings the instrumental records shown on pages 224 and 252 are Crown copyright, and the permission of the Controller of Her Majesty's Stationery Office to reproduce them is gratefully acknowledged. I would also like to thank Dr. Ryozaburo Yamamoto, of the Meteorological Research Institute, Kyoto University, for kindly sending me a copy of one of his microbarograph records of a hydrogen bomb explosion: it is displayed on page 224.

Imperial College   R. S. S.

    November 1957

CONTENTS

LIST OF PLATES

CHAPTER 1

INERTIA FORCES

Newton's laws and the pressure gradient

NEWTON stated that if one piece of matter, A, exerts a force on another piece, B, then B exerts an equal and opposite force on A. This is simply to say that forces cannot be dissipated without trace, as had been thought previously. If B does not gain velocity under the effects of the force delivered by A it can only be because there exist other forces on B equal and opposite to those delivered by A. But if there are no such other forces B will be seen to accelerate in the direction of the force due to A. The important point is that whether B moves or not it exerts a force on A equal and opposite to A's force on it. B is able to offer such a force because it possesses mass, or inertia, and as far as A is concerned it does not matter whether the force offered by B is due to inertia or friction or anything else; A's experience is still the same.

The inertia of a body therefore produces forces upon any other object which exerts a force upon it to change its velocity. Such forces are as real as any other. Indeed they are fundamental in the sense that their existence enables us easily to measure force in terms of the fundamental mechanical dimensions of mass, length, and time. Of course, we could regard force as a fundamental dimension in the place of one of the other three. It would be quite logical, though not so convenient practically, to dispense with time as a basic dimension and use force in its place. The unit of time would then be the square root of the distance travelled by a unit mass under the influence of a unit force in a constant direction. Time has been popular in the past as the fourth dimension into which men have dreamed of wandering out of the present, but such adventure would have an exact counterpart in the experiences of a person who could, by some magic, avoid offering a force in return to any exerted upon him, that is to say have no inertia, no mass. From other people's point of view he

1

would be out of this world, in the sense that it would not be possible to detect him by probing the region occupied by him in the hope of observing his inertia forces. It would be as if he had left the present and become a ghost.

Inertia forces, therefore, are as fundamental a property of our universe as any other. Newton established equations which relate the inertia forces to the motion and which have been the basis of mechanics ever since. Having stated that B exerts a force on A equal and opposite to that of A on B he showed that B could do this only by undergoing an acceleration, i.e.

$$\text{Force} = \text{mass} \times \text{acceleration}$$
or
$$\text{Force applied} = \text{inertia force}.$$

Pressure gradient

There are many kinds of mechanical force which can be applied, such as frictional, gravitational, electromagnetic; but the most important in fluid dynamics is the pressure force. All we need to establish here is that, provided the pressure is large enough to prevent the occurrence of vacuums anywhere, it is only necessary to study the gradient of the pressure.

If we consider a small cylinder of fluid lying at right angles to the surfaces of constant pressure (isobars) the total force upon it from the surrounding fluid in a direction perpendicular to its

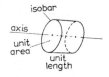

axis is seen to be zero, while the force along its axis depends upon the difference between the pressures at the two ends. If the cylinder has unit cross section area then the difference in the pressure force at the two ends is the pressure gradient multiplied by the length of the cylinder. If the cylinder has unit length then the force is equal to the pressure gradient. This force operates upon a mass equal to unit volume multiplied by the density, and so if the pressure gradient force and the inertia force are the only forces present

$$\text{Pressure gradient} = \text{density} \times \text{acceleration}.$$

It is most convenient to write this as applied to unit mass and so dividing by the density we can write this symbolically in the form

$$- \frac{1}{\rho} \operatorname{grad} p = \frac{D}{Dt} \mathbf{v}.$$

There are several remarks to be made about this equation. The negative sign is placed on the pressure gradient because the force is towards low pressure and by convention gradients are measured in the direction in which the quantity (in this case pressure) is increasing—'uphill' in fact. The symbol $\operatorname{grad} p$ is a vector, having direction as well as magnitude. The symbol D/Dt means the 'rate of change of': and we write D/Dt (instead of d/dt, which some authors write) to make it clear that we mean the rate of change of a property of a particular particle. In this case it is the rate of change of the velocity, $\mathbf{v}$, which is being measured, and it is the velocity of the same particle of fluid that is all the time referred to, not of the velocity at a fixed point, nor of the velocity as measured by a particular instrument (moving or otherwise). The velocity, like the acceleration which is its rate of change, is a vector having direction and magnitude.

Continuity

As many murderers have known to their cost, bodies continue to exist. This law of nature, often referred to as the indestructibility of matter, or at least of mass, is expressed in studies of fluid motion by the equation of continuity. This equation simply states that if fluid is diverging out of a region the density there must be decreasing accordingly, or if it is converging into it the density there is increasing.

Although the idea is fundamental to our thinking we shall not often actually make use of the equation explicitly, but its very simplicity has interesting philosophical implications. In the consideration of these the reader is invited to squander a few moments of this time-starved twentieth century. In studying the mechanics of fluids we do not admit that material can appear or disappear, evade us in time, or lose its inertia, either spontaneously or at the behest of the human will. Yet some people can enjoy a schizophrenia whereby they can believe that material can be subjected to influences which appear to flout the normal code of behaviour of matter, on special occasions. The alleged phenomena of psychokinesis are such. But science is dedicated to the abolition of special occasions; indeed that is its *raison d'être*— to comprehend the world without acknowledging in it the slightest measure of caprice or the existence of will. It is our axiom that ' Nature does not misbehave '.

In this respect we may speak of the perfection of Nature's self-conduct with reverence. Many of our problems in fluid mechanics are very difficult to solve, not on account of any incompletely understood process, but on account of the complexity with which the simple processes become involved. We cannot therefore approach them with mathematical purity, and sometimes we have to appeal to experiment to discover what Nature does and then argue afterwards that things must be that way. Often Nature's mode of operation is extremely beautiful; but there has been no choice on Nature's part to perform in this way. She can only work the way she does: this is the perfect way. In science fiction we often imagine other ways but as soon as the perfect way is known they become drab ideas—dated indeed.

The exciting moments of science which live afterwards to thrill succeeding generations are those in which a philosopher has seen clearly in his imagination how Nature behaves and has then done an experiment to prove his idea. But we are not usually as wise as this; more often the experiments we do are the means whereby we find faults with our theories. The mechanics of fluids is far more complicated than the theory in the sense that the ' general ' theorems do not solve particular problems. They are general in the sense that they apply to all cases but they are only the highest common factor (which clerics and sociologists are often pleased to derogate with the misnomer ' lowest common denominator ') of all cases—the necessary minimum of knowledge for starting upon a problem; but they do not tell us how to proceed next. If we can guess correctly what form the behaviour of a fluid will take— laminar, steady, oscillatory, turbulent—we can then marshal our knowledge of that kind of behaviour to tackle our particular problem. But often our imagination misleads us, and we offer as a mathematical solution to a problem a fiction which bears a superficial resemblance to natural behaviour and which often has to suffice because we have not yet learned to comprehend and describe the truth in simple enough terms.

Machines can be made to conform more nearly than Nature to our simple patterns of thought.   In studying Natural Aerodynamics we must therefore be on guard against thinking of processes in too simple terms.   Ideas we synthesise and make use of in our dealings with machines may be inadequate; and it is therefore urgent that we should continually observe Nature and her fluid behaviour, not forgetting that it is we who are the students, to whom Nature owes nothing.   While knowing that Nature takes no steps to conform to our present state of knowledge let us confess that it is our ultimate desire to be masters of Nature by learning her secrets.   Our conquest is slow but progressive.

Our life is dominated by the behaviour of liquids and gases in motion; we are indeed fashioned to make good use of the properties of fluids.   Many of our best and most spectacular machines exploit them, but however much we build surroundings for them they must ultimately operate in the atmosphere or the sea, where fluid behaviour is complicated and unrestrained except by the inability of Nature to act in other than her own unique way.

But we were discussing the equation continuity, which is a mathematical expression of a logical consequence of the indestructibility of mass.   In some form or other it is used in every mathematical solution of a fluid motion problem.   All we need to do here is to make it part of our thinking—which is not very difficult because it forms already part of our unconscious appreciation of Nature through experience.   It is the simplest of ideas in this book, but if all the ideas written here are absorbed to become part of our thinking there will still remain an infinite variety of Natural aerodynamic phenomena to delight, mystify, and absorb us.   The partial comprehension of the mechanics of a beautiful event detracts not one bit, but rather adds to the appreciation of it. Of all the arts music is the most mathematical, and enjoyment is enhanced by the intellectual analysis of it.   So it is with the beauties of Nature in motion.

Confluence and convergence

Confluence is the coming together of streams of fluid, as a tributary into a river, but there is no accumulation of fluid as a result. Confluence simply refers to the geometrical disposition of the streamlines. *Diffluence* is said to occur when the motion is in the opposite direction through a similar pattern. If there are no changes in density and the streamlines get closer together there must be an increase in velocity as elements of fluid become elongated in the direction of motion, just as where a pipe becomes narrower the flow must be faster. The idea of confluence and diffluence therefore does not take into account the separation or approach of particles along the direction of motion, but only the sideways motion.

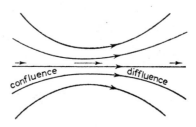

Convergence and *divergence* refer to the accumulation or depletion within a particular volume. We can speak of a convergence or divergence of velocity, or of momentum, or of anything of which there can be a *flux*. The equation of continuity refers to mass only. We could have air entering a tube in which it was heated so that it emerged from the other end with a greater velocity. There would then be a divergence of velocity from the tube, but no depletion of mass within it because the regions of large outward velocity would be regions of low density so that there would be no net outward flux of mass.

If there were a convergence in one or two directions, say horizontally, towards a point on the ground, with no change in the density of the air, the principle of continuity requires that there should be upward motion (a corresponding divergence) above so that the total amount of convergence would be zero.

The importance of sound

Sound waves are possible in the air because it is compressible. Any medium in which there exists a local stress (force) serving to restore particles to a position of equilibrium from which they may be displaced, can have waves propagated through it. Such phenomena will be discussed in Chapter 9. One normally thinks of sound waves as being composed of oscillations which become sound when the air in our ears is affected by them. But the mechanism by which they are propagated may serve also to transport the fluid bodily in one direction in such a way as to reduce the pressure where it is diverging from, and increase it in places to which it is converging. The fact that the mechanism is the same as that of sound waves means that transport is carried out at the speed of sound.

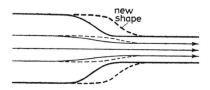

The process may be illustrated by imagining that air is flowing through a channel whose shape is such that the velocity and pressure vary from one place to another. In the course of time the flow settles down to a steady pattern. The density and pressure of air are related according to the ordinary gas laws, and these are related to the velocity by Bernoulli's equation which is described in the next few pages. If we now alter the shape of the channel as indicated in the figure we can expect the flow pattern to settle down eventually to a new pattern indicated by the dotted lines. It is interesting to understand the manner by which the new pattern of flow is assumed, and how quickly. It can depend upon two things. First we would expect that as soon as all the fluid involved in the old pattern of flow has passed out of the channel and had been replaced by fluid which only 'knew' the channel in its new form, the new pattern would be followed. But if the time taken to change the shape of the channel is large compared with the time required to replace the fluid in the tube completely by new fluid, the change in the pattern of flow would, for practical purposes, take place at the same time as the change in the channel shape was made. The second alternative is that the channel walls are altered very quickly, that is in an interval during which the fluid traverses only a small distance down the tube;

then the recession of the walls to the new position causes a
rarefaction in that neighbourhood and fluid accelerates towards
them because in a gas a rarefaction reduces the pressure. The
rarefaction travels outwards, in all directions from where it is
generated, as a sound wave. A displacement of air towards the
walls that have receded takes place throughout all the air that is
reached by this wave. The air affected now ' knows ' about the
new shape of the wall and begins to flow accordingly.

The important point is that not merely a signal but also a
transport of fluid takes place. We may contrast this with the
flow of water with a free upper surface. Audible sound waves
travel through water with a velocity of 1200 m/sec. But if we
were to withdraw a part of the bank of a river suddenly a distance
of say 1 m, water would rush in to the space and a wave would
travel outwards transporting water towards the cavity and lowering
the level of the river everywhere. But the level would only be
lowered over that part of the river reached by the surface gravity
waves, not that part reached by the sound waves, because when
there is a free surface sound cannot transport the fluid in bulk
faster than waves can travel along that surface. This problem
will be discussed at greater length in Chapter 9, but it is interesting
to note that audible sound waves could not travel through a liquid
near a free surface under no pressure unless the liquid could exert
a tension as well as a pressure.

The reader may have visualised the splashes and reflection of
waves from the river banks which would have followed the sudden
withdrawal of part of one bank. Likewise the sudden withdrawal
of part of the walls of the air channel discussed previously would
cause an audible sound. This ' noise ' would depend very much
on the manner of the withdrawal and could be great or small, but
it would consist of oscillations in addition to the bulk transport of
fluid towards the cavity created. It is the bulk transport that
concerns us here, and in the case of air this takes place within the
volume traversed by the sound waves. The additional noise is
for our purposes a separate phenomenon. We might even
imagine that the boundary is withdrawn very skilfully so as to
make no noise or splash as the case may be, but this would make
no appreciable difference to the rate at which the surrounding
fluid became adjusted to the new position of the boundary.

In this book we shall not be concerned with sound waves and shock waves, not because they cannot be a natural phenomenon but because they are not common and cannot be properly observed without special instruments and cannot therefore be studied and investigated by the ordinary reader. Those who wish to experiment with sound and shock waves will find many admirable texts on the subject.

Bernoulli's theorem

The work done against inertia forces becomes energy of motion, or kinetic energy. If the force doing the work is the pressure gradient force, and the pressure distribution is not changing, there is a direct relationship between the pressure and the velocity, namely

Pressure + kinetic energy per unit volume = constant.

If a small element of the air passes to a lower pressure the kinetic energy rises by an amount equal to the pressure gradient force multiplied by the distance the element travels under that force, and this is the change in pressure. Mathematically this is written in the form

$$p + \tfrac{1}{2}\rho v^2 = \text{constant.}$$

The constant is called the ' total head ' of pressure because it is the greatest pressure that the element can achieve. It does this by coming to rest and the work done against the pressure gradient force is equal to the kinetic energy lost. (Note: the work is done against the force due to the pressure gradient, not against the pressure itself.)

This is the simplest form of Bernoulli's theorem, and it is the most useful form. But it is necessary to state the conditions under which it applies.

It holds for each particle separately, the constant generally being different for different particles. If the flow is steady so that the tracks of the particles are fixed lines in space then the constant is the same for all particles along a track, or streamline, but different for different streamlines. It may happen on rare occasions, such as in textbook examples and examination questions, to be true with the same constant for all streamlines in the flow pattern under consideration. Two particles on nearby streamlines at the same pressure but with different velocities must have different total heads of pressure and in natural airflows this is the normal state.

If there are other forces the equation must be modified. For instance, if the force of gravity is important then besides kinetic energy, and potential energy in the pressure field, there is also gravitational potential energy. If a fluid is stably stratified so that the density decreases upwards then an element of fluid displaced upwards will be denser than its surroundings and will be subjected to a force downwards. Vertical displacements require work to be done by or against this force. Bernoulli's equation in this case becomes

$$p/\rho + \tfrac{1}{2}v^2 + gz = \text{constant}.$$

The sum total of the three forms of energy is constant.

When the density of the fluid is uniform and there is no motion the pressure decreases uniformly with height and

$$p/\rho + gz = \text{constant}$$

but if the density is not uniform then the quantity in the left-hand side of this equation is not the same at all heights. The stratification is stable if the density decreases upwards, otherwise it is unstable. In Bernoulli's equation there is thus a quantity which varies with height whether there is a velocity or not, and this represents the force due to the density stratification. When the density is uniform we can simply write

$$p'/\rho + \tfrac{1}{2}v^2 = \text{constant}$$

where p' is the pressure with the hydrostatic pressure subtracted out. This is the same as the first form of Bernoulli's equation we quoted, and it is the difference between the two previous equations.

The equation is no longer applicable if the flow is not steady, but fluctuating. It is sometimes possible to use a form of the equation in which the ' constant ' varies with time in a way which can be computed from the conditions of the problem. If the flow fluctuates the pressure exerted on a part of the fluid by the surroundings may vary; but the pressure over that part may be varied, in time, by an amount which may nevertheless be uniform over the part. If this can be computed from a knowledge of how the surroundings are flowing then the constant in the equation can be replaced by a known function of time.

If the fluid is appreciably compressible the pressure variations also alter the density. Work is done by or against the pressure force as the fluid contracts or expands; furthermore in a given pressure gradient the force per unit mass varies with the density. The modified form of Bernoulli's equation is of less interest and will not concern us.

Finally, if there are forces present which represent irreversible processes the total head must steadily decline as the particle moves. For example, if we cause a fluid to move through a narrow tube the viscous forces oppose the motion and so the pressure must be higher at the entrance than at the exit, in order to provide a pressure gradient force equal and opposite to the resistance. But the velocity may be the same at the two ends so that Bernoulli's equation cannot be true.

Points of stagnation

When the air flows round any solid body, the body divides the flow. At the point of division the air moves neither one way nor the other and is at rest. At this point, called a stagnation point, the pressure is equal to the total head, or very nearly so, the discrepancy being due to the forces of viscosity which are important near the solid surface (see Chapter 4).

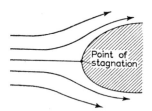

Efficiency of catch

An important phenomenon in nature is the capture, on solid surfaces, of airborne particles such as smoke pollution, cloud and fog droplets, and pollen. The problem posed is becoming daily more important in the case of radioactive substances that may be emitted into the atmosphere from nuclear power stations. It is a complicated one with several aspects: the particles must be transported to a position close to the object on which they are to be deposited, and this involves the motion of the air on the scale of hundreds of metres; they must then make an impact upon the object and, as we shall see, this is generally easier on smaller objects because they deflect the airflow less. But if the objects are too small, perhaps comparable in size with the particle to be captured, we may find that, as in the case of fine hairs, they are blown out of the way by the wind. This last consideration also arises with cloud droplets making impact with each other, because if their sizes are nearly equal the particles all tend to move together and have a very small relative velocity to bring them into contact. In this chapter we are concerned with the effect of the inertia of the airborne particles. Other aspects of the problem of capture of small particles are discussed on pages 91 and 122.

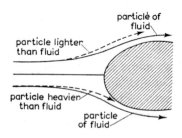

The figure shows the lines of flow of the air on the wind-facing side of a solid body. An airborne particle that is denser than the air will follow a track along which the curvature is less than along the track of the air because the pressure gradient force is the same as that applied to the air but the inertia is greater. Likewise a particle lighter than the surrounding fluid will pursue a track with greater curvature, and it could not come into contact with the wind-facing side of the body. This applies to bubbles of air in water.

All the heavier-than-air particles lying within a certain tube of air advancing towards the body will make contact, the width of this tube being smaller the more nearly the density of the particles approaches that of the surrounding fluid. When the particles are very small the viscous forces (see page 91) become more important than the pressure gradient forces. An experiment can be performed with soap bubbles which are slowly sinking through the air: the greater their sinking speed the more is their inertia in excess of the air they displace and the easier they are to hit with a large object such as a cushion.

For particles of a given density difference from the air the capture is more efficient upon bodies which produce the greatest curvature of the air. For bodies of a given shape the smaller ones produce greater curvature, and so a number of small bodies of the same total frontal area as one large one of the same shape would capture more airborne particles. Likewise a body with sharp corners or complicated shape produces greater curvature than smoothly rounded bodies.

Insects are examples of common airborne objects and, as motorists know well, they are often caught upon the windscreens of fast moving cars. If a car is travelling at 60 m.p.h. the acceleration of the air upwards over the windscreen is of the order of 60 times gravity. An insect in this air suddenly feels as if its weight is increased 60 times and as it ' falls ' through the air its wings and legs are torn off and its bowels drop out on to the advancing car.

The same phenomenon can be seen when snowflakes pile up upon small objects such as poles and wires but scarcely accumulate at all on the wind-facing wall of a house.

Dynamic soaring

Birds are more fortunate than insects in that they can make use of their inertia to remain airborne. The albatross glides with an airspeed of about 20 m/sec. If we neglect for the moment the loss of energy due to ' wind resistance ' we have a form of Bernoulli's equation, namely

$$\text{Potential energy} + \text{kinetic energy} = \text{constant}$$

or
$$gz + \tfrac{1}{2}v^2 = \text{constant}$$

in which z is the height and v is the speed of the bird. When it dives down through a height of 1 m (100 cm) the kinetic energy increases by $100\,g$ CGS units of energy for each unit of mass, and so the new speed would be given by

$$\tfrac{1}{2}v^2 = 100\,g + \tfrac{1}{2}(2000)^2$$

if the old speed were 2000 cm/sec. Since $g = 981$ we find that

$$v = (402)^{\frac{1}{2}} \text{ m/sec approximately}$$
$$= 20 \cdot 05 \text{ m/sec approximately}$$

Likewise if the bird soared upwards a distance of 1 m its kinetic energy would be partially expended in increasing the gravitational potential energy and the velocity would be decreased to about

$$v = 19 \cdot 95 \text{ m/sec.}$$

But if the wind increased by $0 \cdot 05$ m/sec for every increase in height of 1 m and the bird were facing into the wind it would find that although it had gained height its air speed remained 20 m/sec. This shear, or change of wind strength with height, of $0 \cdot 05$ m/sec m (or 5 m/sec in 100 m) serves to maintain the air speed of a bird gliding at 20 m/sec facing the wind shear, and rising through it. If the shear were in excess of this amount the bird would be able to gain air speed as it ascended, or alternatively it would have enough energy to spare to overcome the drag of the air (or ' wind resistance '). On reaching its desired height, of say 20 m above the sea, the albatross can turn about and glide, sinking slowly down towards sea level. As energy is lost in overcoming drag the air speed can be maintained in two ways: firstly by sinking to a lower level and converting potential energy into kinetic energy, and secondly (or rather at the same time) by gliding in the direction of the wind shear so as to sink into air moving more slowly in the direction of flight.

The ascent should be made as rapidly as possible so that the energy lost to drag forces is as small as possible, unless of course the shear is much larger than the minimum required to maintain gliding flight. This minimum depends upon the gliding speed of the bird and is inversely proportional to it, for in finite difference notation

$$g\Delta z = - \tfrac{1}{2}\Delta(v^2) = - v\Delta v,$$

and so

$$\frac{\Delta v}{\Delta z} = - \frac{g}{v}.$$

The left hand side is the rate at which the velocity of the bird decreases in a uniform airstream as it glides upwards. This amount, at least, must be made up by the shear if this kind of soaring is to be practical. It is less for birds with greater flying speeds.

Over the open ocean shears large enough to keep an albatross airborne are normal in temperate latitudes. The shear is greatest very close to the surface which is very convenient for a bird that lives by scavenging from the sea and therefore needs to spend most of its time low down. However, the efficient use of the wind gradient to remain airborne requires that the downwind (strictly it is in a down-shear direction, which close to the surface is approximately the same) glide shall occupy a much longer time than the upwind one in which height is gained. Consequently the bird is carried downwind. The greatest of the albatrosses are only found in the southern oceans where they can soar round and round Antarctica several times a year in the persistent westerly winds without ever encountering a continent. In the northern hemisphere they would be carried irretrievably on to land, where they cannot subsist.

Smaller albatrosses are found in the northern oceans, but on account of their size they can maintain flapping flight with less difficulty and can soar by using the wakes of the waves (see page 120) which is less easy for larger, less manoeuvrable, faster flying birds.

Large air bubbles in water

Large sections of many textbooks on hydrodynamics are taken up by discussion of ' potential flow '. This is a kind of motion in which the only forces of importance are the pressure gradient forces and the inertia forces. These forces are then always in balance. The mathematics with which this kind of flow is treated is extremely elegant and attractive: it is called the theory of ' perfect ' or ' ideal ' fluids. It is a source of continual disappointment to applied mathematicians that this theory is not applicable to many real fluid flow problems. All the greater is their delight when it can be used to solve a problem posed by Nature.

Sir Geoffrey Taylor and R. M. Davies applied it in the following way to the motion of large air bubbles in water. They noticed that these bubbles when rising through water have spherical upper surfaces and ragged, almost horizontal, lower surfaces as shown in Plate 1. When a fluid approaches an obstacle round which it must flow the inertia forces are of paramount importance. As it passes the obstacle and in the lee of it the flow may be complicated in many ways, but potential theory often serves to give a very accurate prediction of the distribution of pressure on the front surface. For a sphere, when gravity is neglected, the

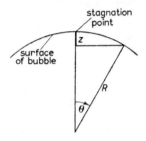

pressure at angle θ from the forward stagnation point is (see figure)

$$p_0 - \tfrac{9}{8}\rho w^2 \sin^2 \theta$$

the pressure being a maximum equal to p_0 at the stagnation point, and w being the velocity of the sphere in fluid which is at rest apart from the motion induced by the sphere. The pressure due to the weight of the water is equal to

$$p_0 + \rho g z,$$

z being the depth below the stagnation point. $z = R(1 - \cos \theta)$, if R is the radius of the spherical surface. Since the bubble is made of air of negligible density compared with water, motion of the air within the bubble can only produce negligible inertia forces and so the pressure inside the bubble is for practical purposes equal to p_0 throughout. If the shape remains unaltered as the bubble rises the pressure in the water in contact with the bubble must also be equal to p_0 everywhere, and so the effect of the inertia forces, represented by $-\tfrac{9}{8}\rho w^2 \sin^2 \theta$, must exactly cancel the effect of gravity represented by $\rho g z$. In fact $\tfrac{9}{8}w^2 \sin^2 \theta = gR(1 - \cos \theta)$ approximately provided that $w = \tfrac{2}{3}(gR)^{\frac{1}{2}}$, because $\sin^2 \theta = 2(1 - \cos \theta)$ approximately for θ less than about $35°$, and so a bubble with a spherical upper surface could rise without change of shape. The lower surface of the bubble is in a continuous state of unrest.

Bubbles smaller than about 2 or 3 cm in diameter have a rounded perimeter and smaller ones still tend towards sphericity because of the influence of surface tension. Bubbles 12–20 cm in diameter can be made by carefully overturning an inverted saucer or dish containing the air under water.

Davies and Taylor thus obtained the formula

$$w = \tfrac{2}{3}(gR)^{\frac{1}{2}}.$$

If we wished to apply the same argument to oil bubbles of density ρ' the formula would correspond simply to altering g in the ratio $(\rho - \rho')/\rho$ and

$$w = \tfrac{2}{3}\left(g\,\frac{\rho - \rho'}{\rho}\,R\right)^{\frac{1}{2}}.$$

But this would only be true so long as the inertia forces in the oil were negligible, which means that there could be no appreciable circulations within the oil.

General form of the law of fluid motion

Except where specially stated otherwise, as for instance in the last article where gravity enters as an important force, we have assumed that there is a balance between the pressure gradient force and the inertia force. In addition to the force of gravity there may be forces of friction. Fields of force can be of two kinds, depending upon the form of the work done by them. The first kind, called *conservative*, is such that it is possible to draw everywhere surfaces which are perpendicular to the force and which nowhere intersect one another, and have no edges. Gravity produces a conservative field, the surfaces being level surfaces enclosing the earth. If a particle is acted upon by such a force it must either do work against it or have work done upon itself by the force, but if it starts and ends upon the same surface perpendicular to the force (i.e. at the same level, or potential) the total work done is zero. In particular, if the particle makes a journey ending at the starting point any work done against the force is regained on some other part of the circuit. Such forces can be represented by the gradient of their potential. Gravity is equal to the gradient of its potential which is $g \times$ height (gz being the potential energy of unit mass). Formally we may write

$$\mathbf{g} = -\operatorname{grad}(gz).$$

Several conservative fields of force can be represented collectively by one single potential gradient —grad Φ.

The second kind of force is involved in the *irreversible* processes of Nature. The work done against friction, for example, cannot be recovered. It is customary, therefore, to represent them collectively by a separate symbol **F**.

The inertia force is thus balanced by three types of force:

Inertia force = total force applied
$\qquad\qquad$ = pressure gradient force + conservative forces + other forces

or
$$\frac{D}{Dt}\mathbf{v} = -\frac{1}{\rho}\operatorname{grad} p - \operatorname{grad}\Phi + \mathbf{F}.$$

In this equation the forces grad Φ and **F** are expressed as forces per unit mass.

CHAPTER 2

MOTION ON A ROTATING EARTH

SOME aspects of the motion of the air are dominated by the effect of the earth's rotation. These are motions which take place over periods of many hours or days. If a motion system endured for only a few minutes or even perhaps for an hour or two the effect of the earth's rotation would not be appreciable.

In this chapter we shall be discussing motion that is *almost* horizontal. The paradox is that although the vertical component of the motion is all-important in producing weather and weather systems, it is not possible to measure it because it is so small, and we have to evolve methods of deducing it from the horizontal components. The vertical motion in convection currents which produce cumulus clouds, and the upcurrents which occur in the neighbourhood of mountains can be measured; but these motions occur on too small a scale for the earth's rotation to have any important effect because a particle of air passes through them in a small fraction of a day. The vertical motion that will concern us is that which occurs over areas hundreds or even thousands of miles across, such that a particle of air traversing the system finds that the earth rotates a few times while it does so.

We shall confine our attention to the NORTHERN HEMISPHERE in order to avoid continual qualification.

The deviating force

The earth's rotation produces two effects on particles of the atmosphere. Both are the effects of inertia forces, because they are due to accelerations which the air undergoes. The first is the centrifugal force which causes the earth to be an oblate spheroid, and this is applied to all particles even when at rest relative to the ground. What we call *vertical* is the direction of *apparent gravity*. The actual force of gravity directed towards the centre of the earth can be resolved into two components—one which we observe as the force of gravity and which is perpendicular to the

19

horizon, the other being equal and opposite to the centrifugal force which the earth's rotation produces. This second component accelerates particles towards the earth's axis and keeps them moving in circles.

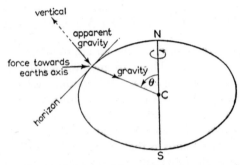

The second effect of the earth's rotation appears when particles begin to move over the earth's surface. To understand how it operates we note that rotation can be represented by a vector in the direction of the axis of rotation and with length equal to the magnitude of the rotation. The difference between gravity and apparent gravity accounts for the changes in velocity relative to the centre of the earth (the effect of the motion round the sun is negligible in comparison and only appears in the form of feeble tides in the atmosphere). The remaining effect can therefore be represented as a rotation about an axis parallel to the earth's axis but through the particle whose motion we are studying. This may be resolved into two components, one vertical and one horizontal.

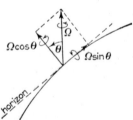

The effect of the horizontal component, $\Omega \sin \theta$, is to alter the weight of a particle moving horizontally over the ground, for if it is advancing towards the horizon which is being tipped up it is being accelerated upwards and the inertia will produce an apparent increase in weight. The magnitude of this effect is about one ten thousandth of gravity for ordinary wind speeds. In a fast moving westerly or easterly air current the pressure at the ground is altered by perhaps two or three tenths of a millibar, and the effect is overwhelmed by other effects which we shall come to in this chapter.

The effect of the vertical component, $\Omega \cos \theta$, of the rotation is the most important. We will find what force it is necessary to apply to a unit mass of air to make it move horizontally with velocity v relative to the ground from the point O. After time t it will have travelled a distance vt and arrived at P. During this time the straight line OP on the earth will have rotated through an angle $\Omega t \cos \theta$ from its original position in space OP_1, and the track of the particle in space is along the curved line from O to P.

In addition to the velocity v along OP the particle has another component which in time t has caused it to traverse the arc $P_1 P$ whose length is $vt \times \Omega t \cos \theta$. In time t with acceleration a a particle traverses from rest a distance $\frac{1}{2}at^2$. The acceleration experienced by the particle in this case is therefore $2v\Omega \cos \theta$, which we shall write as vf for short ($f = 2\Omega \cos \theta$). The direction of the acceleration is at right-angles to the line OP, this being the direction in which velocity in space is added as the particle moves away from the point O to a place where the ground is moving round O with velocity proportional to the distance from O.

We may start this analysis at any point O, but because of the earth's curvature, and consequent variation in θ, the vertical component of the earth's rotation should be measured near to P, the position of the particle.

The conclusion is, therefore, that *if a particle moves with velocity v horizontally over the earth's surface it is being accelerated in space to the left with acceleration vf.*

This is often expressed by saying that *there is an apparent inertia force to the right of magnitude vf* per unit mass. This force is called the *deviating force*.

It will be noted that we have not concerned ourselves with the effects of a uniform velocity through space because there are none. We have considered the accelerations only; but this has required us to assume that there is an absolute zero of angular velocity in space even though there is no absolute zero of velocity.

The magnitude of the deviating force in the horizontal direction is of the same order as that in the vertical direction (they are equal at latitude 45°). The horizontal motion is not restricted by a boundary as the vertical motion is and in consequence motions in which the accelerations are only a small fraction of g can take place—the accelerations persisting for many hours to produce appreciable speeds. There is not room for this to happen in a vertical direction, and buoyancy forces of much greater magnitude are dominant.

The relationship between pressure and wind

In many problems of fluid motion the pressure within the fluid is of minor importance because it adjusts itself to the motion. People, such as designers of flying machines, are concerned only with the pressure at the boundary, and are interested in it as the end product of their calculations. But in the atmosphere gravity produces internal pressure gradients which produce the motion. It is natural therefore that we should concern ourselves with the pressure gradient.

We also wish to draw maps to represent the atmosphere in motion. Various devices have been tried, but maps of pressure prove to be very convenient, one of the reasons being that they are simpler and more accurate to construct than maps representing the motion directly. The pressure at the ground is a representation of the whole atmosphere above and is not therefore subject to such great fluctuations as the wind or temperature, which represent only the condition of the air with which we come directly into contact.

On account of the ease and reliability with which pressure observations can be collected maps of sea level pressure can be usefully drawn, and from measurements of upper air temperature these may be extrapolated upwards to give us maps of upper air pressure.

At very high levels, above 200 mb, or about 12,000 m, the extrapolation becomes unreliable, largely because the radio-sonde pressure-measuring element is not accurate enough, and the measurement of wind by observing the motion of the balloon is the chief source of information.

At intermediate heights, although wind measurements are made use of, the most convenient method of representation on a map is still by means of the pressure. Hence the meteorologist's preoccupation with the isobars.

Our equation of motion for the air is:

$$\text{Acceleration} = \frac{\text{pressure gradient force}}{\text{density}} + \text{deviating force} + \text{friction} + \text{gravity}$$

$$\frac{D}{Dt}\mathbf{V} = -\frac{1}{\rho}\,\text{grad}\,p + \mathbf{V}_\wedge\mathbf{f} + \mathbf{F} + \mathbf{g}$$

In this equation friction is used to refer to internal friction of the air—between two adjacent layers moving at different speeds for instance, as well as between the air and the ground. Since we are concerned with almost horizontal motion the force $\mathbf{F}$ is horizontal. $\mathbf{g}$ is gravity which is vertical. The vector product $\mathbf{V}_\wedge\mathbf{f}$ is simply a mathematical way of writing a vector which is at right-angles to both $\mathbf{V}$ and $\mathbf{f}$, $\mathbf{f}$ being a vertical vector. From this equation we have ignored the horizontal component of the earth's rotation.

This vector equation can be divided into horizontal and vertical components, of which the latter is:

$$0 = \frac{\text{vertical pressure gradient force}}{\text{density}} + \text{gravity}$$

$$0 = -\frac{1}{\rho}\frac{\partial p}{\partial z} - g$$

in which we have put the vertical acceleration equal to zero for this chapter, and written $-g$ for the vertical (downwards) component of gravity. This is the well known *hydrostatic equation*.

The horizontal component is

$$\text{Acceleration} = \frac{\text{horizontal pressure gradient force}}{\text{density}} + \text{deviating force} + \text{friction}$$

$$\frac{D}{Dt}\mathbf{V} = -\frac{1}{\rho}\,\text{grad}_\text{H}\,p + \mathbf{V}_\wedge\mathbf{f} + \mathbf{F}$$

in which **V** is the horizontal velocity and grad$_H$ means the horizontal gradient.

This equation is too complicated to be useful if taken in full always. We therefore discuss special kinds of motion and think of the actual motion in terms of these.

(a) The geostrophic wind

Very often the air travels hundreds of miles with very little change in velocity relative to the ground. If the velocity were absolutely constant and the acceleration therefore zero, and if there were no friction, the pressure gradient force and the deviating force would be in balance, and the wind would be called *geostrophic* (Greek: earth turning). The motion would be dominated by the effect of the earth's rotation.

$$0 = \frac{\text{pressure gradient force}}{\text{density}} + \text{deviating force}$$

or

$$\frac{1}{\rho} \, \text{grad}_H \, p = \mathbf{V}_{G \wedge} \mathbf{f}$$

where **V**$_G$ is the geostrophic wind.

Whether or not the actual wind is equal to **V**$_G$ the pressure gradient may be represented by it.

The pressure gradient is equal to $\partial p / \partial x$ if x is measured across the isobars, and so the magnitude of the geostrophic wind is given by

$$V_G = \frac{1}{\rho f} \cdot \frac{\partial p}{\partial x},$$

and the direction is such that the pressure gradient force is to the left, and is equal and opposite to the deviating force which is to the right of the direction of motion.

(b) The ageostrophic wind

This is the difference between the actual wind and the geostrophic wind. Thus:

Actual wind = geostrophic wind + ageostrophic wind

$$\mathbf{V} = \mathbf{V}_G + \mathbf{V}_A$$

From pressure measurements we can calculate only $\mathbf{V_G}$ directly. We shall therefore spend most of the rest of this chapter discussing how we may estimate the magnitude and effects of $\mathbf{V_A}$.

In the case when there is no friction:

$$\text{Acceleration} = \frac{\text{pressure gradient force}}{\text{density}} + \text{deviating force}$$

$$\frac{D}{Dt}\mathbf{V} = -\frac{1}{\rho}\,\text{grad}_H\,p + (\mathbf{V_G} + \mathbf{V_A})_\wedge\mathbf{f}$$

where we have represented the wind as the sum of $\mathbf{V_G}$ and $\mathbf{V_A}$ in the last term.   But we have already defined $\mathbf{V_G}$ by:

$$0 = -\frac{1}{\rho}\,\text{grad}_H\,p + \mathbf{V_G}_\wedge\mathbf{f}$$

and so by subtraction we obtain:

$$\text{Acceleration} = \text{deviating force due to ageostrophic wind}$$

$$\frac{D}{Dt}\mathbf{V} = \mathbf{V_A}_\wedge\mathbf{f}$$

Comparing this with the equation for the geostrophic wind on page 24 we see that the ageostrophic wind bears a relation to the acceleration similar to that between the geostrophic wind and the pressure gradient.   Thus *the ageostrophic wind is proportional to the acceleration and at right-angles to it to the left,* when there is no friction.

(c) Development

Motions in the atmosphere are all produced in the first place by the action of gravity on masses of air of different density. When cold air sinks, and warm air is lifted above it, potential energy is converted into energy of motion.   On a rotating earth when the scale of the motion is large enough, the motion produced is dominated by the deviating force and the wind systems we observe are the result.   The source of the potential energy is in the exchange of heat by radiation between the atmosphere, the ground, the sun, and outer space; but we are only concerned here with the process of its conversion into energy of motion, which is called *development*.

Development can only occur if there is a vertical component in the motion, otherwise the potential energy cannot be released. Vertical motion can only occur if there is horizontal convergence or divergence of the air below or above the rising or sinking air. If the motion were everywhere geostrophic except for a small effect to be discussed in a moment, the motion would be along the isobars and the speed would be inversely proportional to their spacing. Although the shape of elements of air might be altered there would be no convergence or divergence requiring an increase or decrease in the amount of air at any level. Therefore there can only be vertical motion if there is an ageostrophic component to the wind.

There is one qualification to be made to this last conclusion. If the air moves from one latitude to another there is a change in the ratio of the spacing of the isobars to the speed of the geostrophic

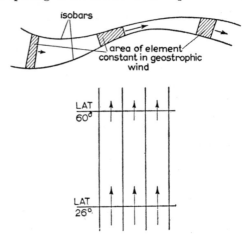

wind. Thus in extensive northerly or southerly airstreams there would be some convergence or divergence even if the motion were geostrophic everywhere. The result is to produce a vertical contraction (and increase in speed) in a current moving towards the equator, if the motion continues to be geostrophic. But to state the situation in this way is very artificial, because since there is no physical constraint upon the motion to remain precisely geostrophic the vertical contraction will not be governed by this alone. Other important effects will interfere and often dominate the flow. In any case the currents in which development mainly occurs are most often moving more nearly along lines of latitude, and we shall therefore concern ourselves with the processes which influence them.

(d) The effect of friction

It is often stated that friction causes the air to acquire a component of velocity across the isobars towards low pressure, and that this effect is greater over land than over the sea where the surface is less rough, and friction less in consequence. This is a gross over-simplification because it ignores the drag produced by layers of air above or below moving with a different velocity.

We will illustrate this by considering the forces upon air near the ground above which the air is moving differently. If there is an interchange of momentum between the superposed layers of air the effect can be represented by a force in the direction of the shearing motion. In the case illustrated the air deviates towards high pressure because of the drag of the air above. For this the equation is

$$0 = \frac{\text{pressure gradient force}}{\text{density}} + \text{force per unit mass due to ground friction} + \text{deviating force} + \text{drag per unit mass due to layers above}$$

and the four forces when drawn as vectors form a closed polygon.

If it were not closed there would be acceleration and the remaining side of the polygon would represent the inertia force.

If the air has a component of velocity across the isobars towards low pressure, we must not assume that it is due, even mainly, to friction at the surface. Both accelerations with their associated ageostrophic components of wind and the drag of the air above may be more important.

(e) Acceleration due to curvature of path: the gradient wind

If r is the radius of curvature of the path of the air then the acceleration is V^2/r inwards along that radius, and so, if there is no friction, and if there is no other acceleration

$$\text{Acceleration} = \frac{\text{pressure gradient force}}{\text{density}} + \text{deviating force}$$

$$\pm \frac{V^2}{r} = -\frac{1}{\rho} \left| \text{grad}_H \, p \right| + Vf$$

This equation is not written in vector form because all the forces are at right-angles to the direction of motion. The symbol $\left| \text{grad}_H \, p \right|$ means the magnitude of the vector $\text{grad}_H \, p$. In the diagrams are seen two cases of circular motion. In one high pressure is in the centre and we take the positive sign for V^2/r because the acceleration is in the same direction as the deviating force, and opposite to the pressure gradient. For circular motion round low pressure we take the negative sign.

In practice we must make two qualifications before using the above equation, which is called the *gradient wind equation*. Firstly we must note that acceleration due to the curvature of the path is not the only acceleration which may occur, as we shall see below. Secondly, in order to measure the radius of curvature of the path of the air we have to know the path, and this in principle assumes that we have solved the equation and found the velocity of the air. Since the air moves with a velocity not very different from the gradient wind it is a fair approximation to assume that the

wind moves along the isobars, and so the curvature of the isobars
is taken as the curvature of the path of the air.   With these

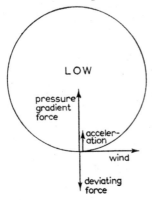

qualifications in mind the solution to the quadratic equation is
called the *gradient wind*.   In normal circumstances it is a slightly
better approximation to the actual wind than the geostrophic
wind.   There are two solutions to the quadratic equation, only
one of which satisfies the physical requirements.   (The other is a
negative quantity, and if the wind were blowing in the opposite
direction the deviating force would be reversed, and this is not
allowed for in the equation).

When the motion is in circles it may be strictly along the isobars,
in which case the gradient wind is exactly equal to the actual wind.

(f) Changing pressure field: the isallobaric wind

The isallobars are the lines of equal rate of change of pressure.
If the wind were exactly geostrophic the acceleration would be
along the isallobars just as the wind would be along the isobars.
When the wind is nearly geostrophic the isallobars nevertheless
give a good estimate of the acceleration and we may take the rate
of change of the equation on page 24 to give us

$$0 = \text{rate of change of } \frac{\text{pressure gradient force}}{\text{density}} + \text{rate of change of deviating force}$$

$$0 = -\frac{\partial}{\partial t}\left(\frac{1}{\rho}\text{grad}_{\text{H}}\,p\right) + \frac{\partial}{\partial t}(\mathbf{V}_{\text{G}\wedge}\mathbf{f})$$

The left-hand side is zero if the rate of change of the acceleration
is precisely zero.   In practice it is generally small.

Provided that there are no great variations in the acceleration from place to place and the wind is approximately geostrophic, the acceleration is equal to the local rate of change of the geostrophic wind $\left(\text{i.e. } \dfrac{\partial}{\partial t}\, \mathbf{V}_{\text{G}}\right)$. The ageostrophic wind is at right-angles to this and to the left of it, the magnitude being acceleration $\div f$. Thus:

$$V_{\text{A}} = \frac{1}{f} \times \frac{1}{f} \times \frac{\partial}{\partial t}\left(\frac{1}{\rho}\left|\,\text{grad}_{\text{H}}\, p\,\right|\right)$$

$$= \frac{1}{\rho f^2}\left|\,\text{grad}_{\text{H}}\, \frac{\partial p}{\partial t}\,\right|$$

and the ageostrophic wind, in this case called the isallobaric wind, is at right-angles to the isallobars, and is directed towards the region of greatest rate of fall of pressure.

On a weather chart there must be a region of maximum rate of fall of pressure ahead of a moving depression. We therefore expect to find convergence towards this region—and likewise divergence from the region away from which a depression is moving.

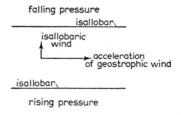

Physically the isallobaric wind may be thought of as motion across the isobars in such a way that the air takes up the geostrophic wind velocity of the new pressure field. If the isobars are getting closer together the air must be accelerating in the direction of motion as the geostrophic wind increases. The air must therefore move across the isobars towards low pressure in order that work shall be done upon it to accelerate it. If the spacing of the isobars is increasing the air is slowing down and must therefore move towards high pressure in order to do work against the pressure gradient force.

On weather charts the barometric tendency shows where the isallobaric low and high centres are. Since these are regions of convergence and divergence respectively they are also regions of up and down motion in the air above. They are centres of development.

(g) The geostrophic acceleration: confluence and diffluence

The air may undergo accelerations even when the isobars are nearly straight, the pressure field is changing very slowly, and the curvature and isallobaric effects are small. This happens when the isobars get closer or farther apart along their length, and the air is said to undergo confluence and diffluence. In a region of confluence where the air is being accelerated in the direction of its motion there must be ageostrophic motion across the isobars towards low pressure. Likewise where there is diffluence there must be motion across the isobars towards high pressure in order to produce the deceleration.

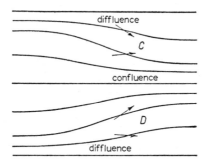

As we have seen, the ageostrophic component of the wind, in this case produced by the geostrophic acceleration (or acceleration along the track of the geostrophic wind), is that which produces convergence or divergence, and it will do this in regions such as those indicated in the figure by C and D where there is motion as indicated across the isobars.

In this case the acceleration is assumed to be equal to the rate of change of the geostrophic wind along the path of the air, namely

$\mathbf{V_G}$. grad V_G. The ageostrophic component of the wind is therefore given by

$$V_A = \frac{1}{f} \mathbf{V_G} \text{ . grad } V_G$$

the direction being towards low pressure for an acceleration.

The regions marked C and D in the figure are centres of development.

Motion in the upper air

What we have said so far about almost horizontal motion is applicable at any level in the atmosphere. In order to discuss the motion aloft more fully we must describe how it is represented on maps.

(a) Upper air contours

In the equations we have used so far the air density has appeared. This is inconvenient in that it varies with altitude and so a different value has to be put in for different heights. We have also spoken in terms of the isobars. It is not convenient to compute them for levels other than the surface. It is therefore customary to represent the upper air pressure distribution by contours of constant pressure surfaces. These are simple to compute using the temperature and pressure records of radio sonde balloons.

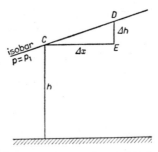

In the figure we have represented a vertical section of the air at right-angles to the isobars. The points C and E are at the same height h. The points C and D are on the same pressure surface $p = p_1$. The pressure at E is $p_1 + \Delta p$; $CE = \Delta x$; $ED = \Delta h$. Since this is a section at right-angles to the isobars

$$\Delta p = \Delta x \, |\text{grad}_H \, p \,|.$$

At the same time, considering the vertical gradient of pressure

$$\Delta p = - \Delta h \frac{\partial p}{\partial z}$$

and by the hydrostatic equation (page 23) this is equal to

$$\Delta p = - \Delta h(- g\rho).$$

Combining this with the first expression for Δp we have

$$\frac{1}{\rho} \left| \operatorname{grad}_H p \right| = g \frac{\Delta h}{\Delta x},$$

or

$$\frac{1}{\rho} \operatorname{grad}_H p = g \operatorname{grad}_H h$$

in vector form, for we know that the direction of the two gradients is in the plane of the diagram and to the right.

Thus the pressure gradient is expressed as the gradient of the height of a surface of constant pressure. The geostrophic wind equation then is

$$V_G = \frac{g}{f} \left| \operatorname{grad}_H h \right|$$

the direction being along the contours of the pressure surface with low values of h on the left.

A map of contour height looks very like a map of pressure but the spacing of the lines may differ according to the units used.

(b) *The thermal wind*

If there is a horizontal gradient of temperature in the air two neighbouring columns of air have different densities. The depth of air between two pressure levels is therefore different and so the horizontal gradient of contour height of two pressure surfaces will differ. There will then be a variation with height of the geostrophic wind.

This variation with height is called the *thermal wind* because it is the direct result of the existence of a horizontal temperature gradient. The figure represents a section of the air perpendicular to the isotherms. If the temperature difference between the columns of air AC and BD is ΔT,

$$\Delta T = \Delta x \left| \operatorname{grad}_H T \right|$$

where the distance Δx is measured across the isotherms. The difference between the geostrophic winds at the upper and lower pressure levels $p = p_2$ and $p = p_1$ is given in magnitude by

$$| \mathbf{V}_{G2} - \mathbf{V}_{G1} | = \frac{g}{f} | \mathrm{grad_H} \, h_2 - \mathrm{grad_H} \, h_1 |$$

$$= \frac{g}{f} | \mathrm{grad_H} \, h' |$$

the direction being perpendicular to the vector $\mathrm{grad_H} \, (h_2 - h_1)$, that is along the lines of constant $(h_2 - h_1)$ which we have denoted by h'. These lines are called the *thickness lines* for the layer of air between pressures p_1 and p_2. The geostrophic wind shear between the top and the bottom of the layer is along the thickness lines, and inversely proportional to their spacing.

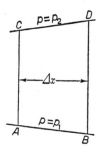

The coefficient of expansion of the air is $1/T$, and so if T is a mean temperature of the layer between p_2 and p_1 the difference in the thickness of the layers AC and BD, is approximately

$$\Delta h' = \Delta T \times \frac{1}{T} \times h'.$$

Dividing this by Δx, the element of distance across the thickness lines, we have

$$| \mathrm{grad_H} \, h' | = \frac{h'}{T} | \mathrm{grad_H} \, T |$$

and so if we define the thermal wind, $\mathbf{V}_G'$, as the geostrophic wind shear in unit height change

$$V_{G'} = \frac{1}{h'} \left| \mathbf{V}_{G2} - \mathbf{V}_{G1} \right| = \frac{g}{f\bar{T}} \left| \text{grad}_{H} \, T \right|$$

the direction being along the isotherms with cold air on the left.

It is important to note that this is a geostrophic wind. If we wish to investigate more closely we must take into account the ageostrophic component in the various ways already outlined. Nevertheless, the thermal wind gives a very useful estimate of the actual wind shear.

Sutcliffe's development theorems

The basis of the theorems we are about to deduce is that if the air in the lower levels is converging or if the air in the upper levels is diverging there will be cyclogenesis, while if there is convergence at the higher levels or divergence at the lower levels there will be anticyclogenesis.

Cyclogenesis means simply the generation of circulation as in a cyclone. It does not necessarily mean that a closed circulation will appear. Since motion in a cyclone is around a centre of low pressure it means that there is a tendency for a centre of relatively low pressure to form. In general this means the appearance of an isallobaric low, or centre of falling pressure.

We shall gain further insight into the process when thinking of it in terms of vorticity, or rotation of the fluid (see Chapter 3, page 75) for when convergence occurs cyclonic rotation is increased. Since the motion is very roughly geostrophic cyclonic rotation must be round a centre of low pressure, and so an increase in cyclonic rotation must be accompanied by falling pressure in the centre.

Development, then, may consist of convergence in the low levels, upward motion above the convergence, and a centre of falling pressure at the ground. At the same time there is divergence and rising pressure (or rising contour height) at high levels, and the growth of an anticyclonic circulation. Alternatively, anticyclonic development consists in the opposite process with downward motion in the middle, convergence aloft and divergence below.

The regions of development can be located by studying the ageostrophic wind which is responsible for the convergence or divergence. It is fundamental to this idea that convergence at one level should accompany divergence at another. The convergence pattern could not be the same at all levels, for if it were air would accumulate over a point and the pressure would rise. If the pressure were rising there the isallobaric wind would cause an outflow of air.

The process of development just described takes place by the conversion of potential energy into kinetic energy or vice versa. It is possible for new potential energy to be created; indeed it is necessary, and this is done by the heating or cooling of air by some outside agency such as the release of heat by condensation of water vapour and precipitation of the water as rain or the loss of heat to space by radiation. There are many such processes.

It is interesting that there must be a convergence of air on the average at all levels when the air is cooled and the pressure rises: likewise there is a total divergence and a pressure fall at the ground when the air is warmed and the pressure falls. This convergence or divergence is in the nature of an expansion wave which travels outwards with the speed of sound and is not observable as part of the wind system (see Chapter 9).

The principle to be applied therefore is that if we can compute the difference between the fields of the ageostrophic wind at a low and a high level we can deduce the vertical motion which must occur between those two levels and so locate the regions of falling pressure (over rising air) and rising pressure (over sinking air) at the ground.

To compute the difference in the ageostrophic wind fields we compute the difference in the acceleration fields at the two levels. Formally, Sutcliffe's derivation is as follows:

The acceleration at two levels, denoted by suffixes 1 and 2, is

$$\left(\frac{D}{Dt}\mathbf{V}\right)_1 = \frac{\partial}{\partial t}\mathbf{V}_1 + (\mathbf{V}_1 \cdot \mathrm{grad}_H)\,\mathbf{V}_1$$

and

$$\left(\frac{D}{Dt}\mathbf{V}\right)_2 = \frac{\partial}{\partial t}\mathbf{V}_2 + (\mathbf{V}_2 \cdot \mathrm{grad}_H)\,\mathbf{V}_2$$

$$= \frac{\partial}{\partial t}\mathbf{V}_2 + (\mathbf{V}_1 \cdot \mathrm{grad}_H)\,\mathbf{V}_1 + (\mathbf{V}' \cdot \mathrm{grad}_H)\,\mathbf{V}_1$$
$$+ (\mathbf{V}_2 \cdot \mathrm{grad}_H)\,\mathbf{V}'$$

where $\mathbf{V}_2 = \mathbf{V}_1 + \mathbf{V}'$.   By subtraction

$$\left(\frac{D}{Dt}\mathbf{V}\right)_2 - \left(\frac{D}{Dt}\mathbf{V}\right)_1 = (\mathbf{V}' \cdot \mathrm{grad}_H)\,\mathbf{V}_1 + \frac{\partial}{\partial t}\mathbf{V}' + (\mathbf{V}_2 \cdot \mathrm{grad}_H)\mathbf{V}'$$

The left-hand side of the equation is the difference between the acceleration at the upper level and that at the lower level.   If we can estimate the distribution of this difference we can deduce the regions of convergence and divergence in the manner already indicated, and illustrated in the examples below.   The right-hand side of the equation consists of two parts.   The first, $(\mathbf{V}' \cdot \mathrm{grad}_H)\mathbf{V}_1$, is the rate of change of $\mathbf{V}_1$, observed at a point moved along with the velocity $\mathbf{V}'$, across the field at the moment in question.   The second and third terms together are at the rate of change of $\mathbf{V}'$ measured at a point travelling with the particles at the upper level (moving with velocity $\mathbf{V}_2$).   We shall examine them separately.

(a) Thermal steering of the surface pressure field

As a practical approximation to the winds we may take the geostrophic wind, and for $(\mathbf{V}' \cdot \mathrm{grad}_H)\,\mathbf{V}_1$ we write $(\mathbf{V}_G' \cdot \mathrm{grad}_H)\,\mathbf{V}_{G1}$. This is a vector in the direction in which the low level isobars turn as we move across the area in the direction of the isotherms (or thickness lines) with low temperature on the left. We now show from this that *the surface pressure pattern moves in the direction of the thermal wind.*   This explanation of the phe-

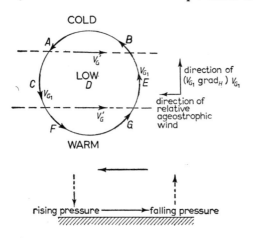

nomenon, which is called *thermal steering*, is Sutcliffe's first result. It states what is the effect of a thermal wind over an area.

In the figure is shown a closed isobar of the surface pressure field. Across it are drawn the thickness lines, or the isotherms, indicating colder air to the north. The low level geostrophic wind is shown circulating round the depression. In passing from A to B, C to D, D to E, or from F to G in the direction of V_G' there is a change in V_{G1} in the direction towards the top of the diagram. This means that the difference between the acceleration at high levels and that at low levels is in this same direction. The difference between the ageostrophic winds at the two levels is therefore towards the left of the diagram. This is shown in vertical section in the lower part of the diagram, which shows that part of the motion which produces convergence or divergence. The vertical motion which results is shown by the dotted arrows; and it is concluded that there is cyclogenesis at low levels on the right and rising pressure (anticyclogenesis) on the left. The low therefore moves to the right in the direction of the thermal wind.

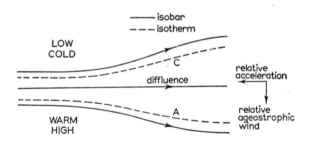

This result, that it is carried in the direction of the thermal wind, can by such argument be shown to be true for any configuration of curved surface isobars. When applied to a region of diffluence, the change of surface wind in the direction of the thermal wind in the case illustrated here is such as to produce cyclogenesis on the left and anticyclogenesis on the right of the diffluence, and to move the pattern forward by intensifying the gradient where it is wide. Compare this with the figure on page 31.

The mechanism can be thought of as a transport of the upper air through the surface pressure pattern. The ageostrophic motion which results carries forward the pattern itself.

(b) Changing thermal winds

The second and third terms combine to form the quantity

$$\left(\frac{D}{Dt}\,\mathbf{V_G'}\right)_2 .$$

We may imagine a particle carried by the upper level wind measuring the rate of change of the thermal wind $\mathbf{V_G'}$, beneath it, as it goes. This rate is the acceleration of the upper air relative to the lower; and the relative ageostrophic motion is at right-angles to it to the left.

Two possibilities arise. One is that some external process should heat or cool parts of the air differently thereby altering the thermal wind. If for instance a circular region were warmed, as it might be over Britain or the Iberian peninsular on a summer's day, the thermal wind would increase in an anticyclonic direction round the region. The relative acceleration would be in this same direction and the relative ageostrophic wind would be outwards. This indicates divergence aloft and convergence below with upward motion and falling pressure in the middle. The generation of a ' heat low ' can be interpreted in this way. Likewise a region of cooling is one of anticyclogenesis (rising pressure).

Sutcliffe's second result may therefore be stated: *Cyclogenesis occurs under heat sources, and anticyclogenesis under heat sinks.* This may seem a little obvious to a reader well schooled in the idea that hot air rises, and produces low pressure because it is less

dense; but this is probably because he is familiar with the result
in the case where the earth's rotation is unimportant and friction
dominant and he presumes it to be the case when the earth's
rotation is dominant and friction negligible. There is no *a
priori* reason why the presence of the deviating force should not
alter the situation; indeed we know that the air does not flow in
towards low pressure but round it. However, while the low
pressure centre is forming there is inflow towards it.

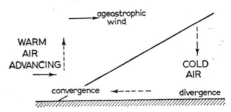

The second possible way in which $\mathbf{V}_G'$ may be changed is by
the closer approach of air of different temperatures. For example
if a warm front approaches a stagnant mass of cold air, as the
temperature gradient increases the thermal wind along the front
increases. The relative acceleration is in the direction of the
thermal wind, and the relative ageostrophic wind is towards the
cold air. This implies subsidence in the cold air and rising
motion in the warm air. The front becomes halted by the relative
rising pressure ahead of it. The cold air sinks and the warm air
rises, releasing potential energy which is converted into energy of
motion along the front, in the direction of the thermal wind.

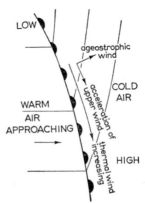

A different result is obtained when a cold front approaches a warm high pressure region. The relative acceleration is towards the cold air, so that pressure falls ahead of the cold front and rises behind it. The cold air penetrates through the anticyclone, largely under the influence of the isallobaric wind, and the high pressure area reforms again behind it.

Analogous results are obtained whereby we find that the arrival of fresh cold air at the edge of a depression will cause a regeneration of it, while the arrival of a warm front will cause it to disappear rapidly.

This result, deduced by Sutcliffe, may therefore be stated as follows: *The intensification of the temperature gradient produces rising pressure in the cold air and falling pressure in the warm air.*

One noteworthy thing about Sutcliffe's results is that they give us understanding of how development can occur in the absence of friction. Whatever part friction may play in atmospheric motion it is not one of the major causes of flow across the isobars, and therefore of development.

Fronts

A front is usually thought of as the boundary between two masses of air with different characteristics, the most important difference being in density. All appreciable motions in the atmosphere derive their energy from the operation of gravity on variations of density, which as we shall see in Chapter 3 is the main reason why they contain vorticity. Density differences in a horizontal direction, therefore, are presumably what the motion serves to relieve; it is consequently paradoxical that Nature should produce large gradients of density out of smaller ones, concentrating the differences into narrow bands with large areas in between in which the horizontal gradients of density are small.

The paradox arises because the motion is on a great variety of scales. Thus the large scale motion of the atmosphere transports heat from equatorial regions towards the poles. In so doing masses of warm air, which are large by human administrative standards but small compared with the whole atmosphere, move towards the poles; while similar masses of cold air from polar regions move towards the equator. The boundaries of these masses are what we call fronts; they are the advancing perimeters of new air which comes to deposit its heat or cold in its new zone of latitude. This method of injecting masses with markedly different characteristics into cool or hot areas is a more efficient one than a steady circulation in which there are no sharp boundaries within the air. The transfer of heat by eddies is much more effective than by molecular motion, and in the atmosphere the eddies are so large that we refer to their component material as air masses.

On the laboratory scale we are used to temperature differences created artificially being evened out by Nature. But, as we shall see in Chapter 7, when the molecular processes and the slow motion that accompanies them cannot do the job, penetrative motion begins and this results in the creation of fronts. The sharp outlines possessed by many clouds are fronts of a kind, and are produced in the course of the motion whose ' purpose ' is to even out density gradients.

Having thus cleared our minds of the idea that the appearance of fronts in the motion is unnatural, we may perhaps excuse ourselves for any difficulty in the matter because it has not yet been possible to demonstrate by arguments, such as we have been using, that fronts will necessarily be generated. Using the equations of hydrodynamics and extensive numerical calculation it can be demonstrated that in certain places, such as where sea breezes are generated, gradients of density will tend to be intensified: but the complicated numerical work cannot be readily interpreted in terms of processes in the same way as formal equations can be, especially when the computation takes place inside an electronic machine. Rather, therefore, let us think of fronts as part of a mechanism of eddy motion designed by Nature to do most of the work of heat transfer by means of the bulk transport of hot and cold fluid, leaving the ultimate transfer, which must be accomplished by molecular methods and by radiation, to take place in a few places where the gradients are much larger than the average. We do not mean that the molecular transfer occurs to an important extent across what we observe as moving fronts but that the fronts are boundaries of the masses of fluid being transported to new surroundings, where, by small scale eddy processes and ultimately by molecular transfer, there will be accomplished the handing over of heat.

(a) The simple model front

The simplest concept of a front is of a wedge of cold air moving under the influence of gravity underneath a warm air mass; the ultimate state towards which the motion tends being with the warm air lying horizontally above the cold. In the simplest case the same particles would continue to remain at the frontal surface, in which case the discontinuity would gradually be smoothed out by molecular and small scale eddy processes.

It is observed that fronts often become intensified in the sense that the discontinuity becomes sharper. This is possible because the particles at the frontal surface are continually replaced by new ones by means of circulations within the air masses such as those illustrated below. The particles originally at A and B approach each other closely at C. Provided that the air at A and B is of different characteristics the sharp discontinuity at C will be maintained.

The motion in this figure is of a kind which generates or at least maintains the sharpness of the front. It is not necessary to have both circulations going, for either alone could maintain the discontinuity against processes tending to destroy it. The sharpness will be greatest at the ground; indeed the presence of the solid boundary there facilitates the creation of discontinuities such as these. We shall see in Chapter 7 that convection currents penetrating upwards maintain fronts but that their intensity steadily decreases after a short initial period while they are close to the ground where they are produced.

At many frontal surfaces observed in the atmosphere the circulations are not as shown above, but are in the opposite direction, and the front tends to become enfeebled. There may be circulation in only one of the masses, but enough to maintain the front.

These circulations are in the direction releasing potential energy because the warm air rises and the cold air sinks, and so it is the most likely during the ' active life ' of a front.

A good example of the motion that can occur at a front that is becoming sharper is when a warm front approaches a stagnant air mass. We saw on page 40 that the warm air rises as it approaches the front and begins to be carried away by the thermal wind in a direction along the front away from the depression. The cold air near the ground in this case moves in (as an isallobaric wind) towards the front and is carried along it towards low pressure. There must also be some rising of this cold air and mixing with the warm air above it but the main motion is due to the changing pressure scene we depicted on page 40. The pattern of flow shown here is typical of the snow producing situations on the western edges of continental anticyclones in winter. It is a significant feature of this kind of motion that particles of air from within the cold or warm air enter the frontal region, pass through it, and are carried away from the area of development within a day or so.

A region of development may remain as a visible entity on weather charts for several days but the air of which it is composed is continuously changing.

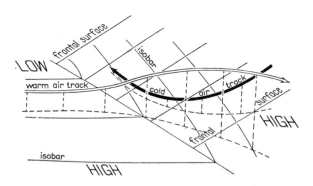

(b) Jet streams and depressions

Fronts are regions where the horizontal temperature gradient is much greater than on either side. The thermal wind is therefore greater, and above a frontal surface there must be a band of strong

winds blowing along the front.   The direction of the wind at the
10,000 m level is usually not far from parallel to the front because
the total thermal wind is stronger than the wind near the ground,
and is therefore the main component of the high level wind.
This band of strong winds is called a *jet stream*.   The name is
unfortunate because it implies that the air is thrown forward in
some way, as from an orifice, whereas it is moving very nearly
geostrophically like most of the air in the atmosphere.

The wind usually reaches a maximum at a height of 12–15,000
m, and above that level the horizontal gradient of temperature is in

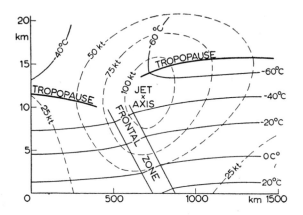

the opposite direction and the wind therefore decreases in strength
with height.   We have illustrated here a typical cross section of a
jet stream taken at right-angles to the front.   In this case the
front is depicted as a zone of large gradient of temperature rather
than as a sharp discontinuity, for this is more realistic.

A looser definition of a jet stream, as an air current on all sides
of which the wind strength is less than within, draws attention to
strong streams of air in the atmosphere which are usually not as
sharply defined as those above frontal surfaces.   They are called
jet streams nevertheless, and occur in the neighbourhood of
latitude 35°, but vary with time of year and geographical situation.   One of the most pronounced sometimes extends from
Morocco to Northern Burma.   There is the warm Sahara to the
south, and the cold plateau of Tibet on the north; but these are

only two of the many features which tend to produce large horizontal gradients of temperature from north to south. Mountains and sea coasts often play an important part in producing jet streams. At any moment a jet stream probably does not extend over the whole length from Morocco to Burma, but it tends to occur in much the same place and can therefore be seen on maps depicting the average conditions over a long period. The jet streams of higher latitudes which accompany the fronts move about mainly between latitudes 40° and 65°, but the variation is so great that although they are usually more intense than those of lower latitudes they do not appear as pronounced in maps of long period averages.

The strength of a jet stream varies along the length of a front as the intensity of the front varies. Fronts are usually most intense in the neighbourhood of newly developing depressions. We have illustrated this by drawing *isotachs* (lines of constant wind strength) at the level of the jet stream in relation to the position of the front at the surface. The front is distorted into a wave of a new depression, as we see it on an ordinary weather chart. Motions of the type shown on page 43 serve to invigorate the front in the region of development.

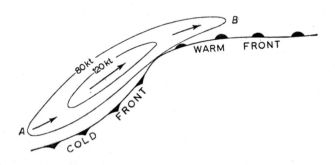

The area in which the jet stream reaches its greatest strength is called the *jet maximum*. The depression moves in the direction of the thermal wind, but not as rapidly as the air at the jet stream level. Typically a new depression would move at 45 kt with a jet stream above it of about twice this strength. The configuration of temperature moves with the fronts of the depression, so that jet stream air is entering the jet maximum at *A*, which is called the *jet entrance*, and leaving it at *B*, the *jet exit*.

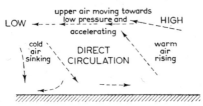

The energy required to accelerate the air into the jet stream must be derived from gravity. Where the air is moving slower than the geostrophic wind it moves to the left across the isobars. This is an example of geostrophic acceleration (see page 31). The ageostrophic motion produces sinking in the cold air and rising in the warm air. This *circulation* is called *direct*; it releases potential energy to accelerate the air into the jet stream entrance. Anti-cyclonic development takes place in the cold air and the depression moves forward ahead of the cold air penetrating under the jet entrance. At the jet exit an *indirect circulation* takes place. The air is decelerated; kinetic energy is converted into potential energy; cyclonic development occurs in the cold air ahead of the depression which therefore moves forwards, and the air of the jet stream deviates across the isobars to the right. In such situations the ageostrophic components of the wind may amount to about 10 kt in a typical case. The wind in the jet maximum is of the order of 100 kt.

The air passing through a depression at high levels is carried through large vertical distances. We have attempted to depict some characteristics of the airflow in the figure below, but this should not be taken as representative of all depressions, but simply as a model depression. The warm air near the ground is gradually caught up by the advancing cold front. The warm air aloft ascends the warm front and is 'thrown out' to the right at high levels. The cold air behind the cold front subsides and is left behind as the depression moves forward. The cold air ahead is carried to the left out of the path of the depression.

The *axis* of the jet stream, which is the line along which the wind at any section is a maximum, is found usually to be higher by about 1000 m at the entrance than at the exit. This is not because the air in the jet is descending but because the maximum is farther downwind at lower levels.

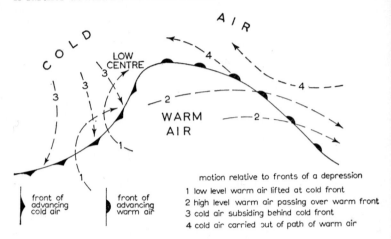

motion relative to fronts of a depression
1 low level warm air lifted at cold front
2 high level warm air passing over warm front
3 cold air subsiding behind cold front
4 cold air carried out of path of warm air

Depressions, in spite of their name, provide one of the most delightful mechanisms in Nature. The motion we have discussed is complicated by the release of energy of condensation when rain is extensive, and it is probable that they are more vigorous on account of this. It seems likely that there are depressions on Mars, but on account of the absence of condensing vapour their time scale is probably very different.

Depressions of this kind do not occur on all scales. Much smaller ones such as tornadoes are not dominated by the deviating force, and so their development is quite different. It may be that in the precise form in which we know depressions they are a rarity in the universe.

CHAPTER 3

VORTICITY

THE MOTION of a fluid can be thought of as composed of *translation*, *distortion*, and *rotation*. Translation serves to move it bodily from one place to another; distortion alters the shape or size of the elements; rotation changes the orientation. There is no difficulty in subtracting the translation from the rest of the motion: we shall concern ourselves here with what remains.

Distortion and rotation of a fluid

We shall illustrate our analysis by means of many examples.

(a) Distortion without rotation

If we have a square of fluid $ABCD$ with centre O, and change the shape of it to the rectangle $A_1B_1C_1D_1$, the change constitutes a distortion. The lines of particles AB and CD have been extended; AD and BC have been contracted. None of these four lines has been rotated. But it is impossible to change the shape without rotating at least some of the lines of particles: OB and OC are rotated to OB_1 and OC_1. The total rotation is nevertheless zero, and to measure it we take the *sum of the rates of rotation of any two lines of particles at right-angles*, and this we call the *vorticity* in the plane of the two lines. When this is zero we have distortion without rotation, as in the example shown.

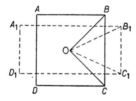

(b) Rotation without distortion

When the fluid rotates as if rigid there is no distortion. This occurs when a bowl of water is placed on a turntable and rotated about a vertical axis with constant angular velocity for long enough for the water to rotate with the bowl. The sum of the rates of rotation of any two horizontal lines of fluid particles is the same everywhere in the water and is equal to *twice the angular velocity of the fluid*, because each line is rotating with the angular velocity of the fluid. The rotation is about a *vertical axis*. The vorticity in this case can be represented by a vector whose direction is vertical and whose length is proportional to twice the angular velocity of the fluid.

If a portion of the fluid were suddenly ' frozen ' rigid but was subjected to no forces by the surrounding fluid, its angular velocity of rotation would be half its vorticity. This imaginary process of ' freezing ' is one whereby the distortion can be sub-tracted out, so that only the vorticity, or rotation, is left.

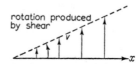

To measure the vorticity in a plane we note that the angular velocity of a line of particles along the x-axis is $\partial v/\partial x$, the rate of change in the x-direction of the velocity v in the y-direction. Likewise the angular velocity of a line of particles along the y-axis is $-\partial u/\partial y$, in which u is the velocity in x-direction. The vorticity in this plane, which we denote by ζ, is

$$\zeta = \frac{\partial v}{\partial x} - \frac{\partial u}{\partial y}.$$

The vorticity in the yz-plane of the coordinates is likewise equal to

$$\xi = \frac{\partial w}{\partial y} - \frac{\partial v}{\partial z}$$

and the component in the zx-plane is

$$\eta = \frac{\partial u}{\partial z} - \frac{\partial w}{\partial x}$$

The vorticity vector $\boldsymbol{\omega}$ is the sum of these three components, thus:

$$\boldsymbol{\omega} = \xi, \eta, \zeta.$$

(c) Simple examples of vorticity

It is a common experience that the wind increases upwards away from the ground. This may be because of friction at the ground or it may be due to the presence of a thermal wind (see Chapter 3). If the flow is at the same time smooth and horizontal, then a vertical line of particles AB is rotated into the position A_1B_1 by the motion. This *shearing motion* produces no rotation of horizontal lines, and so the vorticity is equal to the rate of rotation of vertical ones. If the motion is in the direction of the x-axis and z is vertical the only component of vorticity is about the y-axis, and this is equal to

$$\eta = \frac{\partial u}{\partial z}.$$

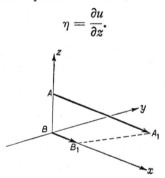

An example of vorticity about a vertical axis is the case of a belt of winds blowing along lines of latitude. If the strength of the wind were greatest at a middle latitude and decreased towards the equator and the pole, then particles of air lying along a line of longitude would be rotated anticlockwise on the polar side of the belt and clockwise on the equatorial side. The vorticities *relative to the earth* would then be as shown. The *absolute vorticity*, that is the vorticity in space, would be ζ, the relative

vorticity as shown, with the earth's angular velocity added.   As we
saw in Chapter 2 for large-scale motion we are not concerned
about the component of rotation about horizontal axes and so
simply add f, twice the vertical component of the earth's rotation,
to get the absolute vorticity about the vertical as

$$\zeta_a = \zeta + f.$$

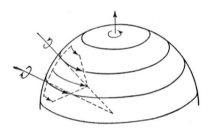

(d) *A line vortex; stability*

When the motion consists of circular motion around a straight
line such that the velocity is perpendicular to the radius and proportional to $1/r$, it is said to constitute a line vortex.

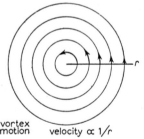

vortex
motion   velocity $\propto 1/r$

This is a mathematical abstraction because it implies that the
velocities become infinitely great on the central line, and the
nearest approach to it in practice would be with a small central
core rotating as if solid.   With this configuration of velocity the
rate of rotation of a line of particles, AB, lying along a radius
would be $\partial u/\partial r$, or $-1/r^2$, if $u = 1/r$.   The rate of rotation of a
row of particles in the direction perpendicular to the radius
would be the same as the rate of rotation of the radius through
a particle, namely u/r, which is $+1/r^2$.   The sum of these two
rotations is therefore zero, and the fluid has no vorticity even

though particles are moving round the centre in circles. In the practical case the 'solid' core would possess vorticity. In the mathematical case only the particles on the vortex line itself would have vorticity, and it would be of infinite intensity.

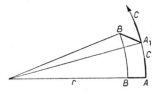

Line vortices have a practical interest because they represent a state of neutral stability. Let it be supposed that the particles within a radius r_0 were moving in circles faster than in the case of a line vortex while outside the motion was equal to that case. Thus:

$$u = A/r \quad \text{for} \quad r < r_0,$$

$$u = a/r \quad \text{for} \quad r > r_0, \quad \text{and} \quad A > a.$$

If some particles from inside $r = r_0$ were displaced outwards, the moment of their momentum, ur, about the axis would remain constant and so their velocity would be greater than that of the particles already outside $r = r_0$, because $A > a$. This would mean that the centrifugal force would be greater than on the neighbouring particles. But in circular motion the pressure gradient force is equal and opposite to the centrifugal force, and the particles which had moved outwards, having a centrifugal force greater than this, would therefore be accelerated outwards. Likewise it can be seen that if particles from outside $r = r_0$ invaded the region inside they would be accelerated inwards by the pressure gradient force which, being equal in magnitude to the centrifugal force of the indigenous particles would exceed the centrifugal force of the invaders.

A situation of this kind arises in an ordinary domestic liquid mixer. The central shaft is made to rotate and carry the fluid in the centre with it. Since this fluid is rotating with greater moment of momentum than the particles surrounding it, it is accelerated outwards. On reaching the walls of the cup its moment of momentum about the centre is reduced by friction and so it is accelerated inwards among the fluid which has not been retarded. In this way the fluid becomes thoroughly mixed.

A stable configuration is one in which the velocity decreases more slowly outwards than $1/r$. A displaced particle finds a pressure gradient force tending to return it to its original radial distance.

The fluid going down the bath plug behaves very like a line vortex because the moment of momentum about the centre remains constant and the velocity of a particle therefore tends to be proportional to $1/r$ as it approaches the outlet. If friction against the bottom of the bath is encountered as the water approaches the centre it will be retarded a little, and so the velocity in the centre will be of smaller magnitude than in a line vortex. The configuration will therefore be stable.

A dust devil likewise is a stable configuration because the air in the centre has experienced friction at the ground (where it picks up the dust) and is rotating more slowly than in a line vortex. The air near the ground is very hot and is therefore buoyant, which means that, if the dust devil column is once established, as the warm air in the column rises under its buoyancy force the surrounding air cannot enter from the sides to replace it because of the stable configuration of velocity. Air must therefore ascend from below, because the only level at which convergence can occur is at the ground where friction reduces the velocity.

Tornadoes and waterspouts are likewise stable configurations. Again, when the vortex develops it soon reaches down to the ground (or sea) because that is the only place from which there can be a supply of air into the centre.

The vorticity vector and vortex lines

The vorticity vector can be found by adding the components perpendicular to three planes at right-angles. The *vortex lines* are lines in the fluid such that the direction of the tangent at every point is in the direction of the vorticity vector. The motion in a teacup serves as a useful illustration of this.

Motion in a teacup

If the tea in a cup is stirred and then allowed to settle for a moment to a fairly steady state of motion, the velocity may be analysed into three components. First there is the rotation (1) round the vertical axis.   On account of the friction at the bottom this rotation is greater at the top than at the bottom.   Therefore we have a second component of vorticity (2) about axes pointing horizontally inwards towards the central vertical axis; the fluid above these lines moving faster round the central axis than those below.   There is also a third component (3) which results from upward motion in the centre and downward motion at the edges, outward motion at the top and inward motion at the bottom. On account of the friction at the bottom the velocity is reduced there and so the centrifugal force is less than in the fluid above. But the pressure gradient force to which it is subjected, owing to the hollowing out of the upper surface, is the same, and so the fluid at the bottom converges inwards.

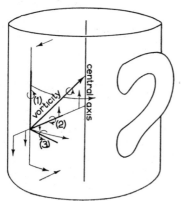

The vorticity at the point O is therefore represented by a vector which is the sum of these three components.

The vortex lines in the fluid are upward converging spirals.

Properties of vorticity

(a) *Flux of vorticity: circulation*

Before proceeding to discuss further manifestations of vorticity in Nature we shall discuss how it behaves within a fluid in motion.

A *vortex tube* is the surface containing all the vortex lines which intersect a closed curve.   The fluid within a vortex tube is called a *vortex filament*, or simply a *vortex*.

An alternative definition of vorticity can be given in terms of *circulation* round a closed curve.   When a portion of the fluid is

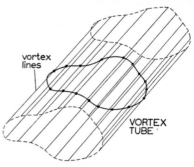

vortex lines

VORTEX TUBE

rotating as a solid, the circulation round a small circle whose plane is at right-angles to the vorticity vector (or axis of rotation) is equal to the product of the speed at the circumference multiplied by the length of the circumference. If the speed of rotation is Ω, and r is the radius of the circle, the circulation is $r\Omega \times 2\pi r$, which is

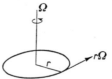

equal to $\pi r^2 \times 2\Omega$. This is the product of the area, πr^2, and the vorticity 2Ω. When the area enclosed by the curve is not in the plane at right-angles to the axis of rotation we take the projection of it on to that plane. This is only a particular case. It can be easily seen that in the case of other simple shapes such as squares and triangles, the circulation is equal to the product of the area

and the vorticity. The circulation has to be defined, in general, as an integral, which is the sum of the products $\mathbf{v} \cdot d\mathbf{s}$. $\mathbf{v}$ is the vector velocity at a point on the closed curve of which $d\mathbf{s}$ is an element of length. $\mathbf{v} \cdot d\mathbf{s}$ is the scaler product (the product of the magnitude of $d\mathbf{s}$ with the magnitude of the component of $\mathbf{v}$ in the direction of $d\mathbf{s}$). The integral is written $\oint \mathbf{v} \cdot d\mathbf{s}$.

The next step in the argument is to note that for a closed curve of finite size the circulation round it, $\oint \mathbf{v} \cdot d\mathbf{s}$, is equal to the sum of the circulations round a number of smaller closed curves which form a network of which the original closed curve is the boundary.

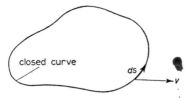

This is because each of the interior circuits is composed of sides which are also sides of other circuits on which the elements of length $d\mathbf{s}$ is measured in the opposite direction. The contributions from all the interior curves are thus cancelled out when the sum of the circulations is taken. The circulation round each of the small circuits is equal to $2\mathbf{\Omega} \cdot d\mathbf{S}$, where $2\mathbf{\Omega}$ is the vorticity at a point within it and $d\mathbf{S}$ is a vector perpendicular to the element of area bounded by the small circuit, and of magnitude equal to the area. By taking the scaler product $2\mathbf{\Omega} \cdot d\mathbf{S}$ we obtain the projection of the area on the plane perpendicular to $\mathbf{\Omega}$. If we now take the sum of the circulations round the elements we have that

$$\underset{\text{round the boundary}}{\oint \mathbf{v} \cdot d\mathbf{s}} \quad = \quad \int 2\mathbf{\Omega} \cdot d\mathbf{S} \quad = \quad \underset{\text{over the surface}}{\int \boldsymbol{\omega} \cdot d\mathbf{S}}$$

The left-hand side of this equation is *the circulation round the boundary*. This, we now see, is equal to the *flux of vorticity through the circuit*, or integrated component of vorticity across any surface having the circuit as boundary, which is represented by the right-hand side.

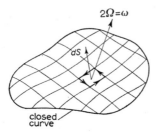

This theorem, which is really a purely mathematical result, whose proof can be found in various forms in books treating the subject of vector fields, enables us to understand the properties of vorticity, as follows.

The strength of a *vortex tube*, or *flux of vorticity* along it, *is constant*. To show this we note that the flux across a collar-shaped surface wrapped round a vortex tube is zero. This is because the vorticity has no component across it since it is composed of vortex lines. Therefore the circulation round the boundary of this collar is zero. Part of this boundary consists of two adjacent sides along which the direction of passage round the boundary is opposite. These parts of the circulation cancel out so that the sum of the circulations round the two ends is zero. But since one is in a negative direction we conclude that the circulation is the same round any two circuits round a vortex tube in the same direction. This is equal to the flux along the tube and so the *strength of a vortex tube*, or product of the vorticity and the area of a section, *is the same all along its length*. (The product must of course be expressed as an integral, $\int \boldsymbol{\omega} \cdot d\mathbf{S}$ if the quantities are not uniform over the area.)

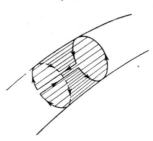

This theorem, no longer holds if the velocity is discontinuous anywhere along a vortex tube. At any discontinuity of velocity the shear, and therefore the vorticity, is infinite. But a vortex tube may have sharp corners upon it and the theorem is still true.

Since the vorticity is unique in direction at every point, vortex lines cannot intersect one another (except where the vorticity is zero). Nor can they terminate within the fluid as long as there are no discontinuities of velocity: this is because it is always possible to define the positive *and* negative direction of the tangent at any point, which could not be done at a loose end. Another way to see this is to note that a vortex tube cannot have a closed end, otherwise there would be a flux of vorticity into the tube at one end and no equal flux anywhere out of the closed end.   Therefore no finite vortex can terminate in the fluid.   This can only be true if it is also true of all infinitesimal vortices; and must therefore be true also of the vortex lines.

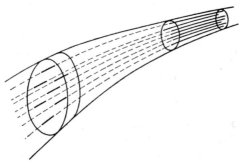

Since no vortex lines can cross the wall of a vortex tube, if the number of lines within a tube is made to represent the circulation round one section (or the flux of vorticity across it) it will represent it at all sections because the number along the tube is the same at all sections of it.

Thus, *the vorticity at a point is proportional to the number of vortex lines across unit area perpendicular to them.*

A corollary is that if the circulation round a closed curve is zero it must lie on a vortex tube.

(b) Change of circulation

We next compute the rate of change of circulation round a closed curve which consists always of the same particles of fluid. The circulation is the sum of elements $\mathbf{v} \cdot d\mathbf{s}$, whose rate of change depends on the rate of change of the velocity $\mathbf{v}$, and upon the change in the element $d\mathbf{s}$ as it moves along with the fluid.   This is expressed by saying that

$$\frac{D}{Dt}(\mathbf{v} \cdot d\mathbf{s}) = \left(\frac{D}{Dt}\mathbf{v}\right) \cdot d\mathbf{s} + \mathbf{v} \cdot \left(\frac{D}{Dt}d\mathbf{s}\right)$$

The first component of the right-hand side is the scalar product of the acceleration with $d\mathbf{s}$.   We saw at the end of Chapter 1 that the acceleration is made up of three components, the pressure gradient force, the conservative forces, and the forces representing irreversible processes.　We shall consider the product of each of these in turn with d**s**.

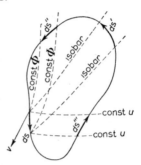

If d**s**′ is the element where the two isobars through the ends of d**s** again intersect the curve then *provided that the isobars are also surfaces of constant density*

$$-\frac{1}{\rho}\operatorname{grad} p \,.\, \mathbf{ds} = +\frac{1}{\rho'}\operatorname{grad} p' \,.\, \mathbf{ds}'$$

because grad p . d**s** is the difference in pressure between the two ends of the element d**s**.　The same is true for the element d**s**′. In composing rate of change of the circulation round the whole closed curve therefore from elements $-\dfrac{1}{\rho}\operatorname{grad} p$. d**s** we obtain nothing from the pressure gradient force because for each element there is an equal and opposite element somewhere else.　The condition that the isobars also be surfaces of constant density is important.　If it is not satisfied then the above equation does not hold because of the difference between ρ and ρ' on the two elements d**s** and d**s**′.　The consequences of the condition not being satisfied are discussed later in this chapter.

Likewise, if we draw through the ends of d**s** the surfaces of constant potential of the conservative forces, to cut the circuit again in d**s**″ we find that because the gradient of a quantity multiplied by an element of length is equal to the difference between the values of the quantity at the ends of the element

$$-\operatorname{grad}\Phi \,.\, \mathbf{ds} = +\operatorname{grad}\Phi'' \,.\, \mathbf{ds}''.$$

There is thus no contribution from these forces to the change of circulation.

Friction and other forces representing irreversible processes may, and generally do, alter the circulation.

Finally, there is the contribution from the change of the element $\mathbf{ds}$, represented by $\mathbf{v} \cdot \left(\dfrac{D}{Dt} \, \mathbf{ds}\right)$. The element is composed of the same particles of fluid always but changes because of a difference of velocity between its ends. Thus $\dfrac{D}{Dt} \, \mathbf{ds}$ is equal to $d\mathbf{v}$, the difference in velocity between the two ends. We therefore have to deal with $\mathbf{v} \cdot d\mathbf{v}$. This scalar product of two vectors is equal to the sum of the products of their three components, namely $udu + vdv + wdw$; u, v, w being the three components of the vector $\mathbf{v}$. If we now draw the surfaces of constant u through the ends of the element $\mathbf{ds}$ to meet the closed curve again in $\mathbf{ds'''}$ then since u and du are the same on $\mathbf{ds}$ and $\mathbf{ds'''}$, but du is opposite in sign, the sum round the whole curve ($\oint u \cdot du$) is zero. Likewise $\oint v \cdot dv$ and $\oint w \cdot dw$ are also zero, and so $\oint \mathbf{v} \cdot d\mathbf{v}$ is zero.

Altogether therefore we find that

$$\frac{D}{Dt}\left(\oint \mathbf{v} \cdot \mathbf{ds}\right) = \oint\left(\frac{D}{Dt}\,\mathbf{v}\right) \cdot \mathbf{ds} + \oint \mathbf{v} \cdot \left(\frac{D}{Dt}\,\mathbf{ds}\right)$$

$$= -\oint \frac{1}{\rho}\,\text{grad}\,p \cdot \mathbf{ds} - \oint \text{grad}\,\Phi \cdot \mathbf{ds}$$

$$+ \oint \mathbf{F} \cdot \mathbf{ds} + \oint \mathbf{v} \cdot d\mathbf{v}$$

$= 0$ (if the surfaces of constant density are also isobars)

$+ 0$ (under all circumstances)

$+ 0$ (if there are no frictional or other non-conservative forces)

$+ 0$ (under all circumstances).

The result may be stated as follows: *the circulation round a closed curve always composed of the same fluid particles cannot change unless the fluid is acted upon by non-conservative forces such as friction or the surfaces of constant density do not coincide with the isobars.*

In particular the circulation round closed curves always composed of the same fluid particles in a frictionless fluid of uniform density cannot change.

(c) Changes of vorticity due to distortion

Now let us consider the properties of frictionless fluids of uniform density. The circulation round any closed curve lying initially on a vortex tube, but not circumscribing it, is zero. In the subsequent motion the circulation round any circuit drawn on the surface composed of the particles originally lying on the piece of tube bounded by the closed curve remains zero; the surface therefore remains part of a vortex tube.

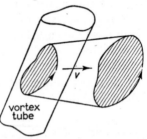

The intersection of two vortex tubes is a vortex line and so evidently the vortex line through a particle of fluid always consists of the same other particles.

Vortex lines and vortex tubes, therefore, move with the fluid and consist always of the same particles.

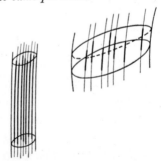

The fluid contained in a short section of a vortex filament always has the same vortex lines crossing it, and if it is distorted *the vorticity is inversely proportional to its area.* As the vortex lines are crowded together the rotation increases in proportion to the number of them crossing unit area.

Since the forces due to the pressure gradient cannot alter the circulation (unless the density varies along the isobars) any ' forcible ' alteration in the shape of a fluid either by pistons or movement of the boundaries or by the action of the surrounding fluid must vary the vorticity in accordance with this law.   The most interesting case is when the fluid is stretched along the direction of the vortex lines because this increases the intensity of rotation on account of the lateral contraction.

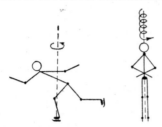

Solids possess vorticity, it being twice their angular velocity. The vortex lines in a solid are parallel to the axis of rotation. If a rotating skater contrives to draw in his limbs in a direction perpendicular to this axis he crowds the vortex lines together and increases the rate of rotation.   To slow down his rotation he only has to stretch out his limbs again.

The production of vortex filaments

In the last article we saw that circulation can be produced in two ways—through the variation of the density along the isobars and through the operation of non-conservative fields of force.   We shall leave the second of these for the next chapter where fluid friction is discussed.   Here we shall consider the first.

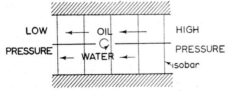

There are two important situations in which the isobars can be tilted relative to the surfaces of constant density.   One is when the pressure gradient is determined artificially, as it might be in a pipe with a light fluid such as oil in the top half and water in the bottom. If the pressure is raised at one end the isobars will be across the pipe while the density is uniform on lines along it. The same pressure gradient force operates on unit volume of both water and oil, but since the density of oil is less the acceleration will be greater. This will produce a shearing motion of the oil over the water, the corresponding vorticity being about horizontal axes at right-angles to the diagram.

The vortex lines produced will be the lines of intersection of the surfaces of constant pressure with the surfaces of constant density because there will be no rotation produced about any axis perpendicular to these surfaces. The direction in which rotation is created is so as to bring the constant density surfaces into coincidence with the isobars.

Alternatively, the pressure field may be produced by gravity, as in the atmosphere and in open water. In this case if the density surfaces are tilted then the pressure surfaces will also be, but by a different amount.

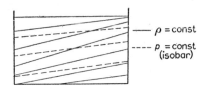

The existence of accelerations in the fluid will alter the pressure gradient, but in general, if the motion is produced by the tilting of the density surfaces in the first place the pressure gradients corresponding to the inertia forces will be small in comparison with those produced by the weight of the fluid. Thus the pressure is approximately equal to the weight of fluid above, and the departure from this value due to upward or downward accelerations of the fluid are generally small.

One can think of cases in which the inertia plays an important part in tilting the constant density surfaces even farther from the horizontal than they already are. For instance when a wave makes impact with a sea wall the inertia causes the water to ride up the wall and tilt the (constant density) surface of the water upwards in the opposite direction to the influence of gravity which tends to make the surface horizontal. As the tilting of the surface increases gravity sets up an increasing pressure gradient such as to produce a rotation of the surface towards the horizontal again.

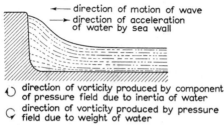

← direction of motion of wave
→ direction of acceleration of water by sea wall

↻ direction of vorticity produced by component of pressure field due to inertia of water
↺ direction of vorticity produced by pressure field due to weight of water

Production of vorticity in the atmosphere by gravity

A fluid is said to be stably stratified when the tilting of horizontal surfaces in the fluid produces a pressure gradient force tending to make them level again. In an incompressible fluid stable stratification implies simply an increase in density downwards. In general it is required that an element of fluid displaced upwards (or downwards) should have a greater (or smaller) density than the fluid at the level to which it is displaced. A neutral state is one in which an element displaced vertically has the same density as its new surroundings. Since the pressure decreases upwards air displaced upwards is expanded and its density decreased accordingly. If at the same time there is no exchange of heat with the surroundings the density is related to the temperature by the adiabatic law, which is discussed further in Chapter 7. This means that we can express the neutral density gradient in terms of a gradient of temperature, which is called the 'adiabatic lapse rate' (see page 169 for further discussion). This is approximately a decrease of 9·9°C per km of height. If the temperature gradient exceeds this the air is unstable: if it is less the air is stable.

(a) Air waves

The surfaces originally horizontal in the atmosphere may be tilted by a variety of mechanisms such as the flow down a mountain slope. (This subject is discussed further in Chapter 9.) Let us suppose that the surfaces are tilted near the foot of the hill so that the crossing of the pressure and density surfaces creates a rotation in the direction shown.   When the surfaces are horizontal, at B, the momentum of rotation will carry the air past the equilibrium position so that when it arrives at C the tilt will be in the opposite direction to what it was at A.   Here the creation of vorticity is in the opposite direction and the air moves over the crest D of the wave by a process opposite to that by which it traversed the trough B.   In the absence of damping by friction this oscillation about the equilibrium position in which the surfaces are horizontal will continue indefinitely and a train of stationary waves will be observed on the lee side of a mountain in a stably stratified airstream.

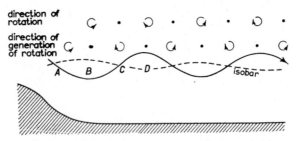

The waves are stationary relative to the mountain, but are being propagated through the air in an *upstream* direction with a speed equal to the wind speed.   If there were some mechanisms for initiating them they could be propagated with a speed different from the wind, and could therefore travel across the ground.

(b) Convection

If air is unstable the upward displacement of a portion of the air surrounds it with air of greater density.   Vorticity in rings round the buoyant air is generated.   The ensuing motion is the

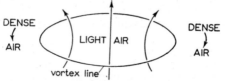

subject of Chapter 8.   If the buoyant air rises up to a stable layer and passes beyond its equilibrium level vorticity in the opposite direction is generated and the ring vortex lines are destroyed.

Vortex rings

A vortex ring is an isolated closed (or re-entrant) vortex. If it is of irregular shape its motion is necessarily unsteady. The motion changes the shape and this extends some parts of the tube and compresses others, thereby altering the velocity field. The mathematical difficulties involved in the study of unsteady vortical motion which is neither two dimensional nor has axial symmetry are almost insurmountable. But the motion of circular vortex rings is of considerable interest even though they do not normally occur naturally. Here we shall describe some properties of vortex rings without proof. The reader interested in the mathematics is referred to Lamb's *Hydrodynamics*.

We suppose that the vorticity is confined within a tubular ring of fluid of almost circular section. This we call the *substance* of the vortex ring. The vortex lines are then circles within the substance. The form of the motion of the external fluid, which possesses no vorticity, is shown in the figure. The quantities which determine how the ring moves are the magnitude of the circulation round the tube, the diameter of the tube containing all the substance, and the diameter of the ring. One extreme case is that in which the tube is contracted into a single circular line round which the circulation is finite. If the fluid is at rest at infinity the ring itself is also at rest, and the velocity at the centre is along the axis of the ring.

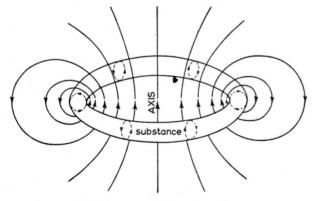

If now the vorticity is spread through a finite volume of fluid the substance moves in the direction of the motion along its axis with a velocity which may or may not exceed the velocity on the axis at the centre of the ring. If the velocity of the substance exceeds that at the centre of the ring the fluid at the centre will be left behind by the ring, and although its motion is in the same direction as that of the ring, it passes, relative to the ring, through it in the opposite direction.

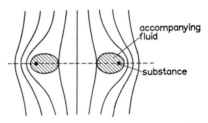

Fluid closer to the substance of the ring will move forwards through it: and such material will travel with the ring even though it contains no vorticity. This situation, in which the *accompanying fluid* is itself ring-shaped, is difficult to realise in practice because it requires that the diameter of the tube shall be less than

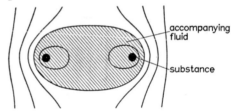

$\frac{1}{86}$ times the diameter of the ring. Normally the velocity at the centre exceeds the forward velocity of the substance so that the accompanying fluid is contained within an ovoid surface. The shape of the surface depends upon the distribution of vorticity within the substance, and only special cases have been investigated. One interesting case is Hill's spherical vortex: the substance occupies the whole sphere, outside which there is no vorticity, and there is no exterior fluid accompanying the substance.

Within the substance of the vortex ring the circular vortex lines are carried through and around one another by the motion. As they pass through one another they alternately contract and expand.

If a feeble ring vortex were present in the fluid accompanying an intense one it would circulate through and around it, but if it were in the exterior fluid it would pass through it or around it at most once. If two vortices of comparable strength and with

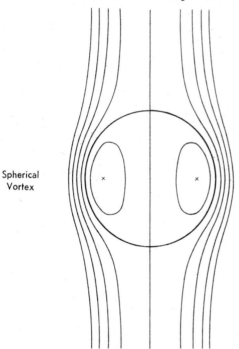

Spherical Vortex

circulations in the same direction are aligned upon the same axis they will continually pass through one another if the one at the rear is either within the fluid which would accompany the other or has a forward velocity of its own, through the surrounding fluid sufficient to catch up the other.

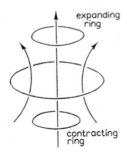

expanding ring

contracting ring

The circulation of each remains constant but the one at the front will be extended while that at the rear will be contracted, each in the field of motion of the other.   This causes the expanding one to be slowed down while the other is accelerated, in such a way as eventually to pass through it if they are close enough together.

The substance of a single vortex ring can be thought of as composed of a bundle of separate thin vortex rings continually passing through each other.   The cross sections of the inner rings of the bundle are larger because they have been compressed, while those on the outside, having been stretched, are smaller.   Therefore the vortex lines within the substance are more closely packed on the outside, so that in the circulations round them the bulk of the fluid is carried forward in the direction of the motion on the inside.

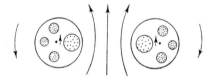

If the substance of the vortex ring is buoyant and the ring is travelling upwards, then as the fluid passes round the outside of the ring circulation in the same direction as round the ring is created by the density difference between the substance and the outside fluid.   As it passes up the inside of the ring vorticity in the opposite direction is created.   The vorticity is therefore greater in the lower part of the substance and so the substance as a whole will have an outward velocity, and the ring becomes larger as it travels.   Likewise a vortex ring whose substance is heavier than the surroundings increases in radius if it is descending.   If they are travelling in the opposite direction to the buoyancy force upon them vortex rings contract.

If a vortex ring is travelling vertically in unstable surroundings the accompanying fluid acquires increasing buoyancy as it advances and so it too will increase its radius: but if the surrounding fluid is stably stratified the diameter of the ring occupied by the accompanying fluid will decrease.   Clearly the motion must change its nature if buoyancy forces operate for any considerable time because their effect, being proportional to time, will ultimately dominate the motion.

In the theoretical case when the vorticity is concentrated into a single circle the circulation of the separate vortex lines round one another cannot occur and so the ring does not progress: this is impossible to achieve in practice, yet the concept is useful in giving us an idea of the velocity field due to an individual closed vortex line. Each vortex line is subjected to motion which is the sum of the separate velocity fields of all the others.

For purposes of discussion we shall state here, without proof, what is the velocity field of closed vortex filament. The exterior fluid possesses no vorticity so that the motion can be expressed in terms of a potential. An equipotential surface is such that at all points of it the solid angle subtended by the closed vortex line is the same. The velocity is everywhere perpendicular to these surfaces and is proportional to the change in the solid angle due to a displacement unit distance along the streamline. Thus the velocity is large where the solid single changes most rapidly in the direction of motion.

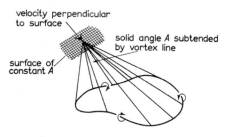

velocity perpendicular to surface

solid angle A subtended by vortex line

surface of constant A

Straight line vortices

If the motion is two dimensional in planes perpendicular to a set of line vortices the solid angles are measured as ordinary angles, most conveniently between a fixed direction and the lines from the point in question to the points where the vortices meet the plane. The direction of measurement of the angles accords with the sense of the vorticity. Each line vortex produces no

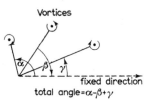

Vortices

fixed direction

total angle $= \alpha - \beta + \gamma$

motion of itself, but moves in the field of motion of the others.
The motion due to the separate vortices can be added vectorially.
In particular if there are only two it can be readily seen that they
will rotate around a fixed point on the line joining them, which is
between them if they are in the same sense, but outside them if
their direction of rotation is opposed. The fixed point may be
regarded as their ' centre of gravity ', their magnitudes being
measured by their circulations. In the particular case of two
equal and opposite vortices the fixed point is at infinity and the
vortex pair progresses at right-angles to the plane containing them.

The equipotential surfaces are the coaxal circular cylinders which
pass through the vortices, and the streamlines, which intersect
these cylinders everywhere at right-angles, are therefore coaxal
circles. The velocity between two vortices is greater than the
velocity of the vortices so that there is always a body of accompanying fluid. This is shown in the left-hand figure. The

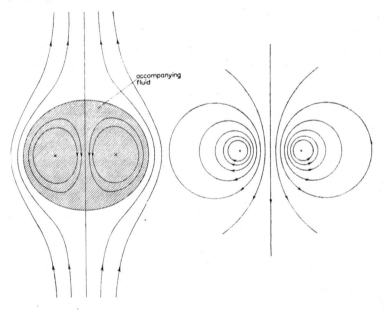

accompanying
fluid

instantaneous motion of the fluid is shown on the right.

The nearest approach to line vortices in Nature is found on a water surface. In a river vortices with vertical axes can often be seen in the wake of a bridge pier or other obstacle. They are rather like line vortices terminating on the upper boundary of the water. They can be seen to rotate around one another: but the motion is not always stable in the sense discussed on page 53 so that small vortices sometimes disappear. It must also be remembered, when watching such vortices, that sinking motion beneath the surface can often intensify vortices while upwelling motion destroys them by horizontal spreading of the surface layers.

Vortex pair

An aircraft wing experiences a force at right-angles to its direction of motion relative to the air by producing a *downwash*. The force applied to the air continuously adds downward momentum to it. The downwash is bounded on each side by a vortex which trails back from the wing-tip. The motion close to the wing is described in most books on aerodynamics: we are concerned with the behaviour of the two line vortices which are produced. The motion is the sum of the motions of two solitary line vortices and this was shown in vertical section in the last figure. There is a strong downward motion between the vortices and a feeble upward motion outside. The vortices move downwards under each other's influence with a speed which is a quarter of the downward speed at the mid point.

Some aquatic birds fly in formation in order, so it is said, that those behind may be in the upward moving air outside the vortex pair of a bird in front. But this may not be the only advantage of formation flight. Possibly the mechanical connection established between the birds keeps a small group together on long migrations or at night. Only one bird need navigate, and the setting of a pace may help weaker birds.

Vortex pairs made by heavy aircraft are sometimes made visible by the condensation of exhaust in the centre of the vortices. The motion is stable because, as we have seen, the rotation in the centre cannot be as rapid as in a line vortex. Consequently mixing between the air in the centre and the air outside each vortex is inhibited and two thin tubes of cloud are sometimes seen to trail for a mile or two behind the aircraft. These trails, and the accompanying fluid, are descending through air that is stably stratified and so there will be a gradually increasing upward buoyancy force acting upon them and their accompanying fluid. This will begin to produce vorticity in the opposite direction so that the vortices will ultimately become embedded in air of opposite vorticity. This is an unstable configuration and so the material rotating in the centre of the vortices will ' burst ' out into the surrounding fluid (see plate 2).

This bursting will occur first on those parts of the vortices which have descended farthest because the buoyancy of the fluid and the creation of vorticity in the opposite direction will be greatest there. These will also be the parts where the vortices have been stretched along their length, for if a part of them becomes stretched the vortices will be brought nearer together, and this will in turn increase their downward velocity and thereby increase the stretching at that point. The vortices are also brought nearer together as they descend because there is an upward buoyancy force on them and their accompanying fluid (see page 70).

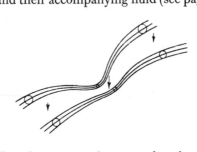

This instability of a vortex pair means that the downwash of an aircraft tends to break up into lumps. If the condensation of exhaust takes place not in the vortices but is generally spread throughout the downwash, it will descend first as a curtain of cloud but soon the lower edge of the curtain will break up into lumps corresponding to those parts of the vortex pair which are descending most rapidly. Alternatively there may be no condensation of exhaust, and if the aircraft is flying above a thin layer of cloud either it may force a tube of clear air down into the cloud, or only the ' lumps ' of the downwash may reach to the bottom of the cloud, in which case a line of clear holes is made.

Two trails from two engines on one side of an aircraft will rotate round one another, the inner one passing first below, then outside, and then above the outer one.

Vorticity on a rotating earth

We saw in Chapter 2 that for many purposes the atmosphere may be considered as being constrained on a large scale to move horizontally, so that the only component of the earth's rotation which we need to consider is the rotation about the vertical. Rotation of the air about the vertical can be changed either by a change of latitude or by vertical motion. We shall consider these processes separately, but first we shall discover how they may be recognised on a pressure chart.

We must not allow our thinking to become confused at this point by asking which happens first—the changes in the pressure field or the changes in the pattern of motion. Of course there must be new pressure gradients if the pattern is to change, in the sense that all the accelerations are due to pressure gradients; but it is unprofitable to try to think of the motion producing new pressure gradient and the new pressure gradient producing more new motion. The pressure and velocity fields develop simultaneously, and the only reason why we are so intimately concerned with the pressure in studying large scale atmospheric motion is that it is easy to measure and to map, and has been developed into a convenient quantity in terms of which to represent the motion (see Chapter 2).

The motion is nearly geostrophic. If it were precisely so in the sense that the pressure map would be a convenient method of displaying the motion exactly, then as the motion changed the isobars would change with it. In considering the vorticity we have eliminated the pressure from the discussion for we are able to say how the motion will develop without reference to pressure; but if we are to say what the motion will look like on the weather chart we must say how the isobars will move. Therefore when we find that cyclonic vorticity (or rotation relative to the earth in the same direction as the earth's rotation in space) is increasing, we can expect to see the development of a centre of low pressure, or at least a region of pressure falling relative to the surroundings. We would likewise expect to see rising pressure where rotation was developing relative to the earth in the opposite direction.

Motion round a cyclone (depression, low—same thing) must possess cyclonic vorticity relative to the earth. Rotation in an anticyclone is in the same direction as the earth in space but slower, so that it is in the opposite direction relative to the earth. The curvature of the isobars when it is large is thus a good indication of the vorticity relative to the earth, but when it is small we must notice also how the pressure gradient varies from one place to another in order to determine the direction of the vorticity.

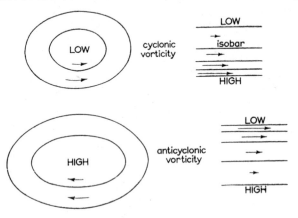

(a) Long waves: change of latitude

If an air current has no vorticity relative to the earth at one latitude and is inclined so that the air moves to a different latitude, say polewards, the component of the earth's rotation in space about the vertical increases and so the rotation of the air relative to the earth decreases and must therefore become negative, or anticyclonic. The most northerly parts of the current move more rapidly and the streamlines (and therefore the isobars also if the motion is approximately geostrophic) curve to the right. This direction of curvature is maintained until the air has returned to its original latitude; but because it is crossing at an angle it passes to a lower latitude where its rotation relative to the earth must be cyclonic because the rotation of the earth about the vertical is less than that of the air. The air therefore again returns to its original latitude.

The wave motion which results was first elucidated by Rossby. If there are no other influences the length of waves executed by a parcel of air (which is not to be confused with the length of waves to be seen in the instantaneous flow pattern or isobar pattern which may be moving), can depend only on the wind speed U, and Rossby's parameter β which is twice the rate of change with

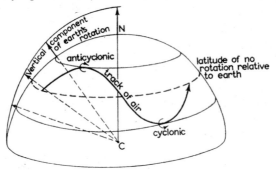

latitude of the vertical component of the earth's rotation. β is, in effect, the rate of change of the vorticity of the ground as we go northwards, and is represented mathematically by $\partial f/\partial y$, if y is length measured along a line of longitude.

The units of β can be radians per second per centimetre, and the units of U centimetres per second. In order to obtain a length from these we have to combine them in the form $(U/\beta)^{\frac{1}{2}}$. Thus the wavelength is proportional to this quantity, the constant of proportionality (as in the analogous case of a simple pendulum) being found by a more complete analysis to be 2π. Thus:

$$\text{Wavelength} = 2\pi(U/\beta)^{\frac{1}{2}}$$

This formula is only for small amplitude waves, for in this argument we have assumed that the amplitude has no effect on the wavelength. (See Chapter 11 for fuller discussion.)

(b) Convergence and divergence

When there is horizontal convergence there must be vertical stretching of the vortex lines. If the air were initially rotating with the earth then it must have had the same number of vortex lines as the solid earth. After convergence it has more vortex lines per unit area and so must be rotating cyclonically relative to the earth. After divergence it has fewer vortex lines and is

therefore rotating slower than the earth in space and anticyclonically relative to it.

An extreme case of convergence occurs in a tropical cyclone
(hurricane, typhoon—same thing, almost).   The curvature of the
isobars is then so large that the wind is more nearly equal to the
gradient wind than the geostrophic.   Occasionally tropical cyclones
are carried in a broader airstream across the equator, in which
case they will be rotating anticyclonically in their new hemisphere.
This is rare, and is a source of confusion to mariners when it
happens.   Generally, however, air is rotating in space in the same
direction as the earth so that regions of convergence generate
cyclonic vorticity with low pressure.

The pressure field is used in forecasting practice to represent
the wind field.   Since the wind field cannot be measured accurately enough to obtain a reliable estimate of the convergence, the
rate of change of the pressure field is used to deduce the rate of
change of cyclonic vorticity.   This is directly related to the
convergence because it is proportional to the density of vortex
lines which is varied by the convergence.

Secondary flow

Secondary flow is the name given to circulations which develop
in a fluid when the main flow is distorted even though these
circulations have, initially at least, no influence on the distortions.

(a) Bend in a canal

If fluid is flowing along a canal of uniform section without
vorticity then at a bend the flow on the inside will be faster and on
the outside slower than in the straight portion.   If this were not
so the fluid would have to possess vorticity.   Consequently a line
of particles arranged across the stream in the straight section will
move forward on the inside of the bend relative to the fluid on the
outside.   On coming out of the bend the fluid has been distorted
but no small elements of it have been rotated.   This deformation
of the main flow occurs whether or not the fluid possesses any
vorticity in addition.

In a practical case, the friction on the bottom of the channel
retards the lower layers of fluid so that the velocity profile is as
shown in the figure.   The dotted line is then a vortex line.   On
emerging from the bend the vortex lines are seen to lie diagonally

and so there is a circulation as shown in the bottom of the figure
because vortex lines cross the section drawn.

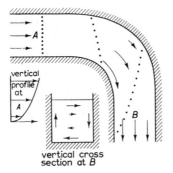

vertical cross
section at B

This secondary circulation will appear even if there is no friction
in the bend itself, so long as the fluid enters the bend possessed
of vorticity.

An alternative way of thinking about the phenomenon in terms
of pressure is as follows. The pressure is higher on the outside
of the bend because the fluid is being accelerated inwards by the
pressure gradient force as it passes round the curve; according to
Bernoulli's equation (page 9) we can see that the fluid on the
outside must therefore be moving more slowly. The lower
layers of fluid are travelling more slowly and therefore the centrifugal force on them is less than on the layers above and is less than
the inward pressure gradient force which is determined by the
slope of the free surface and the motion of the upper layers.
Thus the layers at the bottom will be accelerated inwards and the
secondary circulation results. This analysis is less satisfactory
than that using vorticity because it can only predict accelerations,
not motion. By following the vortex lines the tracks of the
particles can be discovered.

The consequence of this is that silt on the bed of a river is
carried towards the inside of a bend, where upwelling occurs.

(b) Bend in a pipe

By a similar analysis we can see that if the flow in the centre of
a pipe is greater than round the walls the vortex lines are rings
concentric with the pipe at right-angles to the flow. These
rings are distorted by the motion round the bend so that vortex

lines cross a section of the pipe after the bend, and the circulation is as shown in the figure.

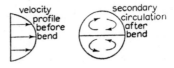

If the bend continues after the secondary circulation is established friction will begin to modify it and it will also contribute substantially to the deformation of the vortex lines. The problem is then very complex.

Circulations such as these can have an effect on the erosion of the walls of a pipe or on the deposition of ' fur ' in hot hard water.

(c) Motion behind a tree

If the wind increases upwards from the ground the vortex lines are horizontal and across the flow. At some distance to one side of a tree the flow is undisturbed. A particle approaching the stagnation point on the wind-facing side of a tree gradually comes to rest there. The vortex lines are therefore wrapped round the tree and on the lee side circulation will be produced with downward motion in the middle and upward motion on each side. The vortex lines are stretched in this region as well as being distorted so that this circulation may be considerable.

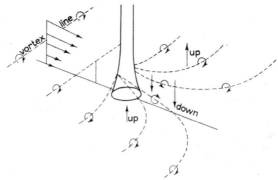

One effect of this type of motion is to bring the upper layers to the ground and to carry the lower layers up. Obstacles on the ground cause the upper and lower layers to be very effectively mixed in this way.

(d) *Motion behind a hump*

The motion behind a hump, or house, or rock, is similar to that behind a tree because near to the ground the vortex lines are retarded in front of the obstacle. There may not be a stagnation point in this case because the flow may pass over the top. In the atmosphere if the hump is as large as a hill and the air is unstably stratified by air being made very hot close to the ground in the sunshine, the lifting of the air over the hump raises it to the same level as air that has not been warmed as much. Vorticity then begins to be generated by the buoyancy forces in the opposite direction, that is with upward motion in the centre in the lee of the hump. Close to the ground where the retardation of the air is dominant the circulation is the same as behind a tree. The complete circulation in a section across the flow in the lee of the hump is then as shown in the figure (Part 3). This problem was first investigated by Hawthorne and Martin.

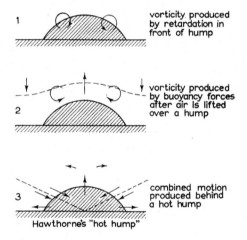

1   vorticity produced by retardation in front of hump

2   vorticity produced by buoyancy forces after air is lifted over a hump

3   combined motion produced behind a hot hump

Hawthorne's "hot hump"

Instability of a vortex sheet

The discontinuity of velocity between two adjacent streams of fluid in each of which the velocity is uniform is called a vortex sheet. On the surface of discontinuity the vorticity is infinite, elsewhere it is zero.

If a slight deformation occurs on the sheet there is a convergence of the fluid towards the sheet in the neighbourhood of B, and a divergence from it in the neighbourhood of A. If we imagine the sheet to consist of a thin layer in which the vorticity is very large, instead of an infinitesimally thick layer of infinite vorticity, we see that the material of the layer tends to accumulate near A, but to be squeezed away from the neighbourhood of B. As the layer accumulates near A the circulation in a fixed circuit round A increases in a direction so as to increase the deformation and so the motion tends to wind up the vortex sheet round A and to stretch it at B, producing a row of vortices instead of a sheet of vorticity.

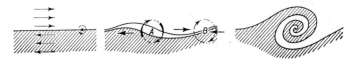

Whirls of this sort can sometimes be seen on the tops of cumulus clouds which are composed of air rising from a lower level into a faster moving layer of air. The tops of the clouds thus tend to become vortex sheets. Whirls are also sometimes seen on the tops of layer clouds in the neighbourhood of mountains where the deformation of the flow by the mountain produces a discontinuity of velocity at the cloud top.

CHAPTER 4

VISCOSITY

SO FAR we have concerned ourselves with forces which have been due to the pressure gradient, the inertia, the earth's rotation, and gravity. Friction has been occasionally mentioned, and in this chapter we shall discuss more fully the phenomenon of internal friction in a fluid.

Stresses and strains

A stress is a force. We are interested in the force which can act between one part of a fluid and another. If the geometrical surface S lies within the fluid it is instructive to discuss what forces there can be between the fluid on one side of a portion A of unit area of this surface and the fluid on the other side. The stresses add up to a single force $\mathbf{R}$ which may be resolved into three components, $\mathbf{X}$ and $\mathbf{Y}$ in the tangent plane to A, and $\mathbf{Z}$ in the direction perpendicular to A. $\mathbf{Z}$ is called the normal stress, $\mathbf{X}$ and $\mathbf{Y}$ are the two components of the tangential stress.

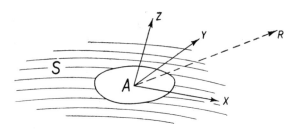

When the fluid is at rest $\mathbf{Z}$ is the only component because it is the property of a fluid that when at rest it can retain no tangential stresses (it cannot resist a distortion because a fluid has no natural shape). The normal stress is then equal to the pressure.

A strain is a distortion. A fluid only resists a strain while it is in the course of being produced; no force other than the normal pressure is required to keep a fluid in the distorted shape. The forces, or stresses, which are produced within the fluid are proportional to the *rate* at which the distortion is taking place, which is called the rate of strain. The simplest example is provided by shearing motion in which the velocity is everywhere in the direction of x but increases with increasing z. In addition to the normal pressure, **Z**, there is now a *shearing stress* or *tangential stress*, **X**, exerted by the fluid below the element of area A on that above. This stress is in the direction which tends to reduce the relative motion of adjacent layers of fluid and is proportional to the shear, or rate of strain. The constant of proportionality is μ, the coefficient of viscosity.

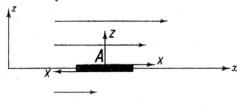

It has, for the most part, been assumed that there is always a linear relationship between the stress and the rate of strain. This is equivalent to assuming that the properties of the fluid which are responsible for its viscosity are unaltered by the shearing motion. As we shall see, the viscosity is produced by the ' random ' motion of the molecules, and there is no *a priori* reason why this should remain unaffected when the shear is very large. For instance if the distance between layers whose difference in speed was comparable with the speed of sound were equal to only a small multiple of the mean free path of the molecules, we could reasonably expect that the ' random ' motion would not be isotropic. But this contingency does not normally occur in nature, except in the air around shooting stars, and will not concern us in this book.

In the case of simple shearing motion, then, we have that

$$\mathbf{X} = \mu \frac{\partial u}{\partial z}.$$

We now consider the effect of these forces on the particles of fluid. If the shear on one side of the particle is the same as on the other side then the shearing stresses due to the fluid on the two

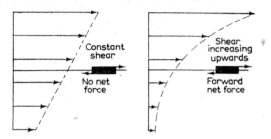

sides will be equal and opposite and there will be no net force on the particle. But if the velocity profile is curved the stress steadily increases up through the fluid as indicated in the figure so that all particles will experience a forward force which will be proportional to the rate at which the shear increases upwards. The frictional force per unit mass is then equal to

$$F_x = \frac{1}{\rho} \frac{\partial \mathbf{X}}{\partial z} = \frac{1}{\rho} \frac{\partial}{\partial z} \left(\mu \frac{\partial u}{\partial z} \right)$$

and this is generally written as

$$F_x = \nu \frac{\partial^2 u}{\partial z^2}.$$

Here F_x is the force in the x-direction due to viscosity and ν, $= \mu/\rho$, is called the dynamic viscosity, whose significance we shall discover later.

$$\frac{\partial}{\partial z} \left(\frac{\partial u}{\partial z} \right), \quad \text{or} \quad \frac{\partial^2 u}{\partial z^2},$$

is the gradient of the shear, and variations in viscosity from place to place are assumed to be negligible.

Clearly, if the velocity, u, in the x-direction varies in the y direction there is also a component of F_x, equal to $\nu \partial^2 u/\partial y^2$. A further distortion of the fluid is produced if u varies in the direction of x and there is a further component of F_x equal to $\nu \partial^2 u/\partial x^2$. The cause of this third component will be understood best by first analysing the cause of the other two components.

Kinetic theory of viscosity: transfer of momentum

The kinetic theory of heat supposes that the molecules are in a continuous state of agitation which increases in intensity with increase in temperature. In liquids this increase is accompanied by a simultaneous decrease in the intermolecular bonds which determine the volume of the liquid. The intermolecular bonds in a gas are negligible, in this context at least. This 'random' motion causes an exchange of molecules between adjacent layers of fluid, and *on the average* the molecules from the lower layer

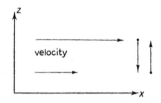

will arrive in the upper layer with a velocity in the x-direction equal to that of the layer from which they have come. Molecules passing from the upper to the lower layer will possess a velocity in the x-direction equal to that of their layer origin, on the average. If the upper layer is moving faster than the lower layer the momentum of the lower layer in the x-direction will be increased and that of the upper layer decreased by these exchanges of molecules. The rate at which momentum is transferred from one layer to the other will depend upon the amount of shear (which determines the excess or deficit of velocity with which molecules from one layer arrive at the other), and also upon the frequency with which the molecules make the crossing and how far they travel across the main stream before being absorbed into their new layer. These last two factors are represented by μ, and the first by the shear $\partial u/\partial z$. μ is a physical property of the fluid, and is independent of the motion (at least so it is generally assumed, and the assumption works well at ordinary fluid speeds).

The force produced by the molecular motion in the direction of the motion is the pressure gradient force. The normal pressure upon an element of surface is produced by the bombardment of that surface by the molecules, or by the molecules crossing the surface and adding their momentum to the fluid on the other side. If the fluid is being stretched in the direction of the motion then the surface is receding from the molecules bombarding it and the normal pressure is reduced on the rear side of a small volume. If it is being stretched more on the forward side the reduction in pressure is greater there and so the volume experiences a net forward force which is equal to

$$\frac{1}{\rho} \frac{\partial}{\partial x} \left(\mu \frac{\partial u}{\partial x} \right)$$

per unit volume. This term represents the unwillingness of the fluid to be stretched in one direction and simultaneously contracted in the direction at right-angles.

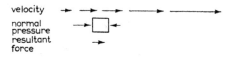

Finally, if the fluid is expanding the normal pressure is reduced because the molecules are all, on the average, moving apart from one another. If the rate of the expansion varies from one part of the fluid to another there will be a net force on the fluid towards the regions where the expansion is greatest. This effect is very small except in very high speed flow. When the changes in velocity are comparable with the speed of sound these effects become very large and ordinary viscous flow does not occur. Shock waves are then produced, in which there is a great dissipation of ordered energy into heat, but we shall not be concerned with them in this book.

The Reynolds number

The equation for the motion of unit mass of fluid with which we began was enlarged to include friction on page 18. We now have an estimate of the friction force in terms of the coefficient of viscosity and the distribution of shear. The equation states

$$\text{Acceleration} = \frac{\text{pressure gradient force}}{\text{density}} + \text{deviating force} + \text{friction} + \text{gravity.}$$

In cases where friction is important we are concerned with motion on a small scale such that the deviating force is unimportant. The force of gravity is usually nearly equal and opposite to the vertical component of the pressure gradient force ($\partial p / \partial z = -g\rho$). When internal friction is important the dominant forces are therefore represented by

$$\text{Acceleration} = \frac{\text{pressure gradient force}}{\text{density}} + \text{net viscous force}$$

$$\frac{D}{Dt} u = -\frac{1}{\rho} \frac{\partial p}{\partial x} + \nu \left(\frac{\partial^2 u}{\partial x^2} + \frac{\partial^2 u}{\partial y^2} + \frac{\partial^2 u}{\partial z^2} \right)$$

The mathematical form of this equation written here is the component in the x-direction only, u being the component of the velocity in this direction, for it is inconvenient to write the friction term in vector form. We note again that what we have written down for friction is only the *resultant* of all the friction forces per a unit mass of fluid.

When we speak of viscous flow we mean flow in which the forces of viscosity are of major importance. When the velocities are very small, as in treacle or glycerine, the inertia forces are negligible and the pressure gradient force is almost equal and opposite to the net viscous force. When the velocities are larger the inertia forces may be of the same order of magnitude as the viscous forces, and in some cases the viscous forces may be negligible in comparison so that the pressure gradient force nearly balances the inertia force.

The Reynolds number R, is the ratio of the inertia forces to the viscous forces: when it is large viscosity is relatively unimportant in determining the pattern of flow in the sense that variations in viscosity do not alter it appreciably. When R is small the viscous forces are dominant and the motion is sluggish and treacly. R may be evaluated in various ways. In the equation we see that

$$R = \left(\frac{D}{Dt} u \right) \bigg/ \nu \left(\frac{\partial^2 u}{\partial x^2} + \frac{\partial^2 u}{\partial y^2} + \frac{\partial^2 u}{\partial z^2} \right)$$

for this is the ratio of the appropriate terms in the equation. But this is not a very helpful form in which to express it because it varies from one part of the flow to another, and is zero at points where the acceleration, or inertia force, happens to be zero. Therefore we take a representative value of the terms contained in it. If U is a velocity and d a length then a representative time is d/U. (In an example U might be the speed in a broad stream and d the width or length of an obstacle.) An acceleration, or inertia force, which is velocity $\div$ time, is therefore $U \div d/U$ or

U^2/d. The velocity gradients $\dfrac{\partial u}{\partial x}$, $\dfrac{\partial u}{\partial y}$, and $\dfrac{\partial u}{\partial z}$ are represented by

U/d and the gradients of these gradients $\left(\dfrac{\partial^2 u}{\partial x^2}, \dfrac{\partial^2 u}{\partial y^2}, \text{ and } \dfrac{\partial^2 u}{\partial z^2}\right)$ by

U/d^2. Then

$$R = \frac{U^2}{d} \Big/ \nu\, \frac{U}{d^2}$$

$$= \frac{Ud}{\nu}.$$

Further insight may be gained by consideration of energy. We saw in discussing Bernoulli's theorem that we can compare the inertia force with the pressure force per unit area, p, by considering how the kinetic energy $\frac{1}{2}\rho U^2$ changes, as work is done by the pressure gradient force. We might call $\frac{1}{2}\rho U^2/p$ the Bernoulli number because it expresses a relationship between the inertia force and the pressure force per unit area, but it has no practical value because the pressure is a result of the motion and adjusts itself to it. Viscosity on the other hand is a property of the fluid and is not determined by the motion, at least so we normally suppose. The representative viscous force per unit area, corresponding with the pressure, and therefore with $\frac{1}{2}\rho U^2$, is the viscosity multiplied by the shear. Shear is velocity gradient, or velocity $\div$ distance, and is represented by U/d. The representative viscous force per unit area is thus $\mu U/d$, and the Reynolds number is

$$R = \frac{1}{2}\rho U^2 \Big/ \mu\, \frac{U}{d}$$

$$= \frac{1}{2}\frac{Ud}{\nu}.$$

That we have arrived at half of the previous value illustrates that a unique value of R is not definable, but having once defined it in a particular way we must stick to the same definition while we make use of the number. The representative length and velocity are not unique; instead of d, which might be the diameter of an object in the flow, we could take its radius, and there is thus a necessary element of arbitrariness in the actual value of R chosen.

Similarity

The form of the flow is determined by the interplay between the various forces, and the external conditions imposed. Thus the shape of the streamlines is determined by the shape and movement of the boundaries, the external forces imposed (such as the force propelling a body through the fluid or the force applied to bodies to keep them fixed relative to one another in the flow, or the pressure difference between the two ends of a tube through which fluid is flowing) and *the interrelation between the inertia and viscous forces within the body of the fluid.* The pressure distribution within the fluid is determined *as a result* of the interplay of the other forces and is not a property of the fluid, like density, or viscosity, or a property of the boundaries like shape or size, imposed before the motion takes place.

The motion thus results from the boundary conditions imposed and the magnitude of the Reynolds number.

If a pattern of the flow were established and the velocity and viscosity were simultaneously reduced or increased in the same proportion the pattern of streamlines would remain the same because the Reynolds number would be unaltered. Again the geometrical shape of the pattern would remain unaltered if the dimensions and the viscosity were altered in the same proportion, because, again, the number Ud/ν would be unaltered. Of if the density and velocity were altered in inverse proportion so that ρU remained constant, the shape of the flow pattern would still remain unaltered.

This result is strictly a mathematical one, and it is argued at length in many text-books. We are concerned to emphasise the physical aspect, and the argument given here is not complete. It is important to ensure, in applying an argument of this kind, that the Reynolds number is the only non-dimensional number which can be composed from the conditions of the problem, if it is desired to establish that two examples of a flow pattern are similar even though the conditions are varied. For instance, if there were two bodies in a fluid stream and we wished to study the flow around them by a model experiment we would have to make the models of the two bodies to the same scale because another non-dimensional number (i.e. a pure ratio) can be obtained as the ratio of the diameters of the two bodies. We shall return to this theme in later chapters. If two flow patterns are to be similar *all* the non-dimensional numbers that can be composed must be the same in the two cases. The Reynolds number is only one such number. In the aerodynamics of machines it is the most important; but in Nature there are forces other than viscous and inertia forces which may be more important. Thus, if the deviating force, or forces due to gravity played an appreciable part in determining the motion, other numbers also would have to be considered in designing model experiments.

Efficiency of catch

We saw in Chapter 1 that when the air follows a curved path in front of an obstacle such as part of a tree, small airborne particles may make contact with the surface if they are heavier than air by crossing the streamlines followed by the particles of air. This motion relative to the surrounding air is resisted by the viscous forces and so the distance that the airborne particles are carried across the streamlines is reduced and the number of particles caught on the surface correspondingly reduced. In addition the velocity of the air close to the surface of the obstacle is reduced by viscosity and so the body produces a flow at some distance from itself which is more nearly like the flow without viscosity past a larger body. Consequently the existence of viscosity reduces the curvature of the streamlines in the fluid in front of the body and the velocity of the particles along those curves: this again reduces the distance travelled across the streamlines by airborne particles because their inertia has less effect when the accelerations are smaller.

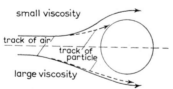

For both causes the obstacle catches fewer airborne particles than if there were no viscosity. The track of an airborne particle when the viscosity is either negligible or large is shown by the dotted lines in the figure above. The full lines show the tracks of air particles approaching along lines initially the same distance from the line of symmetry of the flow. It is more difficult to drop a ball bearing into treacle or glycerine so as to make it collide with a smaller one ahead of it than it is in water.

The boundary condition in viscous flow

We are used to talking about ' the surface wind ', meaning the wind we experience when standing on the surface of the earth. But strictly the velocity at the surface is zero. It may be large close to the surface, but the molecules of air which make contact with the surface on the average lose their component of velocity along the surface. This is an experimental fact. For example the rate of flow of viscous liquid through a narrow pipe can easily be calculated, for various diameters of pipe and pressure differences between the ends, either on the assumption that the velocity at the surface is zero or that there is some slip at the surface, and only the assumption that there is no slip agrees with the measurements in all cases.

As students of Nature we must, of course, recognise that this law is not exact in the sense that $2 + 2 = 4$ is exact. Future generations may be able to state a law which is nearer to the behaviour of Nature; but we do not at present know what sort of law this might be. The law of no slip makes our experience intelligible, and we have not met any phenomena, in the lower atmosphere at any rate, which depart measurably from it. At very high temperatures and in the ionosphere where the air particles are relatively far apart the motion may have to be treated as if the air were not a fluid but a finite collection of perfectly elastic molecules : but so long as we choose to think of the air as a fluid the law of no slip is satisfactory.

From the philosophical point of view it is difficult to imagine any other possible law : for one thing it would involve introducing a new property of the air which would determine what the amount of slip was, and this would be an additional complication which the true philosopher would be loath to invoke unless compelled by experience to do so.

The conduction of vorticity by viscosity

Viscosity produces a non-conservative field of force. The work done against the forces of viscosity is converted into random motion of the molecules, that is heat, and cannot be recovered as bulk motion of the fluid in the way that work done against gravity or pressure gradient forces can be.   According to the discussion on page 61 we would therefore expect that viscosity would give rise to vorticity, and this is indeed so.   The matter is readily discussed by formal mathematics and is treated in many books. We shall therefore not attempt to reproduce the formal theorem here, but will illustrate it in particular cases so that it can be understood physically.   The theorem is as follows:

Viscosity conducts vorticity in a manner analogous to the conduction of heat by thermal conductivity.   The simplest example is that in which a horizontal airstream has a curved velocity profile. We saw (page 85) that there is a forward net force exerted by the surrounding fluid where the profile is concave forwards, and a likewise backward net force where the profile is concave backwards.

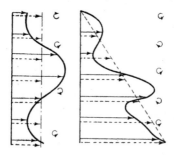

The fluid in the faster moving layers is retarded and that in the slower moving layers is accelerated until the momentum is uniformly distributed.   In the left-hand illustration the vorticity is in opposite directions in different parts of the fluid, and in the ultimate state there is no vorticity at all because the negative and positive regions cancel out as viscosity conducts the rotation from positive to negative regions.   But in the right-hand illustration we have the motion between two parallel planes only one of which is moving.   If the initial velocity profile is irregular so that the vorticity is irregular, the effect of viscosity is to make it uniform so that the velocity profile is straight and the net force on any layer is zero.   The curled arrows show the original direction of the vorticity.

We shall see further illustrations of this theorem in the next chapter. Meanwhile the line vortex provides an interesting example. We saw on page 52 that the vorticity is concentrated along a line, and that although the surrounding fluid possessed no vorticity it was circulating round this line. The velocity is proportional to $1/r$ and so the force tending to retard the rotation of the fluid within a radius r from the centre is $\mu \partial v/\partial r \times$ the area of the surface. This is proportional to $(\mu/r^2)r$ per unit length of the system in a direction perpendicular to the section drawn in the figure. To obtain the moment of this force about the centre we multiply by r, so that the rate of change of rotation within the circular cylinder whose section is drawn is proportional to μ, and independent of r. This means that there is no change in the rotation of the fluid between two cylinders of radius r_1 and r_2; and since there was no vorticity there to begin with there is not at any subsequent time. The line vortex therefore gradually slows down but the vorticity remains concentrated in the central line.

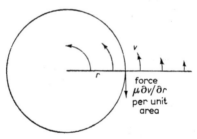

In the more realistic case in which there is a central core, of finite size, rotating with uniform vorticity, surrounded by fluid with no vorticity with velocity proportional to $1/r$, there are, to begin with, no stresses within the core. But the core as a whole is subjected to a slowing down which affects the outside of it first. This means that the vorticity in the central core diffuses outwards into the surrounding fluid as the whole vortex slows down. There are no internal stresses in a body of fluid rotating as a solid; and this is a stable configuration of motion (in the sense discussed on page 53). The motion round a line vortex is in neutral stability. The effect of viscosity therefore is to make the motion in a vortex (of any sort) more stable.

The *total* amount of vorticity within a volume of fluid remains constant as long as none is conducted across the boundaries of the volume of viscosity.

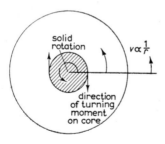

Flow at low Reynolds numbers

As the Reynolds number is decreased the inertia forces become steadily less important and the viscous forces balance the pressure gradient forces. The flow takes place mainly in a direction towards low pressure and is governed by the shape of the boundaries and the pressures applied there. By boundaries we mean the edge of the region under study. They may consist of solid walls or areas where the fluid enters or leaves the region, and in the latter cases the pressure applied is all-important.

If we double all the pressure gradients the viscous stresses are likewise doubled as the velocities are doubled. The configuration of flow is not appreciably altered because although the inertia forces are doubled they may still be negligible. There is thus a pattern of flow which is closely approximate to the flow at any small Reynolds number and can be thought of as being that of a treacly fluid.

When the dimensions of the objects with which we are concerned are very small the Reynolds number is small. A good example of this in Nature is provided by dandelion seeds. These have long, very thin fibres past which the air has to flow when the seed sinks through the air. The drag is large because the flow is at low Reynolds number, and is as effective as could be provided by any form of parachute of comparable overall dimensions.

Flight is impossible in the ordinary sense at very low Reynold numbers. It is impossible to establish a circulation round any form of wing in a treacly fluid, and tiny insects, particularly when swimming in water when their weight has not to be supported, use the viscous resistance to their limbs to propel themselves along.

The method of propulsion used by tadpoles, on the other hand, depends neither on the establishment of circulation round an 'aerofoil' nor on the existence of viscosity. The principle is to propagate a wave along the body in the direction opposite to that of the desired motion. Spermatozoa use a form of helical wave, at one extreme of size, and snakes (on land) at the other use it, but it is not used by birds because they are more concerned to obtain lift than propulsion. The motion of a fish's tail with a to and fro fanning is like the action of a humming bird's wings when it hovers motionless impelling the air downwards; it is a form of reciprocating propeller blade like the single oar used in the stern of a boat; but its path is almost identical in form with that of a portion of a tadpole's tail.

As the Reynolds number is increased the inertia of the air becomes increasingly important so that small variations in viscosity or dimensions may produce large changes in the pattern of flow. But when the Reynolds number becomes very large the form of flow again becomes fixed. These patterns are the subjects of the next two chapters.

CHAPTER 5

BOUNDARY LAYERS

Flow at moderate Reynolds numbers

WHEN the viscosity is large the pattern of flow is controlled by the positions of the solid boundaries, and the pressure gradient force is nearly balanced by the internal stresses transmitted through the fluid by the viscosity from the boundaries. As the velocity or the distance from the solid boundary is increased, or the viscosity decreased, the inertia forces become more important. Ultimately, at very great velocities and far from boundaries the inertia forces are dominant. In this chapter we shall consider the intermediate kind of flow in which only part of the field of motion, the boundary layer, is under the influence of viscosity, and we shall see how the flow can break away from the boundary. This is very much the realm of aeronautics because flying machines have to be designed to exploit the properties of boundary layers: the science is therefore well developed and there is an abundance of good textbooks in which the subject may be studied. We shall therefore be concerned only with the properties of boundary layers in so far as their understanding is necessary in the study of natural phenomena and of turbulent flow, which is very common.

The theory of boundary layers first put forward by Prandtl is sometimes regarded as an artifice whereby approximate mathematical solutions can be obtained to otherwise insoluble problems. This is not a fair evaluation because it does recognise a real phenomenon, namely that the influence of the boundary extends only a small distance from it. We have seen that vorticity cannot be produced within a fluid of uniform density except by diffusion of it through the agency of viscosity either from solid boundaries or from regions of large vorticity. Thus except in regions into which vorticity has been diffused the flow is as if there were no viscosity.

Diffusion of a vortex sheet

If there existed a sheet vortex in the form of a discontinuity of velocity between two layers of fluid, and we could contrive to prevent the surface from becoming ruffled, by having a large density discontinuity for instance, then the viscosity would cause the discontinuity of velocity to become first a shallow layer of large shear and later a deep layer of small shear, as shown in the three stages in the diagram. The change may be regarded as a diffusion of vorticity from the sheet, where it was of infinite magnitude in an infinitesimal thickness of fluid, into the surrounding fluid. The region between the dotted lines is where the velocity of the fluid is less than 19/20 of its original value. Out-

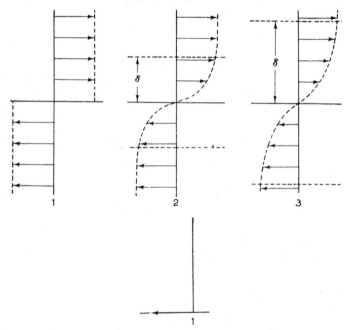

side this the velocity has been altered by less than 5 per cent, and the effect of viscosity may be regarded as negligible. The arbitrary choice of 5 per cent may be unsatisfactory for some purposes and 1 per cent might be preferable, but whatever accuracy we require there will always be a point beyond which the viscosity has had a negligible influence. The region within the arbitrary line is called the *boundary layer*. The experiment we have just imagined is equivalent to having a solid surface as the boundary of the fluid at rest and suddenly making it move. The boundary layer is now the region moving with at least 5 per cent of the velocity of the boundary. The figure is simply the top half of the previous diagram moved to the left with the speed which the fluid originally had to the right. A force has to be applied to the boundary to keep it moving and this corresponds to the increasing momentum of the fluid in the direction of the force.

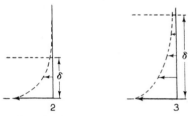

The gradient of velocity is inversely proportional to the boundary layer thickness, δ. The mathematical form of the velocity profile remains the same, but it becomes gradually stretched over a greater thickness of fluid. The rate at which the thickness increases is proportional to the gradient of velocity (as in the case of other diffusion laws) and so

$$\frac{d\delta}{dt} \propto \frac{1}{\delta}$$

or

$$\delta \propto t^{\frac{1}{2}}.$$

The only Reynolds number we can compose is $U\delta/\nu$, where U is the speed of the free stream in the first case or the velocity of the boundary in the second. Since the thickness after time t is proportional to ν, because the rate of diffusion of vorticity is proportional to ν, the Reynolds number defined in this way remains constant; therefore the profile of velocity is similar (in mathematical form) at all stages.

The growth of the boundary layer on a flat plate

The boundary layers we have just imagined are of infinite extent but growing in time. A more practical problem is how the boundary layer grows as the air moves over a solid body in an

otherwise uniform air stream. The simplest case is that of a
semi-infinite thin flat plate. At the leading edge of it there is no
retardation but farther downstream there is a gradually thickening
layer in which the velocity has been reduced by at least 5 per
cent. We can get a rough idea of how this boundary layer grows
by imagining a column of fluid ABCD moving along with velocity
U and having the boundary layer at the plate growing in the same
way as in the previous problem. Since x, the distance from the
edge of the plate, is proportional to t we have that

$$\delta \propto x^{\frac{1}{2}}$$

and so the boundary layer has a parabolic section as indicated by
the dashed line. Because there is less flow across the section (3)
than across sections (2) or (1) there must be a small velocity away
from the plate, but this has a dynamical effect negligible in
comparison with the large retardations in the boundary layer.

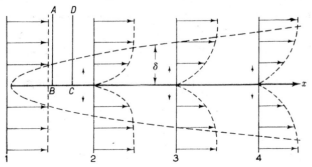

If the plate were of finite width in the direction of the wind then
the velocity profile would gradually resume its original shape
behind the plate, as the vorticity produced at the plate is diffused
outwards over an ever-increasing volume, and is destroyed in the
middle by diffusion of vorticity of opposite signs towards the
centre.

The drag exerted on the plate can be thought of in two equivalent ways. Along the solid surface there is a stress proportional
to the viscosity and the velocity gradient at the surface. This
decreases backwards from the leading edge of the plate because
the shear decreases. This force imparts momentum to the surrounding fluid which is represented by the difference between the

velocity profile behind the plate and in front of it.   The difference between sections 4 and 1 is shaded in the figure.

Using the method of non-dimensional numbers outlined in Chapter 11 we can argue as follows.   A Reynolds number R

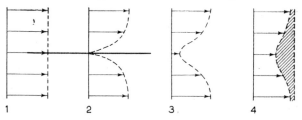

1   2   3   4

can be defined as Ux/v, where x is the distance from the forward edge of the plate.   The only other non-dimensional number in the problem is δ/x.   The number $U\delta/v$ is a combination of these two.   We therefore conclude that

$$\frac{\delta}{x} = F(R)$$

where F is at present an unknown function.   The drag due to viscosity on a strip of the plate of unit width extending a distance x back from the front edge is $x \times$ an average value of the surface stress.   It is also equal to the decrease in the flow of momentum past the plate, which is proportional to the flow U and to the momentum in the boundary layer which itself is proportional to $\rho U\delta$.   Thus

$$x \times \mu \frac{\overline{\partial u}}{\partial y} \propto U \times \rho U\delta$$

The mean value of the shear, $\frac{\overline{\partial u}}{\partial y}$ is proportional to $\frac{U}{\delta}$, and so, since $\mu/\rho = v$,

$$\frac{\delta^2}{x^2} \propto \left(\frac{Ux}{v}\right)^{-1}$$

or $$\delta \propto xR^{-\frac{1}{2}}$$

whence $$\delta \propto x^{\frac{1}{2}}$$

which agrees with the previous conclusion.

Using the knowledge that the answer is in this form it has been possible to solve the equations for the flow over a semi-infinite flat plate, and it is found that if the 5 per cent disturbance is taken as the edge of the boundary layer

$$\delta = 4\left(\frac{\nu x}{U}\right)^{\frac{1}{2}}$$

The boundary layer is thinner for larger velocities and smaller viscosities.

Diffusion through boundary layers

The shape of boundary layers over thick bodies depends on the velocity distribution over their forward facing surface. At a forward stagnation point the boundary layer, according to our definition, is thickened, but not on account of viscosity. It becomes thinner as the fluid accelerates away from this point on either side. This thickening may be regarded as part of the boundary layer when diffusion of heat or water vapour is considered. Nevertheless, except near such a point, the thickness of the layer whose velocity has been altered by 5 per cent or more gradually increases as the air passes back over a body, and the gradient of velocity, or shear, at the surface decreases. Vorticity and momentum are imparted to the surrounding fluid by the surface, and the rate at which this happens is greatest close to the forward edge of the body.

Together with vorticity any other quantity which can be possessed by the fluid can also be diffused into or out of the surface, and the rates of diffusion of the different quantities will be comparable so long as the mechanism of diffusion is the same— that is molecular. Heat and water vapour are the two most important quantities which are diffused in this way, and they may be diffused towards or away from the surface.

We may imagine a drop of water suddenly exposed to a dry atmosphere. If there were no relative motion a boundary layer would grow outwards from the drop, it being defined as the region in which the relative humidity had risen to 5 per cent. But if at the same time there were relative motion, this moisture boundary layer would be made thinner at places where fresh air was being brought close to the surface, and so the gradient of humidity would be greater there than at the rear of the drop. The rate of evaporation would then not be uniform over the surface.

This is of little consequence in the case of liquids, whose shape
is not determined by the condensation; but in the case of condensation of vapour from a supersaturated atmosphere on to ice crystals
the growth is greatest where the boundary layer of the motion is
thinnest.   Atmospheres supersaturated for ice can exist because
condensation does not occur in the free air until saturation for
water is reached.   Below freezing this is at a lower temperature
than saturation for ice because supercoded water exerts a greater
vapour pressure than ice at the same temperature.   Thus if by
some sequence of events ice crystals are present their growth is
different from when no great degree of supersaturation exists and
the gradient of humidity is small and nearly uniform over the
surface.

If a needle of ice is pointed into an air current the boundary
layer of the motion thickens gradually along it from the front.
Since the boundary layer of the condensation process thickens at
the same time, the deposition of ice at the tip of the needle will be
greater than elsewhere.

A form of ice crystal which occurs naturally is the hexagonal
plate.   It is not certain how it falls, but it is probably either

steadily in a horizontal position or rather like the motion of a tray descending a spiral staircase with its edge rolling on the outer wall. However it moves, the boundary layer must be thinner on the rim than in the centre of the plate, and at the angles of the rim than in the middle of the sides. It therefore grows thicker on the rim and the angular points grow more acute and ultimately branch out with long arms.

The drag is greatest at points where the growth is most rapid because the greatest gradients of velocity and vapour concentration more or less coincide. This causes the points of greatest growth on a falling crystal to be turned upwards so that the points where the growth is less are then exposed at the front. In this way the crystals grow nearly symmetrically into shapes such as are illustrated in the figure above. The small branches fill up the spaces between the main ones as they grow. These *dendritic* (tree-like) shapes are common in snowflakes.

The capture of small airborne particles on solid surfaces is, incidentally, also more efficient on bodies whose boundary layer is thin. This is because they also produce greater curvature of the streamlines. We have already seen that the diffusion to the surface is not by molecular diffusion but by inertia forces.

The basis of boundary layer theory

It is instructive to consider how Prandtl, who first put forward the idea of boundary layers, was able to use his idea to obtain solutions to problems. The equations for viscous flow are, in

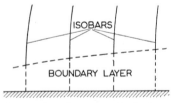

general, too difficult to solve, but are relatively easy when viscosity can be neglected. Provided that the boundary layer is thin the accelerations produced by it in a direction perpendicular to the boundary are very small because the flow is still almost parallel to it. There are therefore negligible gradients of pressure across the boundary layer and the pressure in the layer can be taken as equal to that just outside. The isobars are thus assumed to be perpendicular to the surface.

In the region of viscous flow we therefore start with the pressure given, if we can solve the problem of the non-viscous flow outside; the motion is then much easier to compute. We shall not describe such solutions here; many are well known and are given in standard texts on the subject. The importance of this idea to us is that it makes the phenomenon of separation intelligible.

Separation of the boundary layer

If there is a pressure gradient force outside the boundary layer decelerating the fluid it is possible that, since the fluid in the boundary layer is moving more slowly, it may be brought to rest by the same pressure field. Beyond this point the flow close to the surface is in the opposite direction, that is towards low pressure. As the boundary layer thickens along the direction of motion, the viscous stress which is urging the fluid close to the boundary forward decreases, because the shear decreases. Ultimately it becomes small enough for the pressure gradient force to overcome it and reverse the flow. Separation occurs when the gradient of velocity at the boundary is zero for just beyond this point the only force on the stagnant fluid is the pressure gradient force. Once separation has taken place the rigid boundary no longer exerts a controlling influence over the flow: the streamlines may pass out into the body of the fluid and a *wake* is formed.

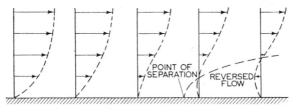

POINT OF SEPARATION REVERSED FLOW

◄——direction of pressure gradient force

The point of separation may often be determined, by boundary layer theory, as the point at which $\partial u/\partial z = 0$, z being measured in the direction away from the boundary. The consequences of separation will be discussed in the next chapter. It is such a common phenomenon that we tend to regard it as the normal behaviour of fluid flowing past a body; it is therefore of considerable interest to see how it can be prevented, and what are the consequences of doing this.

The prevention of separation

Separation occurs in regions where the fluid is flowing up the pressure gradient. This gradient is produced by the form of the flow outside the boundary layer, and must be taken as given. For example, if separation occurs at the convex surface where a channel widens out it cannot be regarded as a method of preventing separation to make the channel of uniform width. The increase in pressure in the direction of motion must be taken as given. It can be computed up to the point of separation from the velocity decrease in the main stream as it widens, by Bernoulli's equation. Thereafter the width of the main stream, and the pressure in it, depend on the form of the eddy produced by separation. The well-known methods of preventing separation are:—

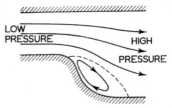

(a) *Addition of momentum to the boundary layer*

This increases the shear at the boundary. It can be done in four different ways:

   (i) *By motion of the boundary*. If the shoulder in the case illustrated is a circular cylinder which is made to rotate the flow adheres to the boundary in the fashion illustrated.

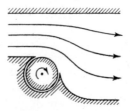

   (ii) *By injecting fast-moving fluid into the boundary layer.* This can be made to produce some very spectacular results, the most notable being the Coanda effect, exploited in the

' jet flap '.   Normally if the flap at the trailing edge of an aircraft wing is lowered separation occurs.   There is nevertheless an increase in lift (and drag) which is exploited by large aircraft to enable them to approach to land at speeds much less than normal cruising speed. The amount of lift is still further increased by a factor of 2 or more if separation is prevented by a jet of air entering the stream parallel to the surface at the top of the flap. This induces the flow to follow the flap shape and greatly increases the downwash, or downward momentum imparted to the air by the wing.

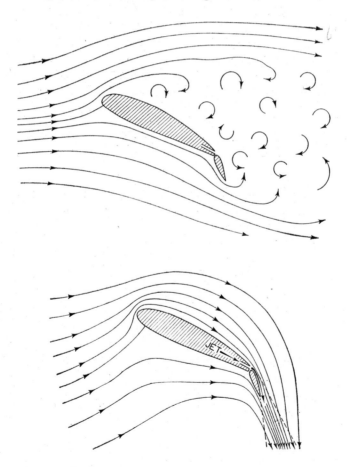

In the upper figure the wing is stalled and a wake (see Chapter 6) is formed. When the jet of air is emitted at the top of the flap there are two important effects. First the jet entrains the wake in the same manner as the jet described in Chapter 8 (page 186) and thereby prevents the separation farther forward along the wing. It also prevents separation on the flap so that the flow follows the contour of the whole upper surface of the wing and the downwash is, in consequence, greatly increased. The lift is obtained by a reduction of pressure on the upper surface of the wing. When the jet operates the stagnation point at the front of the wing is moved downward and there is a greater flow of air over the wing. The velocity below the wing is decreased and the pressure on the lower surface accordingly increased. That this must happen when the downwash is increased can be deduced by considering that the force on the wing is equal to the rate of change of vertical momentum of the air passing by.

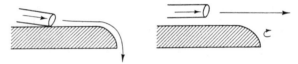

The effect may easily be demonstrated by making jets of water adhere as they pass round corners of vessels (e.g. an inverted saucepan under the kitchen tap) or by making the blast from the tail of a vacuum cleaner pass across a polished table and then vertically downwards over the edge. When separation occurs the air continues horizontally from the table edge: this happens if the jet is lifted slightly from the surface. The phenomenon is also exploited in the slotted wing.

(iii) *By the induction of fluid from the main stream by small inclined blades.* The vortex trailing from the tip of the blade interchanges fluid from the boundary layer with fluid farther away and thereby a large shear is maintained at the boundary. The motion behind one such blade is illustrated in the figure, where it is contrasted with the case of separation on the upper surface of a wing.

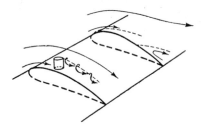

(iv) *By the action of gravity in a stably stratified fluid.* A good example of this is observed on snow-covered mountains, where the air near the surface is much colder than the air above. When the flow is inclined downwards, as it is on the lee side of a mountain, the pressure field due to gravity accelerates the lower layers down the slope so as to make the surfaces of constant density more nearly level. By contrast, the tendency for flow up a slope heated by sunshine induces separation near the top. When air cooled at the surface flows down a slope the motion is called a katabatic wind. Owing to the stability the cooling affects only a shallow layer and so katabatic winds are usually only a few metres deep. But if they serve to prevent separation they may cause a deep flow down a slope that was, during the day, occupied by a feeble up-slope wind in an eddy. The strong downslope nocturnal wind is then much more than a katabatic wind, though it is often given that name. This phenomenon is discussed further in Chapter 9.

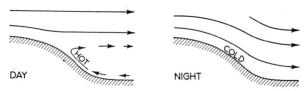

(b) *Removal of the boundary layer by suction*

If the fluid composing the boundary layer is removed by suction, either through a porous boundary or through slots or holes, it is replaced by air from the main stream and so, since the velocity gradient at the surface is maintained, separation is prevented.

(c) Production of turbulent flow

Basically, this is a method of stirring the main stream into the boundary layer, thereby increasing the forward velocity near the boundary. It is discussed further in Chapter 6.

The growth and diminution of boundary layers

Small bodies or protuberances from the surface which lie wholly within the boundary layer of a large body may be thought of as possessing boundary layers of their own, the original boundary layer now being regarded as the main flow. Examples are an ornament on a house, a house or tree on a hill, or a hill within the friction layer on the earth's surface. This friction layer is, however, of a different kind from viscous boundary layers because of turbulence and the earth's rotation.

Boundary layers do not always grow in thickness in the down-wind direction. In particular, if the flow is accelerating the fluid is being stretched in the direction of flow so that the layer of fluid into which the vorticity has diffused is made thinner and the shear is increased. Likewise, if the flow is decelerating, the layer is thickened by contraction along the direction of flow.

Separation is therefore a phenomenon of diffluent flow, and does not occur where the boundaries are getting closer together. The flow through constrictions or over obstacles which form wakes is therefore irreversible, and asymmetrical. Where the flow is

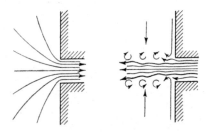

accelerating, and the boundary layer is kept thin, it is very similar to what it would be if there were no viscosity. A good example of this is the pattern of flow from a reservoir into a tube. By contrast, the flow emerging from a tube into a reservoir is a jet with eddies surrounding it because separation occurs at the end of the tube where the boundary widens.

Cavitation and salient edges

The equations enable us to determine only the gradients of pressure corresponding to a flow pattern. If the pressure is given at one point (as when it is atmospheric at an open end of a vessel, for example) it can be calculated at all other points. Where the accelerations are large so also are the pressure gradients, and it may be that on sharp corners the pressure we compute is negative. In order to make the flow possible it is then necessary to increase the pressure everywhere in the system in question in order to make the pressure everywhere positive, otherwise a vacuum will be produced if the fluid is incompressible. This phenomenon is called cavitation. If the fluid is a gas the density will be reduced at such points and the nature of the flow becomes very complicated, but whether it is a gas or a liquid there will always be separation or cavitation at an infinitely sharp angular edge because infinite accelerations would be required to pass round it without. Cavitation can be seen in a transparent liquid, the space being filled with vapour or dissolved gas.

The occurrence of separation and the point at which it occurs are, for practical purposes, independent of the Reynolds number at sharp angular edges. These are called salient edges. Cliff tops, edges of buildings, and walls are such, and the lee space can be seen to be filled with an eddy.

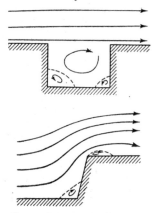

Separation at bends and corners

When the wind blows across the top of a steep-sided quarry

or pit, or against a cliff with an angular corner at the foot, separation may occur where the flow widens out as it approaches the corner. After passing the corner the acceleration of the flow closes up the eddy, which is therefore isolated and stationary.

When the flow is completely enclosed in a tunnel or tube it may be difficult to cause the fluid to flow round a bend without separation. In wind tunnels the bends are usually right-angles and the flow is divided up by a large number of vanes in the corner which

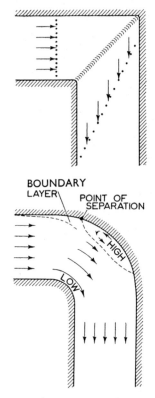

shear the flow as it passes through them. It emerges as a uniform stream again. A line of marked particles lying at right-angles to the wall before the bend emerges lying at an angle of about $26\frac{1}{2}°$ to the wall. Without the vanes the flow would be without vorticity if none were present before the corner. Even in a bend with curved walls the pressure is greater and the velocity smaller on the outside of the curve. Separation is therefore likely to take place on the outside of the bend where the boundary layer grows towards the high pressure region.

In the gas turbine engines of a well-known aircraft the air is taken in round a bend and the direction of motion turned through nearly 180°. Separation may or may not occur on the outside of the bend according to the smoothness of the walls and whether they converge slightly or not. But it is unavoidable that the velocity should be much reduced on the outside of the bend. An unfortunate consequence of this is that snow and soft hail particles taken in with the air tend to stick to the outside wall of the bend because the centrifugal (inertial) force carries them on to it. Because of the small air speed they do not get blown off until there has been a considerable build-up of spongy snow which increases the force of the air on it by constricting the channel. It then breaks off and enters the turbine in large lumps which are big enough to extinguish the flame. The flow round the bend cannot be facilitated by the insertion of vanes as in a wind tunnel because if the aircraft flew into a cloud containing a large amount of supercooled water the vanes would quickly become iced up. The soft hail and snow presents a special problem because heating the wall of the channel does not prevent a spongy accumulation in the thick slow-moving boundary layer and eddy on the outside of the bend. If the ice could be liquefied it would flow away, but the thermal conductivity of snow with a large amount of air embedded in it is too low for it to be melted faster than it accumulates.

To avoid this accumulation the flow should be accelerated as it passes round the bend by contracting the width of the channel. If the outside wall of the bend were made in the form of a circular cylinder even a small draught of air would propel an accumulation of snow and hail particles along the surface, provided that it was lubricated by being kept warm enough to be wet.

CHAPTER 6

WAKES AND TURBULENCE

Flow at large Reynolds numbers

WHEN the velocity is increased the Reynolds number of the flow past a body increases. This means that the inertia forces become more important in determining the pattern of flow than the viscous forces. The only effect is to increase this relative importance provided that compressibility, which we shall ignore in this chapter, is not brought into the scene by having velocities comparable with the velocity of sound. We would therefore expect that there would be little change in the pattern after the Reynolds number had been made great enough for the viscous forces to be negligible. Only by varying the relative importance of the various forces involved can the pattern of flow be changed.

On the other hand, flow at large Reynolds numbers ($Ud/v \rightarrow \infty$) does not necessarily resemble the flow of a fluid with zero viscosity ($v = 0$) because there is always a thin layer of fluid close to the boundary in which the viscosity is dominant. This is expressed by using δ, the thickness of the boundary layer, to form the Reynolds number $U\delta/v$, and then as v tends to zero so does δ in such a way that $U\delta/v$ does not. This means that as the velocity is increased, or the viscosity decreased, we concentrate our attention on the boundary layer, magnifying it under a microscope as it decreases in thickness. In any case, real fluids possess viscosity and the only way to achieve large Reynolds numbers is by increasing the velocity, and it is not realistic to imagine the nature of the flow at infinite velocities.

The phenomenon of separation therefore remains, even though the mechanism is confined to a very thin layer close to the boundary and over the rest of the flow pattern the viscous forces are negligible. At very low Reynolds numbers there is no separation and the boundary layer occupies the whole region. Where separation begins the point at which it takes place moves upstream as the velocity is increased until it approaches a limit beyond which it does not advance however much the velocity is increased.

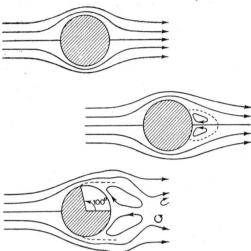

The *wake*, as the system of eddies in the lee of the body is called, is at first composed of small stationary circulations; but as the Reynolds number is increased an unsteady pattern develops in which eddies are shed and travel away in the stream, and new ones are formed behind the body. In the special case of a sphere the limit beyond which the point of separation does not advance is at about 100° from the rear. Howarth demonstrated this theoretically and it has been confirmed by experiment.

When the surface is smooth the point of separation may vary, but if there are salient edges the separation will occur there for all Reynolds numbers large enough to produce separation at all. This is commonly observed, for instance at the corners of houses where the wind is observed to blow towards the corner along both walls, and an attempt to treat it theoretically without reference to viscosity was made in the *theory of free streamlines*. In this it was supposed that the wake consisted of stagnant fluid in which the pressure was constant. Along the boundary of the wake the velocity had, according to Bernoulli's theorem, to be constant, and on these assumptions it was possible to calculate the position of the edge of the wake (the free streamline) and the pressure in the wake. The boundary of the wake is independent of the velocity provided that it always begins at the same point (the salient edge), and since the variations of the pressure are proportional to $\frac{1}{2}\rho U^2$ the difference in pressure between the front and the lee of the body is proportional to the square of the velocity. This law of air resistance is observed to be well obeyed in practice by many bodies.

A good example is provided by a flat plate lying across the stream. Separation occurs at the edge, and the resistance is simply due to the difference between the pressures on the two sides. The only *surface drag* due to viscosity is outwards along the front of the plate and this contributes nothing to the force required to keep the plate in position against the stream.

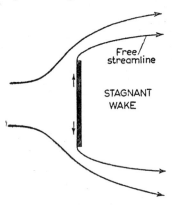

The theory of free streamlines is unrealistic because it requires that there should be a discontinuity of velocity, or vortex sheet, at the edge of the wake, and this is unstable. It will be spread into a thicker layer by the action of viscosity, but it will also be wound into a row or collection of vortices in the manner described on page 81. These vortices will travel at a speed intermediate between that of two streams which originally composed the vortex sheet, and will therefore travel away downstream from the body at a speed somewhat slower than the main stream.

Before discussing in more detail the mechanism whereby a fluid exerts a drag on a body it is illuminating to consider what Nature is up to in breaking up a vortex sheet into whirls instead of letting viscosity diffuse the vorticity outwards into the surrounding fluid. The sheet (organised vorticity) becomes turbulence (chaotic vorticity) and the change is irreversible in the same sense as the effects of diffusion or conduction of heat are irreversible. There is thus an analogy, which we shall discuss more later, between the eddies which are formed and the molecules of a gas: each brings about a spreading of the sharp gradient of velocity, and ultimately the gradients on the smallest scale are dissipated by viscosity. But Nature is impatient, and finds that by straining the fluid she can stretch the area occupied by the discontinuity so that the intimacy of contact between the two masses of fluid is greatly increased. If we examine the eddies carefully we find that this stretching of the interface also brings fresh fluid from the interior of each mass to the surface of contact, thereby intensifying the gradient and making the work of the molecules easier. This process is the same as that by which fronts are created in the atmosphere, and we shall see a further example of it in the next chapter where the buoyancy forces bring fresh buoyant fluid from the interior of a rising mass of hot fluid to the surface, maintaining a discontinuity of density at the advancing front.

In the worlds of politics and warfare this lesson concerning intimate contact between the human molecules of states and armies has long been learned. A general keeps replacing the troops at the front by fresh battalions from the rear, thereby intensifying the battle at the surface of contact with the enemy. The dictator, on the other hand, finds diffusion of foreign ideas into the body of his people embarrassing: he therefore reduces the areas of contact with other nations. He chooses as his ambassadors men least susceptible to heretical influences, replacing them quickly by others fresh from the seminary if they begin to grow weary of the doctrine, thereby emulating the general in those areas of contact he cannot avoid. To muse upon these mechanisms, the reader will understand, is not to argue that human relations can be properly interpreted in terms of mechanical systems, and it would be silly to suggest the converse—that anthropomorphic analogies can be used to ' explain ' mechanical systems which are essentially simpler and more intelligible. Indeed the scientifically minded reader might recall that he is a human being: he might consider for a moment whether he has any criteria for deciding whether he will attempt to solve a problem by methods as certain as those we use in aerodynamics, or whether he will be content to leave problems unsolved. Or will he try to establish other methods of dealing with problems which are urgent, but which are too difficult for science, in order to guide him through life, realising the gravity of the consequences of fallacy, error, fanaticism, and apathy? Now that the nineteenth century mechanistic dream of human power is eluding us we must accept the doctrine of original incompetence, acknowledging that many human problems will always remain outside the domain of logic and scientific method. It is quite another matter to decide whether we need face such problems. We can obviously manage without wondering how many angels can dance on the point of a needle: what about other problems?

The drag coefficient

The force required to keep a body moving steadily through a fluid is equal in magnitude to the force exerted by the fluid on the body. This may be denoted by D, the drag force. If d is a dimension of the body, a pressure force can be represented by $\frac{1}{2}\rho U^2 d^2$ (the Bernoulli pressure $\frac{1}{2}\rho U^2 \times$ an area d^2). A non-dimensional number C_D may then be defined as the ratio between these forces, thus

$$C_D = \frac{D}{\frac{1}{2}\rho U^2 d^2}.$$

The only other independent non-dimensional number we can obtain from the conditions of the problem is the Reynolds number, R. A third number, which might be defined as the surface drag coefficient, or the ratio of the drag force to the viscous forces, is not new, being the ratio C_D/R. According to the argument given in Chapter 11 (page 292), we deduce that

$$C_D = F(R)$$

where F is an unknown function. Since, as R increases, the flow pattern becomes fixed and the viscous forces become negligible, the number C_D must tend towards a constant value, and F therefore tends to a constant as R tends to infinity.

C_D is called the *drag coefficient*, and we can understand how the effect of viscosity upon it becomes negligible at large velocities by investigating the effect of the drag. The force exerted on the fluid communicates momentum to it. When there are moving eddies travelling away downstream from the body, the volume of fluid with this momentum is steadily increasing even though only a negligible amount of momentum has been communicated to it from the surface of the body, or from the wake outwards, by viscosity. The fluid drawn along in the wake is ' sucked ' into the region of lower pressure on the rear of the body: when the wake is well developed the volume so affected is much greater than the fluid leaving the surface into the main stream from the boundary layer at the point of separation. The greater the speed, the thinner is the boundary layer, and so the drag becomes almost wholly *form drag*, that is drag due to the formation of a wake with eddies moving away on it. When the eddies remain fixed and the streamlines close up behind the body the only mechanism for exchanging momentum with the fluid inside is by the viscous stresses across those streamlines. But when the wake is turbulent and contains chaotic vorticity, there are no streamlines with position fixed relative to the body which close up behind it; and the fluctuating nature of the flow may transfer momentum across any such lines. Thus examination of a turbulent wake shows us that turbulent motion can transfer momentum more efficiently than viscosity. It can also transfer other properties, such as heat and water vapour, which can be borne by the fluid. But before investigating the properties of turbulence on its own we shall examine some of the effects of wakes.

The law of fluid resistance

At very small Reynolds numbers, when there is no separation, the inertia forces are small in comparison with the viscous forces. In that case a more suitable drag coefficient would be obtained from a force representing the surface drag, namely viscosity $\times$ shear $\times$ area. Thus

$$C_D = \frac{D}{\mu \dfrac{U}{d} d^2} = \frac{D}{\mu U d}.$$

Again this is a function of the Reynolds number, and tends to a constant value independent of the velocity (but very much dependent on the viscosity) as the Reynolds number tends to zero. This shows that when the inertia forces are negligible the drag is proportional to the velocity because

$$D = \text{constant} \times \mu U d.$$

More generally, for a fixed viscosity and density D is proportional to the Reynolds number (because $R \propto Ud$ in that case).

As we saw above, at large Reynolds number

$$D = \text{constant} \times \rho U^2 d^2.$$

When the Reynolds number is so large that compressibility becomes important a new force is involved, the elastic force of the fluid. This force enables energy to be transmitted through the fluid in the form of waves, and in addition to losing energy by work against viscosity, and by the creation of energy of turbulent motion in the wake, energy is produced in the form of shock (or sound) waves. If we consider the momentum we see that the shock waves must also correspond to a displacement of the fluid in the direction of motion of the body through it. The drag is in this case proportional to a higher power of the velocity than the square.

An interesting example of the square law is provided by the bubbles of air rising through water, which were discussed in Chapter 1. The flow separates from the rim of the bubble and a turbulent wake is formed. We saw that the velocity was given (page 17) by an equation of the form

$$U = \text{constant} \times \left(g \, \frac{\rho - \rho'}{\rho} \, d \right)^{\frac{1}{2}}$$

Since the volume is proportional to d^3 the total buoyancy force, D, on the bubble, is proportional to $g(\rho - \rho')d^3$, and so

$$U = \text{constant} \times (D/\rho d^2)^{\frac{1}{2}}$$

which shows that, as we would expect,

$$D = \text{constant} \times \rho U^2 d^2.$$

In this case no reference is made to viscosity; it is merely supposed that a wake is formed.

Some properties of wakes

(a) Soaring of ocean birds

We saw in Chapter 1 (page 13) how albatrosses can exploit the shear of the wind close to the sea surface to remain airborne

without flapping their wings, provided that their air speed is high
enough. Smaller ocean birds, and possibly albatrosses too,
exploit the gradients of wind at the edges of the wakes at the wave
crests. They are remarkable to watch because they often rise no
more than 2 or 3 m above the sea surface for several minutes
and yet are not seen to flap at all. They appear to behave roughly
as follows: they pass up the lee side of a wave from the top of
which the flow separates; as they traverse the edge of the wake they
experience a sudden increase in airspeed which they use to gain 2
or 3 m of height. During their ascent they choose their
future path among the moving waves so as to avoid the wakes.
While on this path they gradually lose air speed and when they
are near to stalling they turn sideways into the wake of a wave.
Here they receive momentum towards the wave from the air
which is moving in the direction of the wind more slowly (if at all)
than the air from which they have just come. They can then gain
air speed by passing over the wave crest as before.

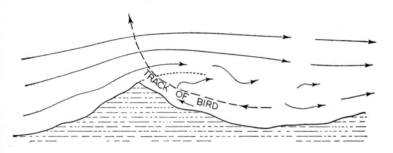

To be able to do this requires long experience of how the waves
move in relation to the wind. I have watched groups of birds
keeping level with an ocean liner travelling at about 15 kt with a
15 kt headwind. This indicates that their gliding speed is something more than 30 kt because their track was not straight.
Generally their motion is not repetitive because the waves are so
chaotic, but on one occasion they were seen circling round and
round one of the moving waves of the wash of the ship, using the
wake of this same wave over and over again. This was, for them,
an unusual experience because the wave was not travelling in the
direction of the wind, but with the ship.

(b) Bubbles of air in water

If a large bubble of air rises through water from the motion of small fragmentary bubbles which break off from its perimeter (see Plate 1) the wake is seen to be like a turbulent ring vortex with the motion towards the bubble extending back for about two diameters. If the bubble passes through a cloud of dye, the dye is carried as a thin column up the middle of the wake behind the bubble. If a smaller bubble is overtaken by a large one the widening wake of the large one eventually engulfs it. It then gets carried inwards towards the centre and if it is close enough to the large one for its velocity relative to the water plus the upward velocity of the water in the wake to exceed the rate of rise of the large one, it will be captured. In the figure the successive positions shown are at decreasing intervals of time. The position of the point 0 where the motion relative to the bubble is zero is not accurately shown. The edge of the wake is unsteady, and the velocities fluctuate around those indicated by the arrows. The small fragmentary bubbles are not shown in the right-hand half of the diagram opposite.

It is interesting that if the captured bubble is large enough, the moment at which it impinges on the wake can be seen by the turning up and distortion of the edge as shown in position 4. The shearing motion inside the wake distorts captured bubbles. In one experiment a captured bubble was broken in half at position 4: the inner half was captured, but the remainder had too small an upward velocity relative to the water and it was left behind!

(c) Capture of cloud droplets by raindrops

We have discussed elsewhere the effect of inertia and viscous forces on the efficiency with which small airborne particles such as cloud droplets are captured by twigs, or wires, or raindrops. In the case of raindrops there is probably a greater capture through the wake than on the forward surface, especially when the drops are of comparable size, for then the smaller one will fall more rapidly down the wake of the larger one. Very small drops (with Reynolds number less than 1) do not form wakes, but when the Reynolds number is 5 or more this effect certainly becomes important. Calculations are extremely difficult when the drop sizes are comparable, so that the phenomenon has only been tentatively investigated so far.

(d) Downdraughts produced by fallout

Particles, such as raindrops, hail, and snow, falling out of clouds carry air down with them in their wakes. When they have reached their limiting velocity the whole force of their weight must be communicated to the air, and so their weight may simply be added to that of the air containing them. This effectively

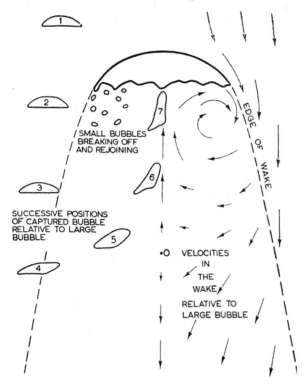

increases the density of the air, and causes a downdraught. This downdraught is, of course, the wakes of the particles, and we recognise it as a downdraught when the wakes of many particles overlap and occupy the entire volume under consideration. When there is a downdraught the particles descend at a velocity much in excess of their terminal velocity in still air. If the weight of all the particles and the volume occupied by them is known, the strength of the downdraught can, in simple cases, be calculated from a formula given in the next chapter (page 161), provided that the terminal velocity in still air of the particles is small compared with the downdraught.

At the front of the downdraught the particles are entering air previously unaffected by the wakes of other particles, and so these particles move more slowly. They are continuously overtaken by others from the interior. A circulation of the particles outwards from the centre of the front of the draught develops, and fresh particles continuously arrive from inside. Since every particle at the front adds air, by means of its wake, to the downdraught the total volume of the downdraught steadily increases. An example of this process is seen in Plate 3, which shows in one picture four positions of a ' cloud ' of air bubbles expelled in a fraction of a second through perforations in a sheet of aluminium at the bottom of a tank of water. The ' cloud ' rose at about three times the speed of a solitary bubble, and grew in volume. The wake of the ' cloud ' noticeably extended 3 or 4 diameters behind it, which should be compared with the case of solitary thermals described in the next chapter. Thermals have no wakes. The formula for the vertical velocity, though of similar form, must have a different coefficient C (see page 161), which has not been measured.

If some sort of fallout emerged from a cloud it would tend to arrive at the ground in the form of a sudden gush because all the particles tend to fall down the downdraught faster than the bottom of it descends. That is to say the velocity within the downdraught is greater than the velocity of the front of the downdraught, so that particles accumulate at the front. Whether the initial intensity of rain or hail from a shower cloud is maintained depends on whether the cloud continues to produce it or not. But it is a common experience for the first onset to be more intense than the more continuous rain after a few seconds, and this is particularly noticeable when the fallout is composed of large particles, as we would expect from this analysis.

The definition of turbulence; decay

If we define turbulence as a kind of stirring motion by which anything possessed by the air is diffused, then, if we mark any two particles of air which are initially near together, the motion will inevitably move them apart from one another. The motion of one relative to the other may be along a very tortuous path, but the average effect must be to separate them. This definition of turbulence is not strictly in accordance with the sense in which the word is often used. For instance if we define it as *any* sort of random or chaotic motion it would include the motion of a jelly carried in a vehicle on a bumpy road; yet at the end of the journey, provided there were no structural damage to the jelly, all its particles would be in the same place relative to each other. When we watch stars at night we see that they twinkle, and this is almost certainly due to varying refraction by the air through which the light passes. The refractive index may vary for one or more of several different causes. It may be because the wind is continually bringing patches of air of different temperature across our line of sight, producing the same effect as when a sheet of glass of variable thickness is moved across in front of our eyes. In such a case we would not describe the glass as being in turbulent motion. Again it may be because the air is undergoing wavy motions and we get a view similar to what a fish would see if we made waves on the surface of the water above it. We know that waves on the surface do not normally stir the water. If on the other hand there were convection going on in the air with warm parcels rising and cool ones descending, so that as the parcels crossed our line of sight the apparent position and intensity of the star changed, then the twinkling would indeed be due to a stirring motion. Often, however, the twinkling is loosely described as being due to the ' turbulence ' of the atmosphere, by which is meant a ' random ' effect not at present understood. In this book we shall only consider motion to be turbulent if any property carried by it is diffused by the motion. If we do not know the nature of the motion which is producing an effect we observe, it is preferable to refer to it as being due to ' motion or motions unknown '. Turbulence, then, would cause a cloud of smoke or gas, or a concentration of water vapour or heat, to be diffused in such a way as to spread it more uniformly throughout the fluid.

This last statement raises a most interesting question: could turbulence carry any quantity borne by the fluid up the gradient of that quantity ? According to our definition this could not happen if the quantity were attached to the material of the fluid, as is smoke, or water vapour, or heat in so far as it can only be communicated by contact between molecules. But momentum can be communicated from one part of the fluid to another by means of pressure gradients which represent orderly contact between molecules over large areas, not random contact as in the case of the communication of heat. The turbulent motion might therefore serve to communicate momentum up the gradient of momentum. Whether it would or not we cannot predict except by reference to each case, but we would certainly expect it to happen only rarely. In fact it does often happen in the atmosphere in the special kind of turbulent motion which carries heat from the equator to the poles; but it is noteworthy first that such motion is produced by buoyancy forces and second that it is almost horizontal and the vortex lines of the large-scale motion are all vertical. If the turbulence were produced by a degeneration of orderly shearing motion into a chaotic three-dimensional distribution of vorticity it would certainly tend to reduce the shear, that is carry momentum down the gradient of it.

Momentum has often been excluded from the list of ' transferable quantities '. In fact, it is generally transferred in a manner very *similar* to other quantities, but we cannot say that it will always be. Since it is not retained by the fluid particles it may be transferred at a different rate from those quantities, such as smoke and water vapour, which are.

In a fluid of uniform density with no viscosity, the vorticity is carried with the fluid (page 62). If we consider two particles on a vortex line we see that they will become separated by turbulent motion, so that vortex lines tend to be stretched, the vorticity increased, and the diameter of the eddies decreased. If the vorticity, which is the angular momentum, is conserved and is proportional to the angular velocity, since the angular velocity is increased the kinetic energy of rotation, which is proportional to the square of the angular velocity, must be increased. This means that as the size of the eddies decreases their energy increases. Therefore the energy of the turbulent motion is continuously being transferred to the small eddies, and the energy of the large eddies decreases.

A vivid analogy is provided by a weight rotating on a string which passes through a small fixed hole and into our hand. We have to pull on the string in order to stop it slipping through the hole.   If we wish the weight to rotate in a smaller circle we have to do work in pulling the string against the tension in it, and this work becomes kinetic energy of the weight.   Its angular momentum is conserved but its energy is increased ($r^2\omega$ is left constant but since ω is increased, $r^2\omega^2$ is increased).   If we let the string slip through our fingers it does work against friction on us and the weight loses kinetic energy.

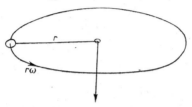

In turbulent motion the eddies distort the elements of fluid composing them.   When a small eddy is embedded in a large one the motion of the large one stretches the vortex lines of the small one and intensifies it.   The small eddy exerts a stress on the large one, reducing the shear in it and absorbing some of its energy. Provided there are bigger eddies present the size of the eddies steadily decreases.

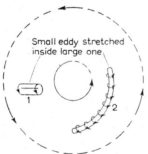

There is, therefore, a *cascade* of kinetic energy, or energy of turbulent motion, from the large into small eddies.

The shearing stresses due to viscosity are proportional to the vorticity (or shear), and the rate of working is also proportional to the shear.   We would therefore expect (and it can be shown rigorously) that if the fluid is not compressed or expanded the rate of doing work against the viscous stresses is proportional to the square of the vorticity. Since the energy of turbulent motion is continually transferred from large regions of low vorticity to small regions of high vorticity, the dissipation by viscosity is increased by this cascade of energy. This beautiful mechanism which Nature has devised for spreading all the properties possessed by the fluid particles uniformly among them is the kind of result we would expect from the second law of thermodynamics. We see, moreover, how a block of marked fluid is stretched out into a tortuous filament which is wound in an ever more complicated manner throughout the volume of the fluid. The existence of viscosity is incidental, in the sense that it does not really make much difference to the properties of the fluid on the large scale, because a fluid in turbulent motion will produce within itself eddies which will ultimately spread any property carried by the fluid throughout its entire volume. But in fact the viscosity steps in and prevents it from producing eddies smaller than about a quarter of a millimetre (in the case of air) or so, by converting the energy directly into heat without passing it through the form of smaller eddies. Eddies of this small size still contain millions of molecules at atmospheric pressure, and so the air in them behaves as a continuous viscous fluid rather than as a collection of a finite number of molecules.

Before discussing some properties of turbulence it is worth remarking that, according to our definition, turbulence cannot be two-dimensional. If it were there could be no stretching of vortex lines because they would all be parallel to one another, and perpendicular to the velocity. There is therefore no analogous phenomenon in Flatland. Although it is possible to imagine a configuration of velocity which will stretch a finite area of marked fluid into a long filament whose length is ever growing, it cannot be made to distribute the fluid from any small volume *uniformly* throughout the whole volume unless it is continually stirred afresh. Three-dimensional turbulence distributes the marked fluid by the same process as it runs its larger eddies down to a standstill.

The Reynolds stresses

Reynolds thought of the flow of a fluid in turbulent motion as made up of two components. The first component, the mean flow, was defined as an average velocity of some sort, and we shall discuss the difficulties connected with this definition in the next article. Reynolds studied the effect on the mean flow of the second component, the fluctuations, and drew an analogy between the fluctuating motion of the molecules, which produces viscosity, and the motion in eddies.

In the simple case of a horizontal stream whose mean velocity u increases upwards but in which there are in addition vertical and horizontal fluctuations w' and u', we enquire whether the vertical motion carries horizontal momentum with it. If the effect of the eddies is to reduce the shear by mixing the upper and lower layers together, thereby spreading the horizontal momentum uniformly, then they can be thought of as producing a stress, just like viscosity. The question is whether eddying motion *necessarily* produces a stress.

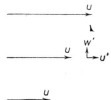

The amount of momentum, additional to that of the mean motion at the level in question, carried upwards by an eddy whose fluctuations of velocity are u' and w', is $\rho u'$ per unit volume, assuming that there are no accompanying fluctuations in density.

This is carried upwards with velocity w' so that the rate at which momentum is transported by the eddy is $\rho u'w'$ per unit volume. The stress experienced by the mean flow is the average value of this, namely

$$\overline{\rho u'w'}$$

where the bar means an average value obtained in the same way as u, the average horizontal velocity, is obtained. This is the Reynolds stress, and is analogous to the viscous stress

$$\mu \frac{\partial u}{\partial z}$$

described on page 84. The significant difference is that μ is a property of the fluid whereas the fluctuations u' and w' are properties of the motion and may be determined by it.

The average value of $u'w'$ may be zero if there is no correlation between the horizontal and vertical fluctuations of velocity. In completely ' random ' motion for every particle with values u' and w' there would be found, on the average, another with fluctuations u' and $-w'$, which would transfer the same amount of momentum in the opposite direction, so that the total effect would be to provide no stress. But we shall see that such random motion cannot exist in a shearing stream. On the other hand *special* types of fluctuating motion can exist which produce no stress, oscillatory wave motion being a simple example. For the understanding of the mechanism of the stresses the best example of eddying motion with no Reynolds stress is when the motion is two-dimensional with uniform shear. All the eddying motion in such a case can, unless it be purely oscillatory, be represented by its vortex lines. Each line adds a rotary motion to the rest, and it is easily seen that for every point at which u' is associated with a positive value of w' there is another at which the same value of u' goes with an equal negative value of w'.

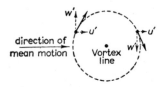

The characteristic which ensures that this kind of eddy shall not produce Reynolds stresses is that the vortex lines of the fluctuations are parallel straight lines lying in planes in which the mean motion is uniform. This means that the eddies do not stretch each other's vortex lines, nor does the mean motion stretch them. But if the vortex lines of an eddy lay across the shearing planes of the mean motion it would be stretched and its kinetic energy increased. This energy can only come from that available in the shear, and must therefore produce a stress tending to reduce the shear. That this is so can be seen by Reynolds's analysis, for upward moving parts of the eddy have a horizontal component of velocity less than the downward moving parts in the case illustrated below. This tends to transfer horizontal momentum downwards on the average, thereby reducing the shear. In this case the fluctuations u' and w' are highly correlated, positive values of w' being associated with negative values of u'. The average $\overline{u'w'}$ is therefore large and negative.

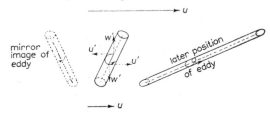

Isotropic turbulence

It is interesting, and important, that the eddies cannot be randomly distributed in such a way that for every eddy in the position of the one shown there is an equal one in the mirror image position transferring horizontal momentum upwards. For if at one instant this happened to be so, the mean motion would distort the eddies in the manner illustrated in the last figure so that after a finite time they would all be transferring momentum from the fast to the slow moving regions. Initially the ' mirror image ' eddy would be compressed, its kinetic energy would be decreased, and it would tend to increase the shear in the mean motion by transferring horizontal momentum towards the faster moving parts of the main stream.

In order that stresses in the mean motion shall be produced by turbulence, the fluctuations cannot therefore be completely random. On the other hand if there existed in fluid which had either uniform or zero mean motion, it could contain isotropic turbulent motion, that is turbulence in which no preferential orientation of the eddies could be found. The small eddies would, on the other hand, be so disposed as to produce stresses reducing the energy of the large ones. If the fluid were then subjected to shearing motion, there would be no Reynolds stresses to begin with, but they would very quickly develop as the majority of the eddies became stretched by the mean motion, and almost none were left in a position to be compressed by it. The turbulence would then no longer be isotropic.

Isotropic turbulence necessarily decays as the energy passes to ever smaller eddies whose energy is ultimately converted into heat by viscosity. By contrast, turbulence in shearing flow continuously extracts energy from the mean motion and can therefore remain at the same intensity even though the smallest eddies are being steadily destroyed by viscosity. Although it does not transfer momentum, isotropic turbulence will, nevertheless, transfer any other quantity borne by the fluid such as smoke or water vapour. In the absence of shear, turbulent motion which was not initially isotropic tends to become so by smoothing out any variations in the motion. For instance, behind any objects of complicated shape such as a grid of wires, or a hedge, the wakes soon merge and compose turbulence. The case of turbulence behind a uniform grid of wires in a wind tunnel has been extensively studied because of its simplicity.

The problem of defining the mean flow

The most obvious difficulty in dealing with turbulence derives from the complexity of the motion which we call fluctuations or eddies, and we soon get used to the idea that we shall only deal with eddies in large numbers, that is statistically, and discuss their properties on the average. It is somewhat paradoxical, therefore, that we then discover a much more fundamental difficulty. This is the problem of defining the mean flow of which the eddies are fluctuations.

If the turbulence being studied is behind an obstacle or grid of wires in a wind tunnel, we can obtain a mean flow without difficulty simply by keeping the flow through the tunnel constant for a time long compared with the life of an eddy or with the time taken for an air particle to pass right through the tunnel. The average value of the velocity u along the tunnel at any point can then be defined as U, given by

$$U = \frac{1}{2T}\int_{-T}^{T} u\,\mathrm{d}t$$

where T is a time long according to the above criterion. Thus U is the average value of u over the interval of time $2T$; and provided that $2T$ is long enough, the value of U obtained will not vary if T is varied. If u' is the fluctuation in velocity along the tunnel then

$$u = U + u'.$$

The average value of u' is, by definition, zero.

We are dedicated to the study of natural motion, and we find that it is often *not* steady for a long enough time for a mean value to be obtained. This is not because the fluctuations are large compared with the mean value, for this would not matter. U may be zero without any serious consequences. But if we vary T we often find that we get a different value of U. There are generally fluctuations not only from second to second and minute to minute but also from hour to hour, day to day, month to month, year to year, and so on, as far as we choose to concern ourselves with the matter. On occasions when the fluctuations from minute to minute are very intense but otherwise the wind is steady all day, we obtain a satisfactory measure of the mean wind by taking an average value over 10 minutes or any longer period up to the whole day.

But if the wind were steadily increasing during the day, the moment during the day, and the length of time over which we took the average, would affect the average we obtained. We could see that any period from 10 to 60 minutes would give roughly the same average, but a longer period would begin to reveal the steady increase during the day. For purposes of studying the small scale (one minute) fluctuations we could define a mean wind at any time of day. But if there happened also to be intense eddies giving large fluctuations every 5–30 minutes this would be impossible, and the properties of the motion could not be satisfactorily described in terms of a mean motion with superimposed fluctuations.

We meet the same problem on a large scale in time when we attempt to define climate. The average wind can be easily defined as the average value of the wind over a period of years, or the displacement that would be experienced by a particle moving always with the speed of the wind at the point in question divided by the period chosen (these are not the same thing); but we have no justification for supposing that the average for one decade will be the same as for another, indeed experience tells us that it is generally significantly different, and that past averages are often a poor guide to the future.

The separation (in our minds) of the mean flow from the fluctuations is impossible when there exist eddies of all sizes of comparable importance. When there is a range of sizes absent we can take an average over a period within that range and obtain a mean value which varies in time under the influence of the larger eddies: the smaller eddies compose the fluctuations. Whether we think of eddies of a certain range of sizes as contributing to a varying mean motion or as fluctuations is *our* choice, not Nature's; and to this extent turbulence is a feature of our thinking, not of the motion.

Unfortunately this problem remains largely unsolved. The ingenious and penetrating ideas of Sutton, which are briefly referred to in Chapter 8 (page 199) have served rather to make us conscious of this problem than to solve it. They offer a solution, which has to be used with understanding, in the case in which eddies of all sizes are present. The attempts to extend the method to many special cases by the use of various coefficients raise the difficulty that we have no theoretical method of ensuring that the values of the coefficients can be deduced for the case in which we may be interested from those in which they have been measured.

In thinking about the mechanisms of Nature, it may often be more helpful, therefore, to think of the behaviour of individual eddies, rather than of them statistically and in terms of coefficients analogous to viscosity, thermal conductivity, and other kinds of diffusivity.

Turbulence near boundaries

When eddies are reduced to less than a certain size they are rapidly taken out of existence by the conversion of their energy into heat by viscosity. There must therefore exist a layer of fluid whose thickness is of the order of the size of such eddies, in which the stress between the fluid and the boundary is due to viscosity alone, and in which the Reynolds stresses are negligible compared with the viscous stresses. Outside this layer, if the flow is turbulent, there is a layer in which energy of the mean motion is converted by the action of the Reynolds stresses into turbulent motion, thereby maintaining the turbulence and the Reynolds stresses in existence.

The Reynolds stress is in addition to, and is generally much larger than, the viscous stress. If the flow is steady the stress is nearly constant in the layer of greatest shear close to the boundary, which is the same as saying that the energy received by the fluid through moving towards low pressure is small compared with that dissipated against the shearing stresses—in that layer. The main stream of the fluid, on the other hand, has work done on it as it moves towards lower pressure, and this is the source of most of the energy dissipated in the region of large shear near the boundary.

The effect of the larger Reynolds stresses is to reduce the shear, where they are operating, in comparison with what it would be if only viscous stresses were present. In a pipe, therefore, when the pressure difference between the ends is kept constant the shearing stress on the walls must be constant. If the flow becomes turbulent the velocity in the main stream must be reduced while the shear at the boundary remains the same. The rate at which work is done on the fluid by the pressure gradient force is reduced when the total flow is reduced because of the increase of the stresses.

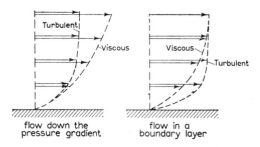

flow down the pressure gradient   flow in a boundary layer

In a boundary layer, however, at the edge of which the velocity relative to the boundary remains constant, the introduction of turbulent stresses concentrates the shear into the layer in which they do not operate, that is close to the boundary. The velocity gradient at the boundary is thereby increased so that separation is delayed. The stress along the boundary is increased.

The effect of preventing separation of a boundary layer is to reduce the size of the wake of a body. The total drag on the body may thereby be reduced even though the viscous stress at the surface is increased. Turbulence to prevent separation may often be conveniently introduced by small roughnesses on the surface.

Turbulence in a stably stratified fluid

One of the effects of turbulence is to make more uniform any property (possibly excluding momentum) possessed by the fluid. If the density of a fluid decreases upwards, either because of a gradient of temperature or of some light constituent such as water vapour in air or salinity in water, the turbulence will tend to make it more uniformly distributed. The carrying of density upwards requires work to be done against gravity, and so the kinetic energy of the turbulence is consumed and converted into potential energy. The centre of gravity of the whole mass of fluid is raised and the fluid becomes less stably stratified.

The rate at which work is done by the turbulence for unit mass of fluid is equal to the rate at which density is transferred by the turbulence in unit gradient of density (which is represented by K_H, the coefficient of eddy transfer of heat or density) multiplied by the gradient of density, multiplied by the gravity force on unit mass. This is equal to

$$K_H \frac{\partial \rho}{\partial z} g$$

per unit mass, or

$$g\beta K_H$$

per unit volume, where β, the static stability, is equal to $\frac{1}{\rho} \frac{\partial \rho}{\partial z}$.

In the atmosphere the energy of turbulence in a stably stratified medium is generally completely consumed in this way unless it is at the same time being continuously created. Thus the presence of turbulence in stable regions of the atmosphere in effect implies the existence at that time of a source of turbulence. Some of the turbulent energy may also be converted into energy of gravity waves: this is discussed briefly in Chapter 9.

There are two possible sources of turbulent energy in the free air away from obstacles and boundaries generally, namely static instability and the Reynolds stresses in shearing flow. The first of these arises when β is negative and turbulent energy is produced, not consumed. The nature of such turbulence is discussed in Chapter 7, and it has special properties which are outlined below. The second source of turbulent energy was considered by Richardson.

Richardson's Criterion

Richardson argued that, if K_M is the coefficient of transfer of momentum by the turbulence, the stress is

$$K_M \frac{\partial U}{\partial z}$$

in the case where the velocity U is horizontal and varies only with height. The rate at which work is done per unit volume against this stress is the stress multiplied by the shear, namely

$$K_M \frac{\partial U}{\partial z} \times \frac{\partial U}{\partial z}$$

or

$$K_M U'^2$$

where

$$U' = \partial U / \partial z.$$

The work done against these stresses is converted into energy of turbulence, and if this exceeds the work done against gravity, Richardson argued, the energy of the turbulence will increase. Thus he concluded that any turbulence will grow if

$$K_M U'^2 > K_H g \beta.$$

The ratio $g\beta/U'^2$ is called the Richardson number, which is denoted by Ri. It is the ratio of the energy available from the shear to the potential energy of the stable stratification.

The derivation of this criterion is certainly illuminating, but it has not been found to accord closely with experiment for a variety of reasons. Richardson regarded it as a criterion for the onset of turbulence, assuming that viscosity was negligible. This assumption is found to be unjustified in cases where the shear is produced close to a boundary by the viscous stresses. We have seen that the presence of a boundary reduces the Reynolds stresses near to it. Schlichting consequently found that turbulence in a stably stratified viscous boundary layer would not grow unless the Richardson number was less than about 0.04. On the assumption that $K_M = K_H$, Richardson originally proposed that the critical value of Ri was unity.   But in the light of our knowledge acquired since then about the conversion of the energy of the large eddies into energy of smaller ones through the existence of Reynolds stresses within the turbulence itself the problem requires reconsideration.   It may also be that the growth of the initial disturbance which later becomes turbulence extracts less energy from the shear flow than fully developed turbulence.   A disturbance whose vortex lines lay within the shearing planes could extract no energy from the mean flow because it would produce no Reynolds stresses (page 130), it might therefore be at a disadvantage in a stably stratified fluid compared with a fully developed turbulent disturbance.   Yet it may be that this kind of disturbance is the one which grows most readily if there is no stable stratification simply because it does not reduce the mean shear in its neighbourhood.

In flow near a boundary roughness increases the likelihood of turbulence and should be considered in Schlichling's experiment, to which, therefore, Richardson's criterion is not strictly applicable.   On a larger scale Durst found that it was fairly well satisfied in the case of the wind in the lowest 10 m blowing over the ground at night.

We saw (page 53) that flow in a curved path can be stable if the velocity decreases outwards sufficiently slowly.   Flow in the boundary layer on the convex surface of a body is therefore stable in the same manner as horizontal shearing flow in a stably stratified fluid.   The centrifugal force corresponding to $g\rho$ is $\rho u^2/r$, and so except near the centre of curvature of the flow

$$Ri = \frac{\dfrac{2u}{r}\dfrac{\partial u}{\partial r} + \dfrac{u^2}{r^2}}{\left(\dfrac{\partial u}{\partial r}\right)^2} = \frac{2u}{r\,\partial u/\partial r} + \left(\frac{u}{r\,\partial u/\partial r}\right)^2$$

The relevant number is now $u/r \div \partial u/\partial r$, of which Ri is a function. On Richardson's criterion the flow is most unstable close to the boundary, at which u is zero if the body is fixed.   As u increases away from the boundary the Richardson number increases and the flow in this sense becomes more stable.   Close to the boundary the Reynolds number $U\delta/\nu$ is very small, δ being the distance from the boundary, and so the viscous forces are dominant and do not permit the growth of turbulence.

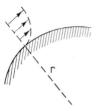

In the case when the main body of the fluid is at rest and the boundary is moving instability may be produced. This happens if a cylinder is rotated in an otherwise stationary fluid (see page 53).

Theodorsen's horseshoes in boundary layer spaghetti

We have been picturing the eddies to be stretched only in terms of pieces of them. In fact as the vortex lines become stretched they become knotted in among each other and drawn out into complicated shapes. Theodorsen likened the element or proton of turbulence to a horseshoe, because the parts of vortex tubes in which the properties of turbulence are generated are the parts that become bent into arcs. They can equally be pictured as pieces of spaghetti which resist being lifted from a plate.

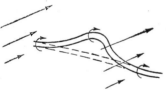

We have seen that close to the boundary of a fluid the vorticity (which is deformed by turbulence and destroyed by viscosity) may be created by the viscous stress (page 93). The vortex tubes thus created lie like spaghetti on the boundary, across the direction of the velocity. When these tubes are distorted, either by eddies or by the mean flow after an initial distortion by an eddy, energy of turbulence is produced. The orderly spaghetti becomes contorted, and as the new eddies decay some are carried out of the region near the boundary where they are created into the adjacent region of small shear.

In fully developed turbulence the spaghetti can be seen to be like a rope spun from fibres, the ' fibres ' being smaller spaghetti extracting energy from the larger and either handing it to yet smaller vortex tubes or to viscosity.   The proton of the turbulence on all scales is the horseshoe bend induced in a vortex tube of any size.

Forced and free convection

Convection is a term used to denote a type of motion which transfers something, usually heat or buoyancy, possessed by the fluid.   *Forced convection* denotes mechanically produced turbulence, that is turbulence which derives its kinetic energy from the stresses at a boundary or from the drag force on bodies in the fluid: it is often composed of the wakes of bodies as when air passes through a grid of wires or over very rough ground covered with obstacles.   *Free convection* is motion generated within the fluid by forces not associated with boundaries which have to be kept in position by a force, and thermal convection is usually meant by the term, though buoyancy rather than heat is the direct agent producing the motion.

Since forced convection is produced near the boundaries but decays as it spreads outwards from them it decreases in intensity away from the ground.   Since also its nature transfers energy to ever smaller eddies the eddies must decrease in size as it spreads into the fluid where it is not generated.   Buoyant convection on the other hand increases in eddy size as distance from the boundary supplying the buoyancy (heat) increases (see also page 171). The force producing the kinetic energy does not act through the boundary but at all heights in the fluid.   Roughly the eddy size in buoyant convection increases with distance from the boundary but variations in the heating rate with time, and the presence of clouds and stable layers complicate this.   Nevertheless, above a certain height buoyant convection is the dominant form of turbulence; below this height mechanical turbulence is dominant. Typically in the atmosphere when thermal convection is taking place and there is a moderate wind producing shear near the ground this height is at a few metres above the ground in open country, but must vary with the nature of the surface.   Over the sea it may be at only a few centimetres, but over a town with large buildings it may be at several tens of metres.   Investigations of this aspect of turbulence are still in their early stages.   Priestley, in Australia, was the first to demonstrate the definite changeover from one type of turbulence to the other.

Shearing motion has an important effect in reducing the vertical distance that can be traversed by a single 'thermal', that is a buoyant eddy.   This is discussed in more detail in connection with the growth of cumulus clouds in Chapter 10.

The significant difference between the eddies of buoyant convection and those we have been discussing, is that they do not tend to be reduced but increased in size, with their vertical velocity decreasing.   Their nature is discussed in the next chapter: for the present we simply note that if we represent the two types of turbulence by means of transfer coefficients and think only of their effect on such things as the distribution of water vapour which we may happen to be interested in, we shall not improve our understanding of Nature.   This will be achieved only by studying in some detail the different mechanisms of the eddies.

Clear air turbulence in the jet stream

In Chapter 2 (page 44) we saw how at a jet stream exit the kinetic energy of the jet stream was converted into potential energy by an indirect circulation around the streamlines.   This process reduces the static stability of the air, and so reduces the Richardson number.   But, because the air of the jet stream is moving faster than the air surrounding it, the air whose potential energy it draws upon to become a jet stream is not that to which it gives potential energy at the jet exit.   In places therefore it may produce so much potential energy that the air becomes statically unstable.   To do this a portion of the air would have, in effect, to undergo an indirect circulation so as to be turned upside down.   If a part of the jet stream were to move across the air below it as it slowed down, on account of the large horizontal temperature gradients it could find itself above warmer air than itself.   On account of the large shears present the flow might become turbulent for a positive value of the Richardson number. It is evident from special radio-sonde balloon ascents made in jet

streams in America to measure the fine structure of the temperature and velocity profiles that while the Richardson number in
layer a thousand metres or more deep may be in the neighbourhood of unity, it may have much smaller values in shallow layers
because the velocity and temperature profiles measured often
show shallow layers in which the shear is 10 times the average or
the stability one tenth of the average.

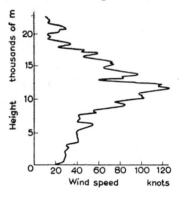

Once turbulence had begun it would spread by increasing the
shear above and below as the shear in the turbulent layer is
reduced by the Reynolds stresses. There is nothing in this
explanation which predicts the size of the eddies to be expected in
clear air turbulence.

CHAPTER 7

BUOYANT CONVECTION

ARCHIMEDES understood centuries ago why it was that things immersed in a fluid would be subjected to an upward force if they were lighter than the fluid which they displaced; but only recently have serious studies been made of the motion that results when the thing that is immersed is also a body of fluid. This is what buoyant convection is about. It is the way in which buoyant fluids move under the influence of the buoyancy forces.

There are several ways in which we can see why the movement should occur. If there is no motion then the pressure at any point is due to the weight of fluid above. The pressure at A in the figure is the same as at A_1 and A_2 at the same level. The fluid above B, on the other hand, is lighter than that above B_1 and B_2 and so the pressure there is less. The fluid will therefore begin to move towards the low pressure region at B and tend to equalise the pressure along the line B_1BB_2. The raising of the pressure in the neighbourhood of B will apply an increased upward force to the buoyant fluid, which will therefore begin to move upwards.

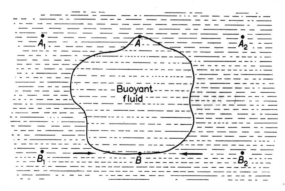

This is rather an artificial way of thinking about it because we have to imagine that we start with the fluid at rest and yet in a state of gross instability. It is difficult to realise in practice

143

because, before we depart very far from equilibrium, motion begins.   If the motion has already begun and is accelerating we cannot make any very ready assumptions about what the pressure is at any point because inertia forces have come into play.

It is desirable, therefore, to discuss fluid in motion as far as possible without reference to the pressure.   One way is to consider the energy changes, for we know that if any mechanical system can move so that the potential energy is decreased and converted through motion into heat, it will do so.   If the buoyant fluid moves upwards, some of the surrounding fluid will move downwards to take its place so that the centre of gravity of the whole will be lowered.   Gravitational potential energy is released if the buoyant fluid moves upwards, and it is converted into energy of motion. The interesting question is how the energy of motion is distributed through the fluid.   What is the pattern of velocity ?

We saw in Chapter 3 that vorticity is created by horizontal gradients of density.   If the density is uniform outside the boundary of the buoyant fluid, and uniform again but smaller in magnitude inside the boundary, then the vorticity will be created to begin with as a vortex sheet with the buoyant fluid sliding up-wards through the surroundings rather like a balloon.   But we know, if only from experience, that Nature will not allow the sharp boundary to remain as sharp, and it is interesting to see what she does about it—not always the same thing.   There are two distinct kinds of convection, the first, slow convection, takes place when the gravitational potential energy is converted immediately into heat and the inertia forces are negligible.   The second, penetrative convection, occurs when almost all the gravitational energy released is converted into perceptible bulk motion and remains as such for a long time—longer, that is, than we are interested in it.

Slow convection

(a) Cellular motion

We can best understand this by imagining how we would set it up.   If two metal plates are placed horizontally one above the other with a fluid in between, and we very gradually raise the temperature of the lower one the fluid in contact with it becomes warmed: it expands, and its density decreases.   In order to permit the expansion we can imagine that the upper plate is allowed to rise a little. The thermal (molecular) conductivity of the fluid will transfer heat upwards through the layer of fluid even when there is no bulk motion, and if we warm the lower plate slowly enough we can ensure that the temperature *gradient* in the

layer is practically uniform. The temperature and density profiles are then straight lines as in the figure. We may wonder how much we can warm up the bottom plate without setting the fluid in motion. The criterion is whether the thermal conductivity can transfer heat upwards to the cold plate more quickly than if there were some motion. Lazy Nature will not bother to have motion if it is not the best way of relieving the temperature and density gradients.

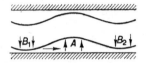

If motion does take place it must be upwards in some places such as A, and downwards in others such as B_1 and B_2 in the figure above. As a consequence of this warm fluid at A will be placed side by side with cool fluid at B_1 and B_2 and the thermal conductivity will begin to conduct heat horizontally, which will take heat from the fluid going upwards and give it to fluid going downwards. This would be 'bad', because the object of the exercise is to convey heat upwards. Nature might try having upward and downward moving parts of the fluid much farther apart so as to reduce this horizontal transfer of heat, but the fluid would then have to travel a large horizontal distance on reaching the other plate in order to return. This would mean that in each circuit a great deal of the gravitational energy available would have to be expended against viscosity in purely horizontal motion parallel to the plates (see figure). Moreover, a particle travelling close to the bottom plate from B to A would acquire enough heat and be ready to rise long before it came to A. The long horizontal traverse would be wasteful from the point of view of getting the heat out of the plate into the fluid. If we had up and down motion much closer together, in addition to the wasteful horizontal conduction of heat there would also be viscous forces resisting the relative motion of the closely placed up and down currents.

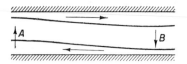

Nature finds a compromise between these two extremes. There is one configuration of the motion which is more efficient than any other shape in conveying heat from one wall to the other. But even this kind of motion, resisted as it is by both the conductivity and viscosity, will not occur unless the temperature gradient exceeds a certain minimum value which must depend upon the viscosity and conductivity of the fluid.

The shape of the ' cells ' (or pattern of up and down motion) is independent of the actual values of the physical quantities and it is the same in all fluids.

This last statement needs some qualification. In the first place it has been assumed that the temperature and density gradients are everywhere proportional to one another, which is another way of saying that the coefficient of expansion of the fluid is independent of temperature. An extreme case will illustrate this point. The density of water is a maximum at 4° C. If we had a layer of water at 2° C and heated it at the bottom there would be no convection at all until the temperature had risen above 4° C, and until then all the heat would have to be transferred by molecular thermal conductivity (radiation being ignored). Even if convection began when the temperature at the bottom was say 5° C it would only extend upwards through that part of the fluid which had been warmed above 4° C. With this proviso, viscosity, which resists the motion which the buoyancy forces tend to produce, and thermal conductivity, which conducts away density differences, have a similar effect. In practice this is very nearly true of gases because the coefficient of expansion is inversely proportional to the absolute temperature, and this varies very little except in very artificial cases.

Secondly, it is also assumed that the viscosity (and conductivity) is independent of temperature, for if it were not it would not behave in the same way at the top and bottom of the cells.

Thirdly, the motion must be slow. If it were not then the accelerations of the particles as they travelled in curved paths would require appreciable forces to produce them and the buoyancy forces would not be almost exactly balanced by the viscous forces. Another way of saying this is that the Reynolds number is very small indeed and the inertia forces are negligible compared with the viscous forces.

Fourthly, although the thermal conductivity and viscosity of the fluid are molecular effects it is the transfer of momentum and heat, not velocity and temperature, that we are concerned with. The effects therefore depend on the density and specific heat of the fluid, and molecular motion may be more effective in transferring heat in relation to momentum in some fluids than in others. Some substances are not true liquids but are gluey: they are very viscous but poor conductors of heat. Slow convection in them has not been studied.

If we attempt the experiment either by gradually increasing the temperature gradient until motion begins, or by gradually reducing it until a much more chaotic motion settles down into a steady state, we observe that the pattern of cells becomes very regular— either hexagonal or square. It seems that the hexagonal configuration can be produced with a very slightly smaller temperature gradient than the square one, but the square one is stable in the sense that it is fairly easy to produce and keep in existence.

To perform the experiment all that is required is a fairly viscous fluid such as paint (as we shall see below the greater the viscosity the deeper the layer of fluid that can be used), and aluminium paint is particularly suitable when diluted with turpentine (as when a paint brush is cleaned after use) because the aluminium is in the form of tiny flakes. Since the motion is governed by viscosity there is shear in every part of it and this causes the flakes to lie almost along the lines of flow. Consequently when the line of sight is at a tangent to the streamlines the flakes are seen edge on and the fluid looks dark. When viewed across the streamlines the flakes are seen to be bright. The temperature gradient is easily produced by placing the tin (or whatever the fluid is contained in) on something warm which is gradually cooling down, so that the motion gradually settles into a steady pattern. A piece of glass placed on top of the container will restrict evaporation and loss of heat from the top: and it can be removed or supported so as to permit some ventilation to suit conditions. The motion is usually said to consist of Bénard cells, after Bénard, who first described this type of motion.

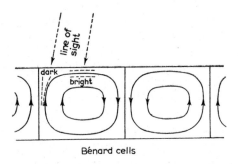

Bénard cells

(b) *Rayleigh's number, and the conditions for motion*

We are now in a position to see how the temperature gradient required to start the motion depends upon the various quantities involved. The motion occurs only because temperature differences produce density differences and buoyancy forces in consequence, so in the first instance we will see how the density differences must depend upon the physical quantities. The viscous force per unit mass is represented by μ/ρ which we denote by ν. The molecular thermal conductivity, as we have seen, operates in a similar way and must therefore appear equally with ν. Since it is changes in temperature, and not changes in amount of heat contained in the fluid, which are responsible for the amount of expansion (and changes in density) the conductivity, k, or coefficient of transfer of heat, must appear divided by the specific heat c_p which relates the heat content to temperature. k/c_p is denoted by κ. The buoyancy force per unit mass is proportional to $g\,(\rho_{\text{bottom}} - \rho_{\text{top}})/\rho_{\text{middle}}$. Provided that the variations in density are only a small fraction of the density itself, ρ_{middle} could be replaced by the value of ρ anywhere in the fluid to a high degree of approximation. The depth of the layer h is the only other quantity involved. It is then found by the argument outlined in

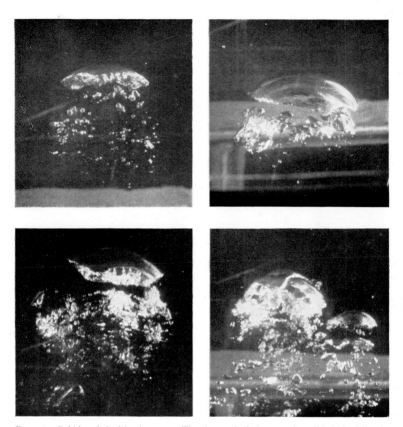

PLATE 1. Bubbles of air rising in water. They have spherical caps and small bubbles follow in their wake. In the fourth case the air was not released as a compact mass, so that there are more fragments; the left-hand edge of the large bubble on the right can be seen to be turned up because it is in the wake of the largest bubble. (*See* pages 15 and 120)

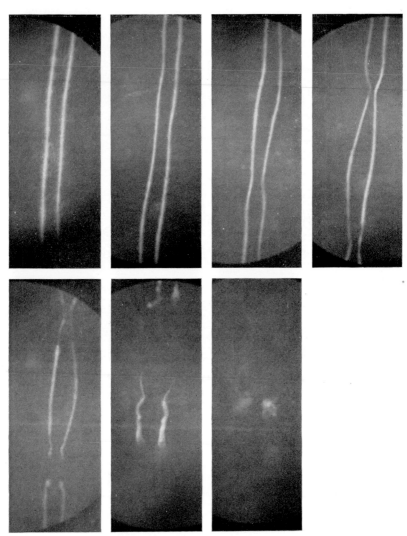

PLATE 2. A condensation trail produced by exhaust from jet engines entering the wing tip vortices of an aircraft, photographed through a telescope (×25). First the fuzzy edges evaporate leaving the tubes of cloud; then the parts which come nearer together descend more rapidly through the stably stratified surrounding air and finally 'burst'. The total time covered is one minute. (*See* page 73)

[*Facing page* 149

Chapter 11, that the only way to express the density gradient in terms of κ, ν, and h, is

$$\frac{g\,(\rho_b - \rho_t)}{h\rho_b} = C\,\frac{\kappa\nu}{h^4}.$$

The left-hand side is the gradient of density required just to start motion. The right-hand side consists of the numerical constant C multiplied by $\kappa\nu$ and h arranged so as to give a quantity whose dimensions are the same as the left side. The reciprocal of C is called the *Rayleigh number*. C depends upon the conditions we have imposed, and to summarise this discussion they will be repeated.

1. The motion is slow: the inertia forces are negligible (the Reynolds number is very small).
2. The temperature and density differences are small, being only small fractions of their absolute values.
3. The coefficients of expansion, heat conduction, specific heat and viscosity are independent of temperature over the range. (It is implied in 2 that the density is independent of temperature too, except in so far as it produces buoyancy forces: its variations do not affect the inertia forces because these are negligible anyway).
4. The conditions at the boundary are the same for temperature and velocity, otherwise κ and ν will not appear in the same way in the equation above.
5. All the heat that goes in at the bottom comes out at the top.

The nature of these conditions will become clearer if we consider what happens if we depart from them. Taking the fourth condition first, one possible case is to have a ' perfect ' solid conductor at the top and the bottom of the layer. The velocity which would be zero, and the temperature, would then both be uniform all over the boundaries, and Rayleigh showed that in that case $C = \dfrac{27\pi^4}{4}$. If we had a free surface at the top the velocity would not be uniform because particles at the surface would be free to move, and the temperature at the boundary would be determined by how the heat was carried away from it. The value of C would then be different—and smaller by perhaps 30–50 per cent because the motion would take place more readily if there were no viscous forces at the top.

The fifth condition means that the fluid is not steadily getting warmer. Buoyancy entering at the bottom is not being absorbed. This must affect the motion, but how is difficult to say. We know that if we deliberately put in heat too rapidly at the bottom then the condition 1 is not satisfied and the motion becomes chaotic and unsteady. The warm fluid rises in lumps, which on reaching the upper surface spread out, forcing the surrounding fluid downwards. This gives an appearance to the upper surface of cells growing from nothing to a very large size, but when they get bigger than a certain size they begin to lose their identity as smaller, better defined ones appear within and around them. If there is a free upper surface it becomes noticeably unlevel, and bulges upwards, particularly where there is an upsurge of fluid and the inertia forces carry it above the mean level before it spreads out.

(c) The direction of cellular motion

The second and third conditions specified in the last article are not separable, because as the temperature gradients grow so do density gradients, and so also do the variations in coefficients of expansion, heat conduction, and viscosity. If all the conditions 1–5 were strictly satisfied there would be nothing to determine whether the motion would be upwards or downwards in the centre of the cell. It is therefore most interesting that the direction which is apparently taken is with the motion in the centre of the cells towards the region of smaller viscosity. For gases, in which the viscosity increases with increasing temperature, this is downwards in the centre: for liquids, in most of which viscosity decreases with increasing temperature, it is upwards. Liquid sulphur has the property that the viscosity has a minimum at 119° C. At lower temperatures the motion in the cells is therefore the same as in other liquids, but at higher temperatures it flows like a gas. Professor Koschmieder has demonstrated this experimentally. At around 119° C the flow assumes the appearance of the diagrams of the intestines one sees in medical books, as the cells rearrange themselves from one direction of flow to the other. Apart from this effect of determining the direction of motion the violation of conditions 2 and 3 has little effect so long as the

motion is steady.   If conditions were such as to disturb the configuration of motion seriously the first condition would be violated
first.   Since κ represents an effect of molecular motion, variations
of it with temperature are likely to produce effects similar to the
variations of ν.

The temperature gradient is related to the density gradient
directly through the coefficient of expansion a.   The left-hand
side of the above equation (page 149) can therefore be thought of as
representing the temperature gradient.   For

$$\frac{\rho_b - \rho_t}{\rho_b} = \frac{\rho_b - \rho_b \left[1 - a(T_t - T_b)\right]}{\rho_b}$$
$$= a(T_t - T_b)$$
$$= \frac{T_t - T_b}{T_b}$$

in the case of gases, for which $a = 1/T$.   Equation on page 149
therefore tells us that for a given temperature difference between
the top and the bottom, the minimum depth of a layer of fluid
which will be set in slow cellular motion is proportional to h^{-3}.
The marginal depth such that shallower layers will conduct the
heat without motion can easily be determined in an experiment by
tilting the bottom of the container of the fluid.   In regions where
the depth is less than this marginal value no cells will appear.

The dimensions of the cells depend upon their configuration
(e.g. square, or hexagonal) but roughly the width is about $2\frac{1}{2}$
times the depth.   This can be seen in the experiment just mentioned because they are bigger in the deeper parts of the fluid.

(d) The effect of shearing motion

Finally, we come to the problem of what happens if there is
shearing motion in the layer in which convection is occurring.
Jeffreys argued convincingly, and the experiments of Graham in
particular seem to support his argument, that the rate of heat
transfer would be best maintained while the work done against
viscosity would be reduced if, instead of assuming a cellular
pattern, the flow took the form of parallel rolls lying along the
direction of shear.   A particle of the fluid would thus execute a
spiral path round one of these rolls.   Adjacent rolls would
rotate in opposite directions, for then there would be no regions of

large shear between the rolls. Particles would pass round the rolls in a manner very similar to that in which they pass round one half of a Bénard cell.

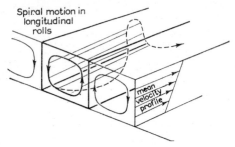

If the rolls were to be across the shear either they would all rotate in the same direction, so that their vorticity was in the same sense as that of the shear under consideration, or alternate rolls would rotate in opposite directions. In the first case, the shear in between adjacent rolls would be very large and the existence of viscosity would make this kind of flow impossible. In the second case alternate rolls would possess a vorticity in the opposite sense to that existing in the flow before convection occurred.

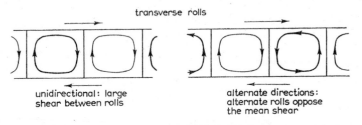

Vorticity can originate in a fluid that is statically unstable, but if it is produced in the form of parallel rolls the rotation of adjacent rolls would be equal and opposite. If a previously existing rotation were added the adjacent rolls would have rotations of unequal magnitude (see figure above) and the shear in between them would be considerable. This difficulty does not arise if the rolls are along the direction of shear. It is found in practice that rolls across the shear are only produced if the shear is very small—presumably the case in which the vorticity generated by the static instability dominates that already existing. The rolls are found experimentally to be along the direction of the imposed shear when it is large.

The experiments done to discover this were carried out by Graham and others under the guidance of Professor Brunt. The fluid was confined between a lower heated surface and an upper

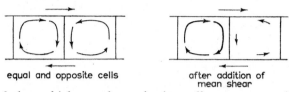

equal and opposite cells   after addition of mean shear

sheet of glass which was drawn horizontally so as to produce the shear. In the free air circumstances are very different. Cellular motion occurs when a shallow layer of cloud becomes unstable. The upper and lower boundaries of the overturning layer are not rigid, and because the density of the air immediately above and below the layer is so nearly equal to that within the layer these boundaries can be distorted. More will be said about the origin of the static instability in cloud layers in Chapter 10. We wish here to remark that the forces inhibiting the formation of transverse rolls in layers with large shear do not operate if the motion can assume a configuration like that shown below. The air above and below undergoes a wavy motion, and the adjacent rolls are not in contact over a vertical area (as they are in the previous figure). All the rolls can take their direction of rotation from the vorticity of the already existing shearing motion; and the motion can therefore take place when only a small degree of static instability is present.

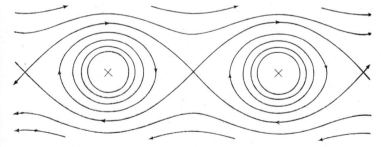

The motion is very similar to what would take place if a vortex sheet were distorted into corrugations (see figure on page 82).

The vorticity would become concentrated into rolls the spacing of which must follow the original corrugations. The only linear dimension from which can be derived the spacing of the rolls, is the depth h of the layer which overturns and forms the rolls. If the configuration of motion is as in the figure above then the air originally in the layer is confined within the closed rolls, and the distance L between rolls is given by

$$L = 2 \cdot 7h$$

approximately. This is, by chance, about the same as the spacing between the upcurrents in cellular convection in a viscous fluid, but it is worthy of note that this relationship was arrived at without reference to viscosity (or thermal conductivity).

In the atmosphere transverse rolls are very common. It is interesting to note that when clouds in the form of parallel rolls (billow clouds) appear in the sky, they do not always form by the breaking up of a layer into rolls, but often by the appearance of new rolls equally spaced at the edge of a region of existing ones. This indicates that the vorticity of the rolls is derived primarily from a redistribution of the vorticity of the existing airstream and not from the generation of new vorticity by buoyancy forces, for the buoyancy forces cannot exist until after the cloud appears. Even in the case of a cloud layer being transformed into rolls the vorticity may be derived from the stream and not from buoyancy forces. This is discussed further in Chapter 10.

Convection streets

Longitudinal rolls (along the direction of shear) occur in cases where the vorticity of the rolls is generated by the buoyancy forces. A good example is the production of a long upcurrent downwind

of a hump in the ground. If the air is unstable over a large area, on account of heating from below, a small displacement upwards of one part of the air will initiate an upcurrent. As long as the surfaces of constant density are horizontal a state of instability can, theoretically, exist. If, as the wind blows, the air is continuously displaced upwards over a small hill convection is continuously initiated there with vorticity being continuously generated in the sense shown in the figure. According to Welch the experience of glider pilots indicates that convection in the atmosphere is often arranged with the upcurrents in long lines lying along the direction of the wind. In this connection it is worth noting that the distortion of the vortex lines by an obstacle in a wind which increases with height is such as to produce a downward motion in the lee of the obstacle (Chapter 3, page 81). Hawthorne has devised a beautiful experiment (Hawthorne's 'hot hump') in which these two effects are combined—the rotation produced by the distortion of the vortex lines being confined to the region of large vorticity in the oncoming stream (that is, near the boundary), and the rotation generated by the buoyancy forces occurring higher up when the obstacle serves mainly to produce an upward displacement and the oncoming stream has less vorticity. This is illustrated in the figure on page 81. The vorticity in the wedge-shaped region near the boundary is initiated by the distortion of the vortex lines close to the boundary by the hump, but it is increased by the forces of buoyancy once the surfaces of constant density have become tilted.

The downward motion on either side of the convection street (see figure above) tends to produce upward motion beyond it because the originally horizontal surfaces become tilted. Another street, parallel to the original one, is thus brought into existence if no other disturbances disrupt the process, and the convection assumes the form of parallel rolls along the direction of the wind, whether there is shear or not.

Penetrative convection

Nature attempts to do things slowly neither for the convenience of the general public nor for the benefit of mathematicians to make their problems tractable. She often supplies heat to the bottom of a fluid so rapidly that slow cellular motion is incapable of carrying it upwards as fast as it is supplied. The atmosphere is often warmed by convection from below, so that the condition

5 on page 149 is not satisfied.   Nature has to devise a mechanism for distributing the heat into the bulk of the fluid, and for removing it from the source at the boundary.

It is observed that the fluid comes away from the heated boundary in lumps, which we call thermals.   The mechanism whereby they are produced will be discussed later, meanwhile we shall study the behaviour of one of these thermals advancing into otherwise undisturbed fluid.   If Nature has a good way of doing things, it is the best, that is good enough not to require alternatives. Thermals will therefore normally behave like each other except in so far as they are born different.   But as we shall see, they mix with the surroundings as they advance, and they grow bigger thereby.   After a time therefore, most of the fluid of which a thermal is composed was originally motionless in the surroundings and most of the momentum and vorticity it possesses will have been generated by the buoyancy forces since its birth.   Its shape and the distribution of density, momentum, and vorticity, within it when it was 'created' have a negligible effect in comparison with what subsequently takes place, and so all thermals tend towards the one ideal configuration as their birthmarks become obliterated.

(a) The ideal thermal

This ultimate form, or ideal thermal, is illustrated in Plate 4 which shows a cloud of heavy fluid released in a tank of water. Its form just after release is shown at the top of the picture.   The fluid in this case was a salt solution made visible by a dense white precipitate of barium sulphate (which is produced on mixing solutions of barium chloride and sodium sulphate).   The con-

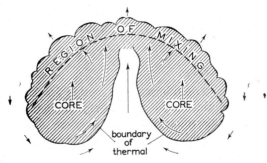

figuration of motion in and around the thermal is shown in the figure, and it can be seen that the vorticity is disposed as we would expect (see page 66) from the distribution of density. Vorticity is continuously being generated but because the volume of fluid containing it is continuously increasing the velocities are steadily decreasing.

The fluid near the ' core ' of the thermal, where the upward velocity is about equal to that of the thermal as a whole, is the most buoyant and so vorticity is being generated in the direction shown in the figure below. Between the core and the surrounding fluid where the density gradients are greatest the fluid is made to rotate as shown. In consequence it is carried round into the rear of the thermal, and when it reaches the central region the vorticity begins to be slightly reduced because the fluid surrounding it is now more buoyant. The core is thus forced to advance* within

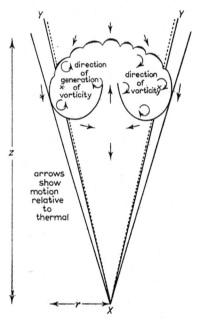

* In the experiments carried out in water tanks to discover the properties of thermals the motion studied was usually downwards. In that case the word ' buoyant ' means heavier than the surroundings and ' advance ' means ' descend '. In the atmosphere, of course, thermals generally rise, though not always (see page 271).

the thermal because it is the most buoyant part of it. The points of zero motion relative to the thermal advance outwards along the dotted lines shown in the figure above.

Mixing takes place only at the front where the thermal is advancing into the surrounding fluid, and the thermal is therefore growing there only. In the figure above we see that the fluid in front is advancing towards the thermal: and all particles inside the lines XY enter it while those outside that line pass round to the rear, as indicated by the arrows in the diagram. The material in the mixing region at the front passes round the outside to the rear to make way for fresh material advancing through the centre. The mixing takes place in a comparatively shallow cap at the front of the thermal and elsewhere the flow is relatively smooth.

The actual configuration of motion is shown in the accompanying figure. This was first plotted out by Betsy Woodward in conjunction with the experiments described below. In contrast with a vortex ring there is a broad region of almost uniform velocity in the centre, moving with about twice the speed of the front cap of the thermal.

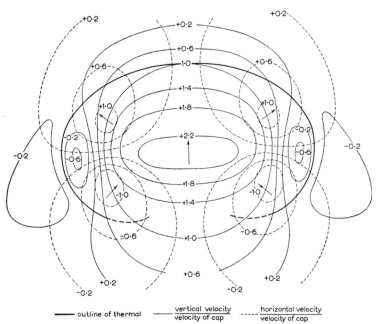

—— outline of thermal $\dfrac{\text{vertical velocity}}{\text{velocity of cap}}$ $\dfrac{\text{horizontal velocity}}{\text{velocity of cap}}$

The mixing takes place by the thermal growing protuberances in between which the exterior fluid is captured. Each of these protuberances looks rather like a small thermal and has little protuberances upon it. The limit to the smallness of the protuberances is set by viscosity, and if a drop of ink is allowed to sink into a glass of clear water generally no protuberances at all are seen upon the ' thermal ' created (the ink being denser than the water). In carrying out an experiment with drops of ink it will be seen that if the ink is allowed to enter the surface of the water with a large velocity it takes the form of a vortex ring (see page 67). The difference between a vortex ring and a thermal is that in the former case all the vorticity and vertical momentum have been supplied by an impulse or by allowing the material to fall through the air before entering the water, whereas a thermal is ideally a configuration of vorticity and momentum produced entirely by the action of the buoyancy forces. The vorticity and vertical momentum produced in the latter manner increase in proportion to the time for which the buoyancy has operated, and will therefore ultimately exceed any impressed upon the fluid at the beginning. A vortex ring composed of buoyant fluid will therefore ultimately become a thermal and the laminar flow will break down so that mixing with the fluid into which it is advancing can take place.

The mixing at the front of a thermal is brought about in two ways. First we have a source of fast moving fluid in the centre of the thermal projecting it into a region of almost stagnant fluid. It is a property of any puff or jet that mixing occurs at the advancing front. This can be seen on the puffs of a steam engine near to the chimney (at some distance the puff becomes a thermal). But in addition we have a second mixing process operating on account of the large density difference between the thermal and the outside fluid. In the top picture of Plate 4 is seen a thermal just after release from rest from a spherical cup which has been quickly overturned. The surface is seen to be covered with protuberances produced by the unstable disposition of density (with light fluid below heavy).

(b) *Simple theory*

We shall begin by assuming that the viscosity of the fluid has a negligible influence on the motion provided that the thermal is big enough to grow many protuberances. It is found that the experimental evidence agrees with conclusions based on this assumption and that the behaviour of a large thermal does not depend upon the Reynolds number. This indicates that the assumption is correct. Consequently when a thermal has arrived at the ideal configuration the only quantities which can determine its vertical velocity are its size and its buoyancy.

The size can be represented either by the radius r, of the largest horizontal section (or some other dimension of the thermal itself) or by the distance z of the front of the thermal from the vertex of the cone indicated in the figure on page 157. Since, as we shall see in a moment, there is only one way in which a velocity can be compounded from the buoyancy and the size, all velocities must be proportional to one another—as they must be once the ideal configuration is reached. The existence of a unique ideal configuration therefore depends upon the existence of only one kind of velocity derived from the quantities determining the motion. There is not a unique configuration for a buoyant vortex ring: it may pass through many forms, as yet unexplored, in changing from a simple ring into an ideal thermal.

The buoyancy can be represented by the total weight deficiency (or lightness) of the thermal or by its mean density excess (or deficit) or by the density excess at a particular point such as the core or the ' centre of volume ' of the thermal. This density excess must be multiplied by gravity because it is only through gravity that it operates and the forces it produces are proportional to gravity. As in the case of slow convection we shall assume that the inertia forces per unit volume are the same inside and outside the thermal. Actually, of course, the density, and therefore the inertia forces, are slightly different inside, but as the thermal proceeds and becomes diluted these differences decrease, and are assumed to have no appreciable influence on the form of the ideal thermal. Although upward and downward moving thermals might behave differently when the density differences are large (say 25 per cent or more), when they are much diluted the behaviour is not observably different. The problem of what happens when the density differences are large is very complicated indeed because there is one more kind of force; there are two inertia forces, those inside and those outside and their ratio is the ratio of the densities. We are assuming that this ratio is not sensibly different from unity.

For convenience we shall use the mean buoyancy $g\overline{B}$ and the distance r. The vertical velocity of the leading cap of the thermal, w, is compounded from these. $\overline{B}$ is of the form density difference $\div$ total density and has no dimensions, and the only way a velocity can be compounded is thus:

$$w = C\,(g\overline{B}r)^{\frac{1}{2}}$$

where C is a numerical constant to be determined either by a complete hydrodynamical theory or by experiment. No complete theory exists, and the mixing process is so complicated that none seems likely to be composed very soon, and so we shall, like generations of scientists before us, fall back upon experiment. It should be made clear at this point that, in the absence of serious flaw in the argument, the constant C measured from experiments on thermals in a water tank in the laboratory would be applicable to thermals in the atmosphere whose volume may be a thousand million times greater.

Since z, the height of the cap of the thermal, is proportional to r we may write

$$z = nr$$

where n is to be determined by experiment.

If the volume and buoyancy at one moment were V_1 and $g\overline{B}_1$ and in the ideal thermal

$$V = mr^3$$

m depending upon the shape, then since the total buoyancy is always the same

$$V\overline{B} = V_1\overline{B}_1$$

and

$$\overline{B} = \frac{V_1\overline{B}_1}{V}$$

$$= \frac{r_1{}^3\overline{B}_1}{r^3}$$

whence

$$w = C(gr_1{}^3\overline{B}_1)^{\frac{1}{2}}/r$$

$$= nC\,(gr_1{}^3\overline{B}_1)^{\frac{1}{2}}/z.$$

But w is equal to the rate of change of z, i.e. dz/dt, and so from the last equation we deduce that

$$z^2 = 2nC \, (gr_1{}^3\overline{B}_1)^{\frac{1}{3}}t$$
$$= \frac{2nC\mathscr{B}^{\frac{1}{3}}}{m^{\frac{1}{3}}}t$$

in which $\mathscr{B} = gV_1\overline{B}_1 =$ total buoyancy or weight deficiency (or excess), of the thermal.

The quantities n, m, C, and $\mathscr{B}$ are constant for a given thermal and so we can say

$$z^2 = t/k$$

where

$$k = m^{\frac{1}{3}}/2nC\mathscr{B}^{\frac{1}{3}}.$$

The first test to make experimentally is to see that z^2 is proportional to time for each thermal. An example of this is shown in the figure below. The vertex of the cone from which z is measured is determined roughly by drawing a cone to envelop the successive outlines of the thermal. The behaviour in the early stages before the ideal configuration has been assumed has to be ignored.

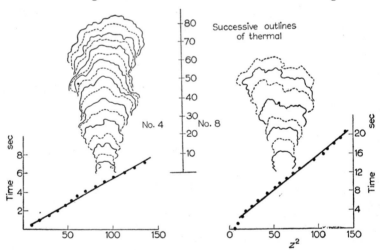

The position chosen for the vertex can only be determined roughly but the indeterminacy makes very little difference to the value of k found from the slope of the line drawn through the points in the figure above.

(c) *Experimental results*

The equation for k shows that

$$1/k\mathscr{B}^{\frac{1}{2}} = 2nC/m^{\frac{1}{2}} = \text{constant.}$$

This constant is the slope of the line drawn through a series of points representing pairs of values of k^{-1} and $\mathscr{B}^{\frac{1}{2}}$ (see figure below). Each point represents observations on one thermal of the kind illustrated in Plate 4.

In the experiments whose results are shown here the total buoyancy (or weight excess) of the thermal was measured by placing a known quantity of salt solution of known density in the spherical cup. After release it was photographed at known intervals. A succession of photographs showing how the thermal retains its shape while growing is shown in Plate 5.

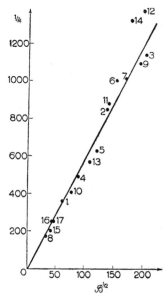

The slope of the straight line fitting the points best in the last figure gives

$$2nC/m^{\frac{1}{2}} = 180g^{\frac{1}{2}} = 5\cdot7 \text{ CGS.}$$

It is relevant to remark here that the straight line drawn was drawn by eye. No sophisticated ' method of least squares ' or any lazy face-saving device was used. According to the theory the points are expected to lie on a straight line and that line is expected to pass through the origin. We have no justification whatever for weighting the observations in any particular way. If one of the points lay far from a line passing very close to the rest, as for example in the case illustrated below, we should not draw the line to miss the origin of the axes as indicated by the dotted line so as to make the sum of the squares of the departures from the line a minimum, but would seek causes why the one point should be

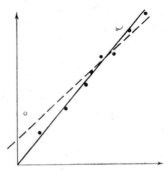

away from the line through the others. If we had chosen to draw k^{-2} against $\mathscr{B}$, or k against $\mathscr{B}^{-\frac{1}{2}}$, or $\log k$ against $\log \mathscr{B}$, we would in all cases expect to find the points lying along a straight line, but an ' objective ', yet arbitrary, method of least squares would give us a different line in each case. On the other hand if this had to be done a great many times, by an automatic computing machine for instance, a method of some sort must be rigidly prescribed because a machine has no judgement, and a least squares method may be convenient (but scarcely ever more than convenient: it should not be given the respect accorded to it by many research workers).

This set of points represents a group of thermals which we have tried to make behave like an ideal one. It may be that they all have imperfections but in varying degrees. It might be that a perfect thermal is more efficient at transporting buoyancy than any of ours and therefore we should draw a line to represent the value of $2nC/m^{\frac{1}{2}}$ for an ideal thermal to one side of all the points—some thermals being closer to the ideal than others.

But some of the points might be beyond this line because of errors of measurement. Others may be far below it because of

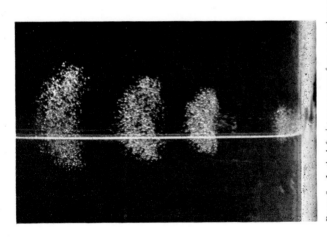

PLATE 3. In the left picture are seen four successive positions of a cloud of air bubbles ejected from a multitude of holes in a metal plate. In the first position not all the bubbles have emerged. In the second the last bubbles to emerge are rising rapidly into the base of the mushroom cloud. In the third and fourth the cloud continues to widen. On the right is seen a similar cloud which has emerged from cloudy water into clear water, bringing some of the cloudy water up in its wake; but it advances ahead into the clear water. (*See* pages 124 and 275)

PLATE 4. Six stages in the growth of a model thermal. The first picture is just after the spherical cup has been removed. (*See* page 156)

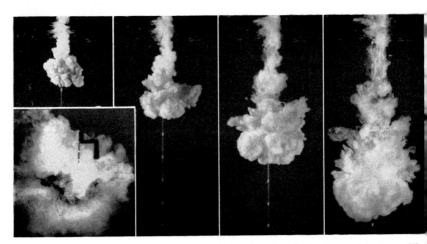

PLATE 5. Another thermal showing the extent to which a thermal retains its characteristic shape. The bottom picture is a view from nearly vertically above of another similar thermal showing the ring shape (the stem obscures part of the dark centre). (*See* page 163)

some abnormality; and often we can gain as much understanding from investigating why some points have strayed from the rest than we do from confirming our expectations by finding that most of the points lie close to a straight line.

In the case of the thermal represented by the point 8 in the figure below the shape was very unsymmetrical (see figure No. 8 on page 162). It appears that the measurements of the most forward point of the thermal were made on a smaller thermal which broke off from the rest which it left behind. The total buoyancy of the part whose motion was measured was thus less than the value ascribed to it. If the thermal had been more compact it would have travelled faster, and the point derived from measurements of it would have conformed more nearly with the others.

The value of m varies from one thermal to another, but is generally in the neighbourhood of 3. This means that the volume of the thermal is equal approximately to the volume of a sphere with caps at the poles chopped off. As it is only the square root of m that we are concerned with we shall concern ourselves more with the value of n because errors in that will matter more.

In the figure below we have plotted the values of n against the

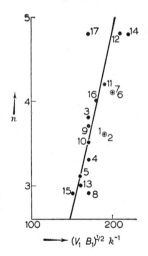

values of $2nC/m^{\frac{1}{2}}$ for each of the thermals, and it is seen that though there is wide variation in the value of n there is a tendency for the larger values of n to correspond with the larger values of $2nC/m^{\frac{1}{2}}$.

The larger values of n are from those thermals which grew along narrower cones than those giving smaller values of n. They travelled a greater distance before achieving a given width; but most often a thermal which started by growing along a wide (or narrow) cone continued to do so. This suggests that Nature does not determine the value of n stringently, but that a slight departure from the ideal shape can continue for some time and that once the motion has approached to within a certain 'distance' of the ideal, only slight forces act to make it conform precisely. Another example of this kind of thing was seen in the behaviour of large air bubbles rising through water: their 'aperture' was found to vary within fairly wide limits although they all obeyed the same law of motion (see page 15).

We may attempt to take account of the variation in n from one thermal to another in the following way. If we admit the possibility that r/z may vary from thermal to thermal we have to decide how to describe the volume. So far we have described it as mr^3 but we could equally call it mr^2z/n. In that case the equation for w on page 161 becomes

$$w = Cn^{\frac{1}{2}}(g\bar{B}_1r_1{}^2z_1)^{\frac{1}{2}}/z$$

and $g\bar{B}_1r_1{}^2z_1$ is now a measure of the total buoyancy. If this were indeed a more fundamental formula for the dependence of w upon z we would expect $Cn^{\frac{1}{2}}$ to be a universal constant instead of C. In the figure above, in which we have plotted n against $(V_1B_1)^{-\frac{1}{2}}k^{-1}$ the line drawn is part of the parabola

$$n = 0{\cdot}00012\,(V_1B_1)^{-1}k^{-2}.$$

To assume that the points lie on this line is better than that they lie on a vertical line (which would take no account of variations in k with variations in n). If this last equation were strictly true it would imply that $Cn^{\frac{1}{2}}$ was the same for all the experiments. In fact, $Cn^{\frac{1}{2}}$ varies less than C over this set of experiments, and so it can be claimed that we have obtained a better description of Nature's behaviour than by assuming n to be the same for all thermals.

It must be emphasised that this digression into the effect of variations of n has no sound theoretical basis; but one may often justifiably grope for a simple formula in the hope that if one emerges a natural process will be revealed.

If we take m as equal to 3 and n as equal to 4 the formula on page 163 gives us

$$C = 1 \cdot 2 \text{ approximately.}$$

The experimental results alternatively give

$$Cn^{\frac{1}{3}} = 2 \cdot 4.$$

(d) Comparison with the atmosphere

The only thermals which are easy to observe in the atmosphere are those which emerge from the tops of cumulus clouds. The outsides of them can be seen and their motion measured by photography in much the same way as for the model thermals, but it is not easy to measure their buoyancy. In a study of cumulus cloud towers which had been recorded by cine camera (see Plate 6) an estimate of the constant C was made by Malkus and Scorer before any model experiments had been performed. Their value was 8/9, and it was based on estimates of buoyancy which now appear to be too great because the motion was assumed to be of a different nature from what has been revealed by the experiments. The great dilution in the interior of the thermal was not properly allowed for. If a better estimate of the buoyancy is made a value of C for clouds nearer to $1 \cdot 2$ seems more probable.

Ludlam and Saunders have also made measurements of the motion of thermals emerging from the tops of cumulus clouds. They made no attempt to measure their diameter and so, in order to compare their observations with the experiments they assumed that the point source of the thermals was on the ground. They also chose the thermals with the greatest upward velocity at any level on a given day for their analysis. This meant that any smaller ones which may have originated at a higher level, within the clouds for instance, were ignored: and it is likely that the largest had their point origin near the ground. Their observations gave a value of C of about $1 \cdot 0$.

But too much should not be made at present of any very close agreement between the values of C for clouds on one hand and thermals in a water tank on the other: the important point is that they do not disagree materially, although the Reynolds number in the laboratory case is about one thousandth of what it is in the

case of cloud thermals. This can only mean that in the model
experiments the Reynolds number was great enough for the viscous
forces to be negligible and so an increase in it, even by a factor of a
thousand, has a negligible effect on the part played by viscosity in
determining the nature of the motion.

Further comments on the behaviour of cloud thermals are made
in Chapter 10.

(e) Successions of thermals

If two thermals are released in succession from the same point,
their height and size increase like $t^{\frac{1}{2}}$ while the interval between the
moments when they pass a given height remains constant. The
difference in height between their tops therefore decreases while
their size increases. After a finite time they begin to overlap and
become joined into a single thermal.

Because of this possibility of the amalgamation of thermals, the
rate of rise of thermals observed in Nature may be greater than if
they had all ascended alone. If two equal thermals are joined
into one the rate of rise of the material within them is increased
by a factor $2^{\frac{1}{2}}$.

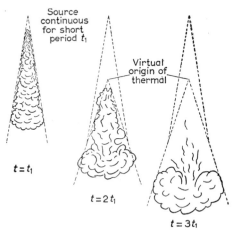

If instead of sending up a succession of thermals a source sends
up warm air continuously but only for a finite time. The buoyant
air may break up into a succession of thermals as in the case of a
pulsating candle flame, but these thermals will then gradually
amalgamate into one large one at greater heights.

Alternatively, if the source is continuous for a short period it may produce a cone-shaped thermal, whose top is like that of a lone thermal. Soon (i.e. within a time comparable with the duration of the source) after the source has ceased the cone of buoyant fluid is gathered into a compact mass, like a solitary thermal, by the advance of the buoyant material released last up into the leading part.

Thermals in the atmosphere

Only when cloud is formed can we normally see thermals in the atmosphere. Below clouds the form taken by convection currents varies according to how the heat is fed into the air. In order to understand what takes place it is necessary first to discover the condition for buoyant convection to occur at all.

(a) The adiabatic lapse rate: potential temperature

The rise of thermals mixes the buoyant air with the surroundings and thereby decreases its buoyancy per unit volume. Since the mixing process is not precisely describable we start by seeing what would happen if there were no mixing, knowing that in practice a thermal will differ less from the surroundings than we shall compute.

We imagine first the situation in which, if a parcel of air is carried to a different height, either upwards or downwards, it always has the same temperature as the surrounding air. If the displacements are made without mixing the changes occurring within the parcel will be adiabatic, and will therefore accord with the equation (to be found in any textbook on heat)

$$p = K\rho^{\gamma}.$$

This equation relates the changes in pressure p, to the changes in density ρ. γ is the ratio of the specific heats of air and is approximately 1·4. K is a constant which depends upon the original condition of the air, and is found simply by inserting in the equation the initial values of p and ρ. The rate of change of pressure with height, z, is given by the hydrostatic equation (page 23), which is

$$\frac{\partial p}{\partial z} = -g\rho.$$

Air also obeys the gas laws of Boyle and Charles which are expressed in the equation of state, namely

$$p = R\rho T$$

in which T is the absolute temperature and R is the gas constant, which for air is about $2 \cdot 86 \times 10^6$ in CGS units. The precise value of R varies with the humidity because water vapour has a different value from dry air. If we differentiate the first and third of these equations with respect to height we get

$$\frac{\partial p}{\partial z} = K\gamma\rho^{\gamma-1}\frac{\partial \rho}{\partial z}$$

and

$$\frac{\partial p}{\partial z} = R\left(T\frac{\partial \rho}{\partial z} + \rho\frac{\partial T}{\partial z}\right)$$

so that

$$\frac{\partial T}{\partial z} = \frac{1}{\rho R}\frac{\partial p}{\partial z} - \frac{T}{\rho}\frac{\partial \rho}{\partial z}$$

$$= \left(\frac{1}{\rho R} - \frac{T}{K\gamma\rho^{\gamma}}\right)\frac{\partial p}{\partial z}$$

$$= \frac{1}{\rho R}\left(1 - \frac{1}{\gamma}\right)\left(-g\rho\right)$$

$$= -\frac{(\gamma - 1)g}{\gamma R}.$$

This is the rate at which the temperature would change in a parcel carried up or down in surroundings whose pressure it took up and which were such that their temperature was the same as that of the parcel. If their temperature were slightly different, in the second equation ρ would be the density of the surroundings, while in the first and third equations it would be that of the parcel. This would produce a slightly different change in the temperature of the parcel, but the difference is academic for three reasons. First the effect is, in Nature, swamped by the process of mixing; secondly the presence of water vapour produces much greater effects; and thirdly with existing instruments we could not detect the effect even if the first two reasons were absent. It is therefore quite acceptable to assume that an unmixed parcel would change its temperature at the rate $(\gamma - 1)g/\gamma R$, which when evaluated is about 9·86° C per kilometre or about 1° C per 100 m. This is called the *adiabatic lapse rate*. 'Lapse rate' means rate of decrease of temperature with height, in this context.

If the decrease in temperature with height of the surroundings is less than this amount a parcel would be cooler than them if displaced upwards and warmer if displaced downwards, so that the air is stable because the parcel would tend to return to its original level on account of buoyancy forces. If the temperature gradient is greater than this amount the lapse-rate is described as super-adiabatic and the air is unstable because buoyancy forces would be in the same direction as the displacement of a parcel.

In an incompressible fluid the adiabatic lapse rate is zero, because the parcel density does not vary (K, γ, and R are not defined). The unstable state is then one in which the density increases upwards, or in which the temperature decreases upwards in most liquids and all gases, because they expand on heating.

In the neutral state, that is when the lapse rate is adiabatic, both the temperature and the density decrease upwards. The *potential temperature* is therefore defined as the temperature a parcel of air would have if brought adiabatically to a standard pressure, which for convenience is usually taken as 1000 mb. If the air at all levels had the same potential temperature then parcels from every level would arrive at 1000 mb with the same temperature and the lapse rate would be adiabatic.

The potential temperature is denoted by θ.

If the potential temperature increases with height the air is stable because parcels displaced upwards would be colder and those displaced downwards would be warmer than their surroundings. If the lapse rate is superadiabatic the potential temperature decreases upwards. From the point of view of convection temperature in an incompressible fluid is analogous to potential temperature in a compressible fluid.

(b) Superadiabatic layers and the growth of thermals

We saw earlier in this chapter that in order to obtain a uniform lapse rate by heating the bottom of a fluid, the heat had to be applied very slowly, otherwise penetrative convection began. If the heat is not applied slowly then the temperature near the bottom rises rapidly and a superadiabatic lapse rate is set up. The instability decreases upwards from the surface, and at levels to which thermals have not yet penetrated the air is not unstable at all. When the sunshine heats the ground the temperature in the lowest layers rises most rapidly, the temperature higher up rising only as thermals from below reach up. The extent to which the lapse rate becomes superadiabatic depends upon the rate at which heat is being carried upwards and the mechanism available to do the carrying. Rayleigh established a criterion for this (page 148) on the assumption that the mechanism was slow cellular convection controlled by viscosity and conductivity, telling us when motion would begin because the conductivity was no longer as efficient as cellular motion. But if the temperature gradients greatly exceed Rayleigh's value penetrative convection occurs. We shall first examine the mechanism whereby thermals originate in the superadiabatic layer and we shall then be able to compute how the lapse rate varies with height.

If a superadiabatic lapse rate exists and a portion of the air is displaced upwards or is made hotter than its surroundings in a manner to be discussed in succeeding pages, it becomes a thermal, mixing with the air into which it rises. Since all the air is unstable, when the air with which the thermal mixes, and the air which it pushes upwards ahead of it, are displaced upwards, they acquire buoyancy: the total buoyancy of the rising mass thus increases rapidly and corresponds at each height to some sort of average value of the buoyancies which air from all the layers below would acquire if displaced up to that level.

But we cannot treat thermals as if they were unaffected by each other. While thermals rise there must be downward motions between them, and downward displacements produce negative buoyancy in an unstable layer of air. Every thermal therefore has a chance of encountering air of negative buoyancy which will tend to nullify it on mixing. Many thermals therefore die within the superadiabatic layer. We can conceive that the number of thermals over unit area of ground decreases with height, but that of those which exist the size increases upwards.

Since these processes are taking place on a scale on which the molecular properties (viscosity and thermal conductivity) have negligible influence the motion must be similar at all heights, the same fraction of any horizontal area being occupied by thermals at any level. This must be so unless there are conditions which discriminate between the air at different heights, as might be the case if the heating were changing rapidly or had only been in existence for a short time so that the convection had not affected a deep layer. But as long as the conditions are not changing appreciably and the thermals are not comparable in size with the depth of the whole layer in which the convection is occurring, the motion must be similar at all heights.

The only dimension which can determine the size of the thermals is the height above the ground, for there is no other length dimension in the conditions imposed. The buoyancy force is proportional to $\theta_0^{-1}g\,(\theta_1 - \theta)$, where θ_1 is the potential temperature a certain constant fraction of the way up the layer, and θ that at height z; for we saw that the potential temperature of the thermal is some sort of average value for all the air up to its level. The kind of average it actually is determines only the constant of proportionality if $\theta - \theta_0$ is proportional to $z^{-\alpha}$ which, we shall see, can be the case. θ_0^{-1} approximately is the coefficient of expansion of the air, which varies negligibly with height. The vertical velocity, w, is therefore given (by argument similar to that which we used for isolated thermals) by

$$w \propto [\theta_0^{-1}g(\theta_1 - \theta)z]^{\frac{1}{2}}.$$

In the special conditions we are discussing the upward transport of buoyancy is the same at all heights: that is to say we are not considering a mechanism for warming the air, but only for transporting the heat upwards through it. Therefore, since the same fraction of the total area is occupied by upcurrent at all heights

$$w\theta_0^{-1}g(\theta_1 - \theta) = \text{constant (independent of height)}$$

because this is proportional to the total upward transport of buoyancy. If $\theta - \theta_0 \propto z^{-\alpha}$ then so is $\theta_1 - \theta$, and so eliminating w from these two equations we have that since g is constant.

$$z^{\frac{3\alpha + 1}{2}} = \text{constant,}$$

therefore

$$\alpha = -\tfrac{1}{3}$$

and the lapse rate of potential temperature is

$$\partial\theta/\partial z \propto z^{-\frac{4}{3}}.$$

The constant of proportionality is related to the magnitude of the transport of buoyancy (and heat) and increases with increasing transport.

This is the lapse rate under the rather special conditions supposed to exist. Very close to the ground the transport of heat is effected by molecular properties of the air, and within a few metres of the surface by radiation (mainly through the agency of the water vapour constituent). Above that, if the rate of transport of heat is increasing with time so is the lapse rate; the lower layers are thus being warmed and the heat flux decreases upwards. The lapse rate therefore corresponds to a steeper gradient $(\partial\theta/\partial z \propto z^{-\alpha'}, \; \alpha' > 4/3)$. If the heat supply is diminishing the lapse rate decreases upwards more slowly than $z^{-\frac{4}{3}}$.

But all this argument is very special in that we have supposed that the surface itself has no properties which could determine the size of thermals and we have supposed that there is only one kind of mechanism in operation to transport the heat. Besides the molecular and radiative mechanisms for this there is the purely hydrodynamical mechanism of the eddies produced by wind over obstacles. This must reduce the lapse rate near the ground, but since thermals increase in size away from the ground and the mechanical eddies are related to the size of the obstacles producing them, above some height the thermals will provide the dominant process. Finally, there is the possibility that eddying motion might be derived from larger scale shearing motion in the manner discussed on page 137. Whether sufficient shear can exist when thermal convection is operative for eddies of this kind to be important is doubtful. We shall avoid the issue by saying that the different kinds of eddy cannot even theoretically be distinguished by observation of them, and the problem has not yet been formulated in a manner in which it can be discussed in a treatise of this nature, though some advance has been made by Priestley, for instance.

Experience shows that the nature of the surface can be of overriding importance. This is illustrated by the difference in the form of convection over cultivated land, sea, and desert.

(c) Thermal sources over land

Glider pilots have provided almost all the information available on this subject. They have recognised, in their search for thermals in which to soar, three main types of thermal source: thermal streets, fixed thermal sources, and drifting sources.

Smoke from a town can often be seen to accumulate in the lower (50–100 m) layers of air when shadows of clouds pass over. Dispersion of smoke is a visible measure of the stirring upwards that occurs over ground warmed by sunshine. Sunshine is the most important factor; other influences are secondary or merely serve to divert or channel the buoyancy it produces.

Thermal streets consist of thermals arranged in long parallel lines roughly along the direction of the wind (see page 154). Sometimes there are lines of cumulus clouds associated with them. Occasionally a single street is associated with a single line of cumulus clouds but this is a special meteorological phenomenon which we shall not discuss here.   It was demonstrated on page 81 how a hump in the ground could start convection in the air passing over it if it were unstable.   A continuously strong thermal source such as a steelworks or power station could have the same effect. In any case there is always a tendency for thermals to be arranged in lines downwind from such places and to be spaced at distances apart such that they are not inhibited by the downward motion around their neighbours. These distances must depend upon the depth of the layer in which the convection is occurring because this determines the width achieved by the largest thermals. Ordered streets therefore tend to occur if the convection is confined to a layer of fairly uniform depth which is also fairly shallow, say 2000 m deep, so that most thermals nearly reach the top. Such a condition is only likely to persist if the layers higher up are also being warmed by some large-scale process, such as the subsidence in an anticyclone or ahead of a warm front.   Otherwise the streets tend to be a rather transient configuration, found when the convection has extended up to a stable layer, but reaches no farther until the whole layer below has been warmed enough for the thermals to pass upwards into the air above.   Streets are most common, therefore, when the whole troposphere is getting warmer.

Fixed thermal sources are places where the ground is hotter than nearby. Thermals tend to originate over them and by producing successions of thermals they create larger thermals over themselves than over the surroundings. Only in almost calm conditions does air rise continuously from a source, and even then it tends to break up into isolated thermals on account of the drifting about of the upper air. Continuous thermals may occur over long ridges which face the sun and along which the wind is blowing slowly such that the thermals originating all along the length of the ridge rise into the same part of the airstream. The inflow towards the ridge then becomes perceptible as a wind of up to 2 or 3 m/sec. Similar inflow often occurs towards large mountain ranges over which the thermals produce thunderstorms in the afternoon and evening. Volcanoes also produce plumes of cloud, but not necessarily winds up their slopes because the heat source is at a high level. No heat source can produce motion at levels below it.

Towns and sun-facing slopes are recognised as good thermal sources for the soaring pilot: towns because more energy is absorbed by wet ground and vegetation so that the surface temperature rises higher than over the countryside, sun-facing slopes because of the greater receipt of solar energy per unit horizontal area. In the countryside chalky areas because of the dryness and lower thermal conductivity of the ground, fields of ripe corn which do not consume solar energy in transpiration, gas works, and wind shadows, are well-known producers of thermals. Chalky areas may simply be areas of higher ground, which act as thermal sources because the temperature of the surface receiving the sunshine rises above that of the free air at the same level.

Wind shadows are also said to be good thermal sources but may be spurious: it is often said that the air gets hotter on a lee slope because the wind is less strong there, but the wind velocity alone cannot have any effect on the heating of the air as it moves over the more or less uniformly heated countryside; nor can the reduced mechanical stirring which would keep the heat in a shallower layer have much influence on the course of a thermal emerging above the layer affected. Most probably they are often sun-facing slopes inappropriately described. Or it may be that in the lee of a hill there is an eddy, with flow up the lee slope, which increases the convergence of surface air towards the hill top and, therefore, also the number of thermals originating there.

Drifting thermal sources are probably produced when the wind strength increases upwards.   When part of the superadiabatic layer begins to rise all round it there is sinking motion.   If there is shear, the air from behind the thermal will penetrate farther under it and the forward tilting of the thermal will tend to cut off the downward motion in front of it.   Since the downcoming air is moving faster than the buoyant air close to the surface it has a shovelling action and the consequent lifting of the superadiabatic layer continues to supply the thermal.   This explains how glider pilots can sometimes remain circling in an upcurrent 200–300 metres above ground for 10–15 minutes all the time drifting in the direction of the wind but more slowly than the wind at their own level.   This would be impossible in one isolated thermal.

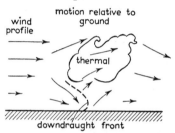

Drifting thermal sources very often produce cumulus clouds. The cloud then grows on the upwind side and evaporates on the other.   The individual thermals into which the almost steady stream of warm air from the source has by then been broken, appear as a pulsating growth of the cloud.   Each thermal may have a life within the cloud of 5–10 minutes, but the cloud as a whole, defined simply as the visible outline, may last for up to 15 to 30 minutes and have 6–10 thermals pass through it.   The upwind edge of such a cloud, where the growth occurs, moves with a speed less than the wind at its own level and more nearly that of the wind at the ground.   The individual thermals composing the cloud move approximately with the surrounding air, and therefore through the cloud (see Plate 6).

(d) Thermals over the sea

When the sunshine ceases to fall on the ground or when cool air from the top of or above the superadiabatic layer spreads out on the ground the temperature of the surface immediately falls below that nearby. The temperature of the ground, when convection is taking place at least, is greatest at the surface and decreases downwards. Heat is lost downwards by conduction as well as upwards while the surface temperature is rising in the morning and early afternoon.

The temperature of the ocean, by contrast, is scarcely affected by sunshine unless there is a complete calm, in which case the surface may become noticeably warmer. Normally there is enough motion for the heat received to be spread over a great depth of water. The energy in the shorter (visible) wavelengths is in any case mostly absorbed over a depth of a few metres. Because also of the large thermal capacity of the heated water there are no appreciable diurnal variations of surface temperature. There are therefore no thermal sources, and instead of a few appreciable thermals the heat appears to be transported upwards by a larger number of less vigorous ones. Soaring in a glider over the open ocean is probably not practicable. Oceanic soaring birds soar by other mechanisms (see pages 13 and 120). Over some landlocked seas which are warm in the autumn, strong upcurrents may be produced in air blowing from cold land. But usually the lapse rate close to the surface of the sea is much less unstable than by day over land when convection takes place. The clouds may become larger simply because the convection continues day and night.

The motion over the ocean has occasionally been observed to assume the form of streets, but this is not normal. The configuration of up and down motion is much more affected by clouds (see page 270). No adequate description of the configuration of convective motion over the ocean has yet been given.

(e) Thermals over the desert: dust devils

In contrast with the ocean the desert undergoes very great diurnal changes in temperature, amounting to perhaps 70° C or more. Yet a few inches below the surface the variations may be less than 1 or 2° C in a whole year. This happens because a surface composed of loose sand with air spaces in between the particles is well insulated from the ground below either for upward or downward transfer of heat. There are several reasons why loose sand has these properties: conduction is very inefficient because of the poor contact of the particles, convection cells cannot occur in the gaseous interstices because of their small dimensions, and radiative exchange has only the same small distances to operate across.

Very high surface temperatures are reached in bright sunshine because the thermal capacity of the surface material is very small. As a result of these high temperatures the lapse rate of temperature over the desert reaches its greatest natural values, and the superadiabatic layer extends to greater heights than elsewhere. The lapse rate may be measurably in excess of the adiabatic value up to 500 m and sometimes as far as 1500 m from the ground; but conditions are very variable across the world and the matter has not yet been fully explored. These values are given to indicate magnitudes rather than precise values.

If a thermal is formed within the superadiabatic layer or within the lower part of it, the air descending and taking its place upon the ground must be a few degrees colder. Since the heat capacity of the ground is so small the place just vacated by the thermal becomes a cool patch from which no further thermals will rise for several minutes. If the desert surface is fairly uniform so that there are no places from which successions of thermals may ascend, the largest thermals produced will be smaller than if good thermal sources were scattered over the surface. Thus on account of the uniformity and low thermal capacity of the ground the thermals at any height are smaller and so the upward transport of heat is smaller for a given lapse rate of temperature than over ground with good thermal sources. In order, therefore, to transport upwards the actual amount of heat received as sunshine a greater lapse rate is found to be required over the desert. Moreover, less heat is absorbed by the ground than over ordinary damp country and so more is available for the atmosphere.

Dust devils occur when lapse rates exist like those over the desert. The rapid rotation is due to the convergence in a horizontal direction and extension in the vertical of air that already possesses rotation about a vertical axis. The stability of the rotating column (i.e. the prevention of mixing between air in the centre and that around it by the distribution of centrifugal force: see page 53) prevents dilution of the rising air, and so the buoyancy tends to increase upwards. The great vertical extent of the static instability means that the stretching process continues as the air ascends.

The only ways in which air can flow into the centre of low pressure of the rotating system are at the top and at the bottom. At the top cool, dust-free air, not originally possessed of vorticity, may enter and descend down the core. At the bottom the friction

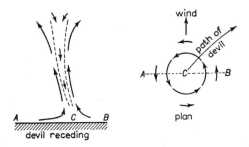

of the ground reduces the velocity round the centre and this permits an inflow (as in a stirred cup of tea, page 54) of warmed air. If there is a light wind the devil continuously gathers surface air from a new piece of hot ground. The friction is greater on the side on which the wind speed is added to the motion due to rotation and so the inflow is greater on that side and the devil tends to move across the wind direction towards that side. Dust devils tend to occur where there is a supply of rotating air. This is often on the edge of where the air is most retarded, where there are trees or buildings for instance.

The demise of a dust devil may be due to the cutting off of rotating air at the base. The bottom may then rise off the ground and the cloud of dust will fairly quickly assume the form of an ordinary thermal. If, on the other hand, it ascends into air that is not rotating not only can cold air enter the centre at the top but the configuration of rotating air is unstable because the centrifugal force carries it outwards into the surroundings. Most dust devils are not very high and the dust can be seen to be thrown outwards at the top. A dust devil may reach upwards several times, each time the buoyant rotating air mixing outwards into the surroundings and losing its rotation. Occasionally the thermal based on the dust devil may reach up to cloud base, but clouds visibly rotating at the top of a dust column have not been reported, so that it is probable that mixing with the surroundings begins well below cloud base level (say 3000–4000 m).

Swinn has elaborately described his exploration of dust devils by glider in Egypt.   He soared to over 7000 ft in one, and often noted a down-current in the centre.   The centre was often dust-free, the most remarkable case being when the devil passed over a coal dump: he was able to look down the hollow centre surrounded by a wall of black coal dust.

Dust devils can be destroyed by mechanical opposition to the rotation, for instance by driving a vehicle through one side against the rotation.   Presumably the tribesmen of old who used to attack them with swords to kill the devil had some similar technique.

The chief difficulty in the way of a proper theoretical discussion of the phenomena is that they are not steady.   They pulsate or are transient or mixing occurs at the end of the vertical column.   Nevertheless, as we have seen, their main characteristics can be understood.

(f) Thermals in a valley: heating a stable layer

When air is heated from below thermals rise, so long as the air is unstable or neutrally stratified, gathering surrounding air to themselves as they advance.   On meeting a stable layer they lose their buoyancy and slow down, raising slightly the temperature at the level at which they finally flatten out.   The air through which they rise sinks slowly, itself to be warmed when it reaches the ground or when it is gathered into an ascending thermal.   To warm a stable layer either the lower layers must be warmed until the layer becomes unstable, or the heat must be applied at a higher level.

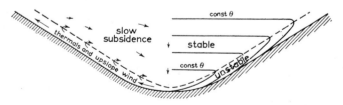

This latter process is important when the air in a valley is stable and the mountainsides are heated by sunshine.   A circulation is produced in which air slowly ascends close to the mountain slopes and is continuously warmed: it spreads out across the valley when a layer of sufficient stability to prevent its further rise is encountered and then descends in the middle. Thermals rise from the surface into the upslope winds. In this way the whole air mass may be warmed and well mixed although all the time it remains stable and free from penetrating thermals except close to the mountain slopes. The extent of the mixing can be judged by the following example. In the morning there was a pall of smoke below 300 m above an industrial plant in a French Alpine valley about 10–15 km wide. The smoke had accumulated overnight. In the early afternoon the smoke had been distributed throughout all the air up to about 1300 m although no thermals could be detected away from the slopes and the lapse rate in the centre of the valley was stable. The upslope winds reached 2–5 m per sec during the day. This was in January, and in the summer winds of 10 m/sec are not uncommon up sloping valleys and mountain sides.

Natural exploitation of atmospheric thermals

In many parts of the world there are birds which make use of thermals to reduce the effort required to remain airborne. The buzzard and several kinds of seagull do this in temperate latitudes: On migrations many large birds use thermals and are said to follow routes along which thermals can best be exploited. The meteorologist is reluctant to accept that the naming of a route ' thermal flyway ' is an adequate summary of all the influences which determine it as the birds' path of migration, because there are many other possible circumstances which could make it favourable. Nor is it certain that the use of thermals is vital to the birds. But there are birds, of which the vultures and albatrosses provide the outstanding examples, which are not possessed of sufficient muscle to remain airborne long enough to find their food by flapping alone. The dynamic soaring of albatrosses is discussed elsewhere (pages 13 and 120).

In the morning in countries where thermals abound for most of the year, that is in near desert areas, scouting vultures test the air for thermals from time to time. When one is seen to be able to soar others join it, and they glide around searching the neighbourhood for carrion. They depend absolutely upon the thermals to keep them at a vantage point from which they can seek out their food.   When a cloud passes across the sun they often descend to earth because the supply of thermals ceases.   The smaller species of birds take the air first because they depend less on soaring and also have, in many cases, a smaller sinking speed.   Only when thermals have reached the required strength do the large birds also go up.   These large birds which are weak in wing but strong in beak and claw do not require sudden flight to escape from predators.

Birds such as swallows, which feed on insects, benefit from the upcurrents in thermals because the density of insects originating at the ground is greater in thermals and this is where they therefore tend to congregate.

Some kinds of dragonfly which feed on aerial plankton have been carefully watched by Hankin.   He described how they soared to and fro above the same stretch of ground, presumably over a more or less continuous thermal source such as a stone wall.   It is not in their interest to be too far from the ground from where the small bodies they devour ascend in the thermal and they lower their legs and abdomens to increase their sinking speed when the up-current strength becomes large.   There is a curious mixture of ' motives ' and convenience in this behaviour.   The thermal brings up the food and saves them energy for flapping; the extension of their legs for catching the food and dealing with it is more often required in strong thermals when food is plentiful. One wonders whether they react most to the food or to the thermal: do they tend to stay in thermals and, as it were, come by the food incidentally, or have they a mechanism which makes them stay where food is plentiful and soar incidentally ?   Considerations of this kind should make one wonder before concluding that the most obvious reaction to circumstances according to our way of thinking is necessarily the most simple Nature can devise.   Do dragonflies fly into the warmer air (up the temperature gradient) thereby entering the food-bearing upcurrents ?   There are many other possibilities.

Tiny insects such as aphids whose airspeed is small compared with horizontal and vertical air motions allow themselves to be dispersed over a wide area by thermals in the summer.   The whole pattern of their behaviour is fascinating to any student of natural aerodynamics and has been made an object of major study by Johnson. But their propensity to fly on warm, sunny days when thermals are likely suggests that their transport by thermals has played a necessary part in evolving a method of seeking pastures new.

The swarms of desert locusts which range from Morocco to Baluchistan, from Iran to Mozambique, exploit the atmosphere in a most subtle way. Rainey and Waloff have elucidated their behaviour in a series of papers in recent years; here we shall describe briefly their reaction to air motions.

During their great migrations the swarms, which may be a few miles across, consist of groups of locusts each occupying an area a few hundred metres across flying in various directions apparently with purpose when viewed from within the swarm, but evidently in a random manner when the swarm is viewed as a whole. Close to the ground they flap their wings but higher up they may be gliding in thermals. The swarm does not become spread by this random flight because those on the edge tend always to turn and fly inwards. Some locusts are at rest on the ground under the swarm. Those which fly out at the front tend to settle; those which are left behind on the ground quickly take to the air and join the swarm, which thus moves with the wind at a speed less than the wind because some time is spent on the ground by each locust. The speed approaches more nearly that of the wind in the heat of the day perhaps because they remain airborne longer when thermals are present, perhaps because at higher temperatures they automatically fly more.

Since the swarms proceed with the wind, does this mean that the wind completely determines the direction of their ' migration '? No particular geographical location appears to be their objective as it is with many species of birds and apparently also butterflies, but the places most suitable for the laying of their eggs are where copious rain has recently fallen upon the desert—a most chancy event by any meteorological standards. The locusts, however, tend to fly only on occasions when thermals are prevalent, which happen generally to be also those occasions when the wind is blowing towards the tropical convergence where copious rains fall. When the wind is in the opposite direction thermals are less prevalent and the locusts often decline to fly. According to

Rainey this pattern of behaviour has occasionally led the swarm to a miserable death through the perversity of unusual weather, but on the average it benefits the species in leading them to suitable breeding grounds.   The variability of the weather from year to year which would soon destroy any species which relied upon exceptional desert weather in a particular place is thus even exploited by the locust swarms, as they follow the different trend of the tropical rains each year.

Only recently has this concept of the motion patterns of the air (on all scales from small thermals to weather systems of continental dimensions) as a part of the environment in which species have evolved become widely recognised, and the possibilities for further investigation are enormous.   Coastal waters are populated by species which depend upon the tides, and we may justly wonder whether there may be fishes whose very existence rests on some special properties of the motion within the sea.   Porpoises have been observed to ' soar ' in the bow wave of a ship, and we may ask if this is not probably a kind of behaviour which they commonly practise in Nature.

CHAPTER 8

PLUMES AND JETS

THE MOTION in plumes and jets is extremely complicated and it is necessary to study some of its bulk properties first before we can see our way to a more detailed analysis.   We start with an orifice from which is emerging a fluid possessing buoyancy, momentum, and vorticity.   It enters the environment which may be in motion relative to the orifice, which may be stably or unstably stratified, and which may be in laminar or turbulent flow.   According to how we combine these various conditions we obtain plumes with various different properties.   Our plan is, therefore, to describe several special cases in order to be able to see how they are combined in the plumes we meet in daily life.

Pure jets, or momentum plumes

When fluid possessing momentum emerges into stagnant surroundings of the same density, it constitutes a pure jet or momentum plume.   The jet occupies a cone of semi-vertical angle 12°.   The motion consists of a large number of whirls, and particles are seen to be momentarily motionless when they are

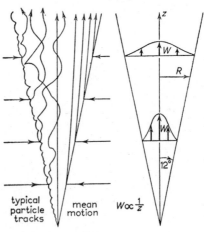

typical particle tracks   mean motion $W \propto \frac{1}{z}$

carried to the edge of the jet.   Such motion can easily be observed
in the jet produced when a locomotive lets off steam.

The surrounding fluid is entrained towards the axis of the jet
and mixed into the jet when it encounters the whirls on the edge.
When it gets inside the jet, a particle of the surrounding fluid
follows a tortuous path under the influence of the whirls.   No
study of these tracks has yet been made but many people have
studied the distribution of the mean velocity.   It is found to
decrease along the axis of the jet but the shape of the profile across
the jet of the mean velocity along the jet is found to be the same all
the way along it.   This is illustrated in the figure above in which
it is seen that the particles diverge up the jet and the velocity in the
centre is gradually reduced.

Since there is no velocity in a direction along the jet in the fluid
outside the momentum emerging from the orifice must be transported steadily along the jet.   If W is the maximum velocity in
this direction then both the momentum of a particle and the volume
of fluid crossing any section are proportional to W so that the
amount of momentum crossing a section is proportional to W^2.
It is also proportional to the area of the section, i.e. to R^2, where
R is the radius, and so

$$W^2R^2 = \text{constant} = W_0{}^2R_0{}^2$$

the suffix 0 denoting the value at a distance z_0 from the vertex of
the cone.

Also $$mR = z$$

where z is the distance from the vertex of the cone. m depends
on the angle of the cone.   This means that

$$W = W_0R_0/R = mW_0R_0/z \propto 1/z.$$

If the jet contained marked passive particles, carried by the
motion but possessing no buoyancy, their concentration would
decrease along the jet.   Since none is entrained from the surroundings the number crossing any section of the jet must be the
same as at any other section.   Therefore if σ represents their
maximum concentration at any value of z

$$\sigma W R^2 = \text{constant (indep. of } z) = \sigma_0 W_0 R_0{}^2.$$

From this and the above equations we deduce that

$$\sigma = \sigma_0 m R_0 / z \propto 1/z.$$

Consequently $\sigma \propto t^{-\frac{1}{2}}$ for an element of fluid carried by the mean motion of the jet.

This equation tells us how rapidly the contents of the jet are diluted as we proceed along the axis. The total amount of fluid, F, crossing a section is proportional to WR^2 and so

$$F_0 = A W_0 R_0^2,$$
$$F = F_0 W_0 / W = F_0 z / m R_0 \propto z.$$

The quantity A depends upon the shape of the velocity profile of the jet.

The inflow at any distance z from the vertex is equal to the rate of increase of the flux F in the direction of increasing z, and this is constant ($dF/dz = $ constant) so that the inward velocity in the fluid outside the jet is the same for all z at a given distance from the axis. At the edge of the jet the inward velocity is proportional to $1/R$ (or to $1/z$).

In all this discussion we have assumed that the orifice is small compared with the distances from it that we are considering. Close to the orifice the motion is determined by how the fluid is ejected, but it soon assumes the configuration described as it moves away on account of the turbulent nature of the motion.

All the relationships we have derived are expressed in terms of F_0 the strength of the jet, and σ_0 the initial concentration of substance, which are characteristic of each individual jet, together with the constants A and m which are the same for all jets of this type whether large or small, in air or in water; but not in treacle. If the viscosity were large enough to have any effect the form of the plume would be changed completely. In the cases under discussion the inertia forces are very much larger than the viscous forces. In a pure jet there are no forces other than inertia forces and, of course, normal pressure gradient forces.

Pure buoyant plumes

When buoyant fluid emerges into uniform surroundings it travels upwards along a vertical cone which looks very much like the cone of a pure jet. But this time, instead of the transport of momentum being constant the transport of buoyancy is constant.

Buoyancy, τ, can be thought of as residing in the particles, and we will take τ as representing the maximum buoyancy at a given z.

τ has the same dimensions as g, and is of the form $g\Delta\rho/\rho$ or $g\Delta T/T$ where $\Delta\rho$ and ΔT are the density and temperature anomalies of the fluid in the plume. The flux of buoyancy is

$$B\tau WR^2 = \text{constant} = B\tau_0 W_0 R_0{}^2$$

where B depends on the profiles across the plume of velocity and buoyancy, which may differ from each other.

The rate at which the flux of momentum up the plume increases upwards is equal to the buoyancy force on a horizontal slice and so

$$\frac{\mathrm{d}}{\mathrm{d}z}\left(A'W^2R^2\right) = C\tau R^2$$

where A' depends on the velocity profile (and is not equal to A in a pure jet because the profiles differ) and C depends on the profile of buoyancy. B must be related to C and A'.

Since

$$R = nz$$

where n is characteristic of a pure buoyant plume, and differs from m for a pure jet, if we assume that W and τ are proportional to powers of Z, the only powers which will satisfy these equations are

$$W \propto z^{-\frac{1}{3}} \quad \text{and} \quad \tau \propto z^{-\frac{5}{3}} .$$

Consequently $\tau \propto t^{-\frac{5}{4}}$.

By measuring the profiles of velocity and buoyancy in one plume the constants A', B, C might be computed, and n can easily be measured (the half angle of the cone is $9°$ approximately). All the mean properties of the plume would then be known—or so you might think; but there is one big snag. The quantities A and A' measure the transport of momentum along the axes of the jet or plume. If there were no fluctuations of velocity from the mean values the problem would be straightforward, but in fact there are large fluctuations, and because the transport of momentum is proportional to the square of velocity a greatly fluctuating flow produces a greater transport than one in which the velocity is nearly equal to its mean value all the time. The mean value must be measured by observing the velocity for a sufficiently long time for many fluctuations to occur.

The quantity B is even more complicated because if the greatest upward velocities are associated with the greatest buoyancies, as they almost certainly are, then again a fluctuating flow will transport more buoyancy upwards than a steady flow equal to the mean value. Nature is certain to employ the fluctuations to bring about a more efficient transport of buoyancy.

The simplest measurements to make are therefore the values of m and n and the values of W_0, R_0, τ_0 (and σ_0 if desired) somewhere in the plume. Their values elsewhere are then given, in the case of a pure buoyant plume, by equations of the form

$$\frac{W}{W_0} = \left(\frac{z}{z_0}\right)^{-\frac{1}{3}}; \quad \frac{\tau}{\tau_0} = \left(\frac{z}{z_0}\right)^{-\frac{5}{3}}.$$

As in the case of a pure jet, our buoyant plume will not behave like the formulae predict very close to the orifice. The approximations will be better the more nearly the upward momentum emerging from the orifice is equal to that which would have been gained by rising from the vertex of the cone under the influence of the buoyancy force. As in the case of thermals, in order to obtain a simple theory, it is necessary to suppose that the buoyancy has a negligible effect on the inertia of the fluid. This assumption cannot be valid close to the vertex of the cone because the buoyancy increases to infinity there, so that if the buoyancy force is imagined to be provided in the ordinary way the density within the plume would have to be zero at a finite distance from the vertex, and negative at smaller distances.

The upward transport of fluid is proportional to WR^2, which is proportional to $z^{\frac{5}{3}}$. The inflow is proportional to the rate of change of this with height, i.e. to $z^{\frac{2}{3}}$. The inward velocity of the surroundings at a given distance from the axis is proportional to $z^{\frac{2}{3}}$, and at the boundary of the plume to $z^{-\frac{1}{3}}$.

Since the inflow at a given distance from the axis increases with height and is therefore not the same at all levels, the horizontal pressure gradient in the exterior fluid must also vary with height. The fluid has a uniform density and so the vertical component of velocity cannot be zero. If the inflow velocity is $-u$, and the upward velocity is w the condition that the plume be similar at all heights requires that u and w are of the form

$$u = f\left(\frac{r}{z}\right) \times z^{\delta}$$

where r is distance from the axis. The equation of continuity then determines w. In this case it is

$$\frac{\partial(ru)}{\partial r} + \frac{\partial(rw)}{\partial z} = 0.$$

The velocity must satisfy the equations of motion, and if p' is the difference between the actual pressure and the hydrostatic value, then

$$\mathrm{D}u/\mathrm{D}t = - \partial p'/\rho\partial r$$

$$\mathrm{D}w/\mathrm{D}t = - \partial p'/\rho\mathrm{d}z.$$

p' and ρ may be eliminated if ρ is constant to give the ' vorticity equation '

$$\partial(\mathrm{D}u/\mathrm{D}t)/\partial z = \partial(\mathrm{D}w/\mathrm{D}t)/\partial r.$$

This equation, with that for u and the equation of continuity quoted, determines f, but it has not yet been solved. Some idea of what the flow is like can be obtained by assuming that

$$u = Dr^\alpha z^\beta.$$

Continuity then gives

$$w = - D\frac{\alpha + 1}{\beta + 1} r^{\alpha-1}z^{\beta+1}$$

and if the vorticity equation is to be satisfied we find, on substituting these values (and putting $\mathrm{D}/\mathrm{D}t = u\partial/\partial r + w\partial/\partial z$), that

$$\beta(\alpha - \beta) r^2 = 2(\alpha^2 - 1) z^2.$$

This equation is simply not true because α and β are constants and r and z are independent. Therefore u and w, and therefore the function f, are more complicated than we have supposed. But close to the plume r is small compared with z because the angle of the jet is only $9°$, i.e., $r = z/6\cdot3$. Therefore near to the plume

$$\beta(\alpha - \beta) = 80(\alpha^2 - 1) \text{ roughly.}$$

But on $r = z/6\cdot3$, i.e. on the edge of the plume, the velocities are proportional to $z^{-\frac{1}{3}}$ (or $r^{-\frac{1}{3}}$) and so

$$\alpha + \beta = - \tfrac{1}{3}.$$

Solving these last two equations we find that since $\alpha < 0$,

$$\alpha = -\,0\cdot993, \quad \beta = \,0\cdot66 \text{ roughly.}$$

The velocity is inwards so that u, and therefore D, is negative. The formula for w shows that it is positive so that the exterior fluid inclines upwards slightly as it approaches the plume.

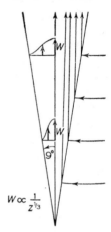

$$W \propto \frac{1}{z^{1/3}}$$

The streamlines are given by a relationship between r and z which satisfies

$$\mathrm{d}r/\mathrm{d}z = u/w$$

which in this case

$$= -\,(\beta + 1)r/(\alpha + 1)z$$

and so

$$r = \text{constant} \times z^{-(\beta+1)/(\alpha+1)}$$

$$= \text{constant} \times z^{-240} \text{ approximately}$$

the constant being different for different streamlines.

At a great distance from the plume, where $r \gg z$, we know that the motion must be almost horizontal and so $u \propto r^{-1}$ and $w \to 0$ for a fixed value of z as $r \to \infty$. Therefore $\alpha \to -1$. Since the vorticity equation is still satisfied $\beta \to 0$. It is left for the reader to demonstrate that $\alpha \to -1$ from above and $\beta \to 0$ from below and that at a great distance the streamlines curve *upwards*. Nevertheless the streamlines are for practical purposes horizontal because, for all values of z/r greater than 6.3, α exceeds -1 by a very small quantity, but a more rigorous treatment is required to demonstrate this.

Transition from a jet to a buoyant plume

If buoyant fluid emerges with a velocity greatly in excess of that corresponding to its buoyancy, to begin with its upward momentum and the kinetic energy of the eddying motion will be like that of a pure jet. As the fluid rises and becomes diluted the momentum added to it by the buoyancy forces steadily increases because it is proportional to the time for which the forces have operated. The total momentum (and kinetic energy) gradually increase until the difference between them and that of a pure buoyant plume is only a small fraction of the total. From then onwards it behaves like a buoyant plume.

Another way of looking at it is in terms of the balance between forces. A pure jet is governed completely by inertia forces. A pure buoyant plume is governed by the ratio of the inertia forces to the buoyancy forces, and since the motion (and therefore the inertia forces also) has been set up by and only by the buoyancy forces, the two forces always bear the same relationship to each other and the plume has the same properties all along its length. A buoyant plume must tend upwards towards being conical.

In the transition zone the analysis becomes more complicated, and it is necessary to appeal to observations to elucidate what happens. However, since the dilution is more rapid ($\tau \propto z^{-\frac{5}{3}}$) in a buoyant plume than in a pure jet ($\sigma \propto z^{-1}$) if it is desired to make a plume rise as high as possible the transition to a buoyant plume should be delayed to as great a height as possible. For instance, if the surroundings are slightly stably stratified there is a limit beyond which the plume cannot penetrate. If additional vertical momentum is given, in the form of a greater exit velocity, then the height at which a given dilution is achieved is raised, so that the equilibrium level at which the plume flattens out is raised.

An extreme case is that of a buoyant plume which can just not penetrate through a sharp inversion or stable layer. If the emission velocity is increased it may just penetrate.

This conclusion should be contrasted with those reached for a bent over buoyant plume in a smooth crosswind (page 196) and in a turbulent crosswind (page 198).

Jet in a smooth crosswind

The dilution of any plume in a crosswind is so rapid that when the material emitted has travelled a short distance its horizontal velocity is almost equal to that of the surrounding air. When the mixing is in the ratio of 10 parts of surroundings to one of effluent the velocity is $10/11$ of that of the surroundings approximately. Not far from the orifice therefore the jet is bent over into a nearly horizontal ' cone ' and it behaves from then onwards as if it had come from a point source a little above and upwind of the ' orifice ', and had been emitted with no relative horizontal velocity. The angle of the cone depends upon the windspeed. When this speed is large a vertical section of the cone will behave very much as if the sections on either side of it were identical with it, as if it were part of a cylindrical puff emitted from a line source with an impulse. Neither the bent over jet nor the line puff have circular sections but are more like a pair of parallel vortex lines with mixing occurring on the outside, as in a vertical section of an isolated thermal (page 156).

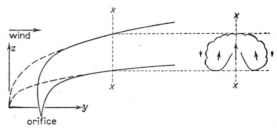

As each vertical section rises and travels along the plume the total upward momentum in it is constant. Its width, $2x$, increases but its thickness (or length) remains constant, and so if W is the vertical velocity of its top, all the velocities are proportional to W and the upward momentum of unit mass is proportional to

$$Wx^2 = W_0 x_0{}^2 = \text{constant}.$$

As before $$x = pz$$
(where p is a number)

and so
$$\frac{W}{W_0} = \left(\frac{z_0}{z}\right)^2$$

or $$W \propto z^{-2}.$$

This type of jet is therefore diluted more rapidly than if there were no crosswind. Since $W \propto dz/dt$, $z^3 \propto t$. The horizontal distance travelled, y, is approximately proportional to t in a steady crosswind and so the uppermost (or lowest, or any representative) point on the vertical section travels along the curve $y \propto z^3$. The 'cone' enveloping the jet is therefore curved.

The rate of dilution is easily shown to be given by

$$\sigma \propto z^{-2}.$$

Buoyant plume in a smooth crosswind

The method of treating a bent over buoyant plume is now straightforward. The total buoyancy in a vertical section is constant, so that

$$\tau x^2 = \tau_0 x_0{}^2 = \text{constant}.$$

The time rate of change of upward momentum is equal to the buoyancy force (compare this with the alternative equivalent statement on page 189 for a buoyant plume) and so

$$W \frac{\mathrm{d}}{\mathrm{d}z} (Wx^2) \propto \tau x^2 = \text{constant}.$$

Also

$$x = qz \quad \text{(where } q \text{ is a number)}$$

whence we deduce that

$$W \propto z^{-\frac{1}{2}}, \quad \tau \propto z^{-2}.$$

We notice immediately that the bent over buoyant plume is slowed down much less rapidly than the bent over jet (for which $W \propto z^{-2}$). In the same way as in the previous section we deduce that $z^{\frac{3}{2}} \propto t$ and the 'cone' grows around the curve $y \propto z^{\frac{3}{2}}$.

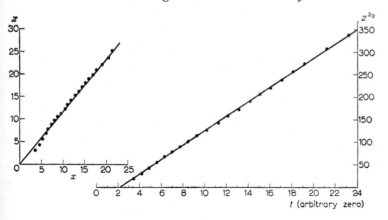

This type of thermal may be subjected to an analysis similar to that given on page 161 for a solitary thermal, on the assumption that it is cylindrical.   In that case, with the present notation,

$$W = C \, (\bar{\tau}x)^{\frac{1}{2}}$$

One set of experimental values obtained by Saunders by releasing cylindrical thermal into a water tank is given in the accompanying figure. The relationship $z^{\frac{3}{2}} \propto t$ is very well obeyed. He finds that roughly $q = 2\frac{1}{4}$ and $C = 0.8$, the cross section area of the thermal being about $2.5x^2$.

The constants of proportionality in all these relationships have to be obtained by means of observation. They will depend on the rate of emission of upward momentum in the case of the jet and on the rate of emission of buoyancy in this case, and on the strength of the crosswind in both cases.

The rate of dilution upwards is the same in both these bent over cases, for

$$\sigma \propto \tau \propto z^{-2}.$$

The addition of vertical momentum to a bent over buoyant plume makes no difference to the dilution achieved at any height. The constants p and q, which represent the rate of widening of the two types of bent over plume, are nearly the same, and the dilution is much more under the influence of the strength of the crosswind. A plume could, by the addition of vertical momentum at the orifice, be made to arrive at a stable layer with a greater vertical velocity than otherwise. It would therefore reach farther into that layer before flattening out. Since the buoyancy at a given height is not increased, if the plume impinged upon a sharp inversion it could not be made to penetrate it by increasing the efflux velocity. A picture of a plume being stopped by an inversion is shown in Plate 7.

Plumes in turbulent crosswinds

The dilution in the plumes so far discussed has been caused by some of the energy of motion of the emerging fluid, or some of the work done by the buoyancy forces, being converted into kinetic energy of stirring motions. But the air into which the plume emerges may already be undergoing stirring motions. These may be produced in one of two ways—by mechanical stirring produced by obstacles on the ground or by thermal convection. The former is sometimes called forced convection: but the term ' forced ' is abhorrent to the student of natural aerodynamics for Nature's unique behaviour is not to be thought of as constrained, even though the motion of the particles may be.   The question of forcing does not arise except in the sense that all motions are associated with forces of some kind.   Thermal convection for instance is the result of buoyancy forces.

As we saw in Chapter 6 the Richardson number is the most obvious non-dimensional number to associate with the occurrence of turbulent motion, but we have to be very careful indeed in the case of the effect of stirring motions on plumes.

Mechanical stirring is fairly straightforward, and we can see it at work on the smoke plumes emitted from small chimneys on the roofs of buildings.   In such cases it is usually so violent that neither the emission velocity nor the buoyancy has any appreciable effect on the motion.   The smoke is carried passively by the air passing the chimney top.   (See Plate 8.)

The larger visible eddies in the atmosphere are produced by thermal convection so that stirring due to convection is more important in the case of plumes from tall chimneys.   We saw in Chapter 7 that the lowest few hundred feet or so of the atmosphere are often in a state of static instability, and are continually producing thermals which emerge from this layer into the air above. If a chimney is emitting enough heat it can be a thermal source, so that whatever the turbulent motion of the air may be as a result of the convection, with some up and some down-currents, all the gas emerging from the chimney may be turned into thermals so that none is brought down to the ground until it has first reached up to the stable layers which limit the further upward movement of thermals.

The motion of smoke emitted with small buoyancy may be quite different, for it may be carried passively in the convection currents both upwards and downwards.   It is not correct simply to superimpose the stirring motions of the surrounding air upon those of a buoyant plume because the plume may play a large part in determining where the upcurrents are.

If a jet emerges with large upward momentum the rate of mixing is increased above that which would be produced by the stirring motions of the surroundings alone. It may be that when a large volume of gas is emitted with sufficient upward momentum the mixture with the surrounding air may be carried far enough upward to initiate a thermal, and the effluents may continue to rise rather as in the case of a buoyant plume. The jet then acts as a thermal source very much as a hump does (see pages 81 and 175) in a crosswind, by displacing unstable air upwards.

In any crosswind the length of plume emitted in a given time is proportional to the crosswind speed. On account of this, in addition to any other effects, there is a dilution approximately proportional to the wind speed. If the plume does not initiate thermals, any effect of buoyancy or efflux velocity must be achieved close to the orifice before the dilution by the stirring motions of the surrounding air becomes dominant.

The objective in choosing the position and design of a chimney is to keep the effluent gases as far away from the ground as possible. In strong winds therefore we should have as great an exit velocity as possible because the pure jet stage dominates the flow close to the orifice. The addition of buoyancy can have little effect because, before appreciable upward momentum has been generated by the buoyancy forces, the dilution will have proceeded so far that the stirring motions in the environment take control.

The case of moderate or light winds with slight environmental stirring motion is most instructive. Let us suppose that during one minute after emission the buoyancy forces can generate sufficient upward velocity to give appreciable vertical displacements before the eddies of the surrounding air take control. If we add additional vertical momentum at efflux the rate of dilution in time is increased simply because all the relative velocities are increased in magnitude, even though the rate of dilution in a buoyant plume is proportional to a higher negative power of t than in a pure jet. Therefore the dilution beyond which the buoyancy forces can only produce vertical velocities negligible in comparison with the environmental eddies is reached in a shorter time. With a high enough exit velocity this time may be so short that the buoyancy forces never produce ' useful ' upward velocities, and the ultimate effect of the high emission velocity and buoyancy forces may be reduced.

If the stirring motions of the surroundings are dominant the most useful analysis is provided by Sutton's theory, which, in spite of any practical limitations, is of considerable philosophical interest.

Sutton's theory

There is a danger, in the problem of pollution from a chimney, that a formula based on rather subtle ideas may be used by engineers who, through lack of opportunity to delve deeply into the matter, have not understood its limitations or its purpose. Sutton's formulae have been widely quoted and have been tentatively improved upon by making allowance for buoyancy and efflux velocity. Here we shall be concerned only with principles, our objective being to elucidate both the niceties and the inadequacies.

We have to consider what is the effect of eddies of different sizes upon the behaviour of the plume. The motion of the atmosphere may be thought of as composed of a whole spectrum of eddy sizes, ranging from as small as 1 cm or less to several thousand miles. The large eddies, which are the cyclones and anticyclones we see on weather charts, have a time scale of hours or days: that is to say they affect one point on the earth's surface for that length of time. When one of these eddies takes a long time to pass us we think of the wind as being constant in direction for several hours or days. It is only if we think in terms of weeks, months, or years, that the weather system becomes an eddy among many.

At the other extreme we are not normally concerned at all about the tiny eddies except when large numbers of them occur. We think of their collective effect only as the smoke we are observing is diffused over an ever-increasing volume, large compared with an eddy. In much the same way in 1883 the weather system eddies were seen to diffuse the clouds of dust from the volcano Krakatoa and spread them over the whole globe in the succeeding two years, a period long compared with the duration of a weather system.

If we stand 100 m from a chimney we regard the large eddies as producing ' the wind ' for our time scale will be comparable with the time required for the particles of smoke to travel from the

chimney to us—say 15 sec. The large eddies, therefore, do not
stir the plume at all, at least, not to our thinking. The tiny
eddies on the other hand are so small that their effect is swamped
by the medium-sized eddies. What we call medium-sized
depends on how far we are from the chimney. At 100 m an
eddy of 10 m diameter would be medium-sized, but at 2 m from
the chimney the eddies only a few centimetres in diameter would
concern us, while the 10 m eddy would cause variations in ' the
wind '.

When the plume is narrow large eddies cause it to wander
about while the tiny eddies widen it. When the plume has
become wide the tiny eddies have a negligible effect while the
larger ones widen, or spread, the plume, and the very largest still
cause it to wander. Thus an *instantaneous* picture of the plume
is one in which a gradually widening plume wanders within
gradually widening limits. If we want to know the concentration
of smoke in a part of the instantaneous visible plume we have to
ascertain the effect of the eddies which are small compared with the
width of the plume. But clearly this would not be very useful
because in a few moments the position of the wanderings will
have changed, and we have therefore to concern ourselves with an
average value of the concentration over, say, a few minutes, during
which the plume wanders about within the limits indicated.

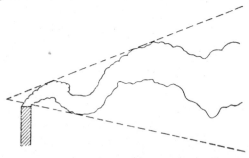

We are immediately in difficulties because as we go farther away
from the chimney we find that the limits within which the plume
wanders also begin to wander about if we watch them over a
longer period of time appropriate to the greater distance. And at
any distance the extent of the wanderings increases the longer we
watch the plume. Over a period of a year the wind blows some

PLATE 6. Pictures at half-minute intervals of cumulus clouds growing over Nantucket with base at 800 m and tops up to 1500 m. The island is a thermal source surrounded by sea, and thermals can be seen to ascend individually and be sheared over and carried away by the wind which is stronger at higher levels. The evaporation of the towers can also be seen to occur at the time the upward motion ceases. These pictures were taken by J. S. Malkus. (*See* page 167)

PLATE 7. The upper picture shows the smoke accumulated under an inversion in a valley during one night from a cement works. The plume is not buoyant enough to rise in the air above and therefore sinks back into the cooler air below. The inversion is about 100 m above the chimney top. The lower picture shows the accumulation of smoke over an aluminium works in a valley during one night. The more buoyant plumes are passing through the inversion which is at about 25 m, and that from the taller chimney is carried away in the light wind at higher levels. Both these pictures were taken in winter shortly after dawn at places where the output of smoke is steady and continuous day and night. (*See* pages 196 and 210)

[*Facing page* 201

time or other from each direction, and so the pollution is no longer
represented by a plume but by contours of pollution centred on the
chimney, showing gradually decreasing average pollution in all
directions, but decreasing more slowly down the direction of the
prevailing wind.   Even if there were no small eddies and the
smoke came away from the chimney as an undiluted tube of
smoke there would be a similar dilution shown by these contours as
distance increased from the chimney, on account of the wanderings.

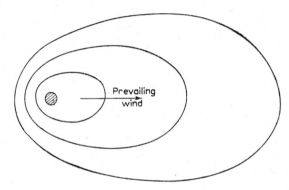

It is now clear that according to the time for which we observe
the plume and the distance we are from the source the dilution we
measure will be produced mainly by eddies of one size scale;
the smaller and larger ones having no relevant effect.   The
question is, what is this one size? Sutton argued that the only
relevant size is plume size.

Before proceeding let us analyse the logical step made.   Any
problem, if it is determinate at all, must have a solution which is
derived from the data.   The only data are the characteristics of the
atmosphere, in which no eddy size is picked out especially, and the
plume itself.   The only relevant dimension in the plume is
distance from the orifice, which must therefore determine the eddy
size.   If the dominant eddy size is proportional to distance from
the origin then all parts of the plume are similar to each other, and
the plume is conical, the width being proportional to the distance
from the orifice.   This argument is fundamentally the same as that
whereby we deduced that the size of an isolated thermal is proportional to the height through which it had ascended (page 160)
or whereby we deduced that buoyant plumes or pure jets in calm

air would be conical.   Sutton's formulae represent this situation, but with modifications.

Clearly the plume cannot be conical because of the presence of the ground.   This difficulty is overcome by assuming that there is an equal source an equal distance below the ground level and that the atmosphere extends downwards as well as upwards. The effect of the plume is then added to that of its image in the ground.   Again the atmosphere has upper limits.   This can be expressed by saying that when the eddies are very large they only spread the plume horizontally.   When the air is stably stratified the intensity of the eddies for a given windspeed is less than when the air is neutrally or unstably stratified.   The intensity of the eddies also depends upon the amount of wind shear (which we saw in Chapter 2 depends largely on the horizontal temperature gradient) and the roughness of the ground.   Following the simplest possible course Sutton gave values for the coefficients in his formulae for various stable stratifications, the intensity of the eddies depending also on the wind speed which was incorporated in the formulae.

These formulae are an attempt to represent the behaviour of Nature.   We normally prefer to do this by deriving equations from basic laws or principles such as Newton's laws of motion. This is impossible in the case of stirring motions and the principle adopted has been first to treat the problem statistically by referring only to average values over a period of time, and second to base the formulae on the principle of similarity.   This necessarily means inserting measured values of the coefficients into the formulae (as we did in the case of a thermal, page 161) and so even if the formulae are not strictly correct they are likely to be fairly good if conditions are not greatly different from the conditions under which the coefficients were measured.   Our objective is by argument to arrive at a formula which will be valid in conditions as far as possible from those in which the coefficients are measured. If we could measure all our coefficients in the laboratory under controlled conditions and then use the formulae for the atmosphere our ideal would be achieved, but apart from the difficulties inherent in obtaining complete similarity between the model in the laboratory and the atmosphere there are other more urgent ones. We shall now discuss these.

It is not practicable, in any formula for the dispersion of

effluents from a chimney, to make allowance for the variations with height of the static stability of the atmosphere. Yet these variations can completely change the behaviour of a plume, as we shall see on pages 207 to 210. This is one aspect of the complexity of the atmosphere. Another, more involved in the theoretical basis of Sutton's formulae, is that there are not always eddies of every size present in the atmosphere. Thus when the plume width or length reaches a certain size such that according to the theory it would be coming mainly under the influence of the eddies of corresponding dimensions we may find that there are no such eddies present. The plume cannot then continue to grow conically. On the other hand if the eddies of a certain size have a greater intensity than other sizes, when the plume grows to that size its further growth will be more rapid, so that the angle of the ' cone ' must change at that point. It is a fact that, although sometimes eddies of all sizes seem to be present with about the right intensities, at other times eddies of certain sizes are almost completely absent.

The final difficulty stems from the theory itself. It requires that the time over which the concentration of effluent shall be measured shall be appropriate to the distance from the orifice. Exactly what this time is has never been determined. Sutton suggested from practical experience that 10 minutes would be about right, but this period is necessarily tied to the values he gave of the coefficients which represent the spreading and dilution process. The values of the coefficients measured by some observers depend quite seriously upon the time over which the average concentration has been measured.

If we try to modify the formulae for different atmospheric conditions we shall be betraying the great purpose which bore it, namely to design the formula to conform to a simple theoretical idea. It is no use adding more and more modifications to the formula to cover all kinds of weather turning it into little more than a collection of experimental values of which we choose those which seem most suited to our immediate problem. This is a way of getting through life and we have to do it if we have neither the time nor the ability to make a more penetrating analysis, but it achieves no philosophical purpose, and the moment has now come to make a fresh approach.

The contemporary concern about the dispersion of effluents stems from the disastrous consequences of air pollution mostly in modern cities. The greatest disasters occur under weather conditions which depart most seriously from the average in such a way as to invalidate formulae designed to apply to average conditions. Our social consciences cannot be salved by scientific studies, however elegant, of dispersion of pollution in average weather. We must study especially those weather conditions which render the pollution noxious, learn to understand the processes which then operate, and plan our towns accordingly. The behaviour of the atmosphere is so varied (and for this we should be grateful for life is thereby enriched) that no manageable theory can possibly treat all its behaviour. If we are to treat some aspects rather than others, then we see that the consequences of pollution require that special, rather than average, conditions shall receive immediate attention. Two final remarks: average conditions in a medium of such varied behaviour as the atmosphere are practically a fiction, as rare as most of the special conditions which concern us as social beings: but he is a poor scientist who in his ivory tower heeds not special human problems if they are relevant to his discipline.

There is another approach to the problem of plume dispersion in which Sutton has played a leading role. As he has himself discussed it at length we will only recite the essential idea. Turbulent motion in the air transfers any property carried by the air from regions where it is dense to where it is less concentrated. Thus smoke, water vapour, and heat are dispersed from sources thereof. Momentum is another property which is transferred and the rate at which it is transferred depends on the gradient of it. If we can measure the gradient of horizontal momentum, which is the wind shear, we can, with two additional assumptions, calculate the rate at which momentum is transferred by the eddies. These two assumptions are that there is no thermal wind, because otherwise there would be shear with no stresses between the layers, and that the wind is geostrophic, which means that no work is done by the pressure gradient on the air. We can therefore assume that the force on a layer of air due to the air above is equal and opposite to that due to the air below.

These assumptions are not seriously in error if the shear is large (i.e. much larger than the thermal wind) as it usually is near the ground, and if the component of the wind along the isobars is measured. This latter precaution is not really necessary in view of the accuracy attainable in this problem.

It is then necessary to assume that smoke, or heat, or whatever it is that the plume consists of, is transferred by the eddies in the same way as momentum, and that the horizontal transfer is the same as the vertical transfer. This latter assumption is not true very near the ground but is a reasonable approximation in practice. But since momentum can be communicated from one parcel of air to another without mixing, whereas smoke and heat cannot, it is probable that a given configuration of eddies does not transfer them in an identical manner. The relationship between the coefficients of transfer of momentum and heat by eddies has been the subject of much discussion and is at present far from resolved.

Effective stack height

If the emission velocity from a chimney stack is increased we have seen that close to the stack the upward momentum possessed by the effluent dominates the motion. It behaves like a pure jet. If, a few seconds after emission, the gases come mainly under the influence of the surrounding stirring motions their concentration some distance downwind is the same as if they had emerged with a smaller vertical velocity at a higher level. The large velocity of efflux therefore raises the 'effective stack height' which is good from the point of view of the pollution to be experienced at the ground.

The amount by which the stack height is effectively raised depends upon how soon the surrounding motions dominate the pure jet motion. In the case of the Bankside power station in London the height may be as low as 30 ft in a strong crosswind (Plate 8), in which, quite apart from the greater turbulence in the air, the dilution is increased by the horizontal extension of the plume; but it may be as high as 300 or 400 ft in almost calm conditions when the plume goes nearly straight upwards.

The addition of buoyancy also reduces the concentration of

pollution at the ground from a chimney but less certainly than the addition of upward momentum when the stirring motion in the surroundings is great. The buoyancy generally takes several seconds, and sometimes as much as a minute to become more effective than impressed upward momentum, and in that time the surrounding motion may have so diluted it that the upward velocities due to buoyancy are negligible.

On the other hand, as we have already remarked (pages 196 and 198), when the air is very stable added buoyancy is more effective than added upward momentum, while when thermal convection is very active a hot plume can behave as a thermal source and raise the effective stack height by perhaps several thousand metres.

The only reliable way in which to increase the effective height of a chimney stack at all times is to increase its height. If we are concerned to raise its effective height mainly when pollution tends to accumulate, namely when the eddies in the surrounding air are feeble, then an increase in buoyancy is most useful. These are not the only important aspects of stack height. As we shall see below (page 209), the height of the orifice in a stably stratified atmosphere may at times be more important than any other single consideration.

If the plume is approximately conical, as Sutton's theory indicates it will be when the eddies of the environment become dominant, then the concentration of effluent in it is proportional to x^{-2}, where x is the distance from the vertex of the cone. This means that, since the distance at which the cone impinges on the ground is proportional to the height h of its vertex (which is the effective stack height), the concentration experienced at the ground is proportional to h^{-2}. In moderate winds the buoyancy of the effluent from a large chimney often doubles or trebles the effective stack hieghts, and in light winds often increases it by a factor of as much as 10. The pollution is, of course, spread over a larger area but it is mainly the large concentrations that do damage, and with sufficient stack height it can be reduced below a negligible intensity at the ground.

Nevertheless, the foregoing is mostly a theoretical discussion. We shall now turn to some of the phenomena in the face of which these, and other, theoretical ideas must be applied.

Diurnal variations in plume behaviour

It may be disappointing to find that precise figures cannot be given to the effects so far described. The influences vary in their importance by several orders of magnitude according to the meteorological situation. But if the processes are understood it is fairly easy to see, by observing the behaviour of a plume, which effects are dominant at any particular moment. It can be nothing but helpful to get on nodding terms with plumes—to become plumes watchers.

(a) Coning

A plume is said to be coning when it is expanding roughly along a cone. Plumes, bent over and vertical, do this when either the efflux momentum or the buoyancy or both together are dominant (see Plate 9); man-controlled influences are paramount and some control can be exercised over behaviour.

(b) Thermalling

When a hot plume acts as a thermal source there are often distortions in it as in looping (below). Nevertheless the gases continue upwards and the eddies never carry any effluents down to the ground. This is thermalling. It differs from coning mainly in that the plume *appears* to be under the influence of surrounding air motions.

(c) Looping

When the environmental eddies twist the plume so violently (see Plate 10) that the efflux momentum and buoyancy are ineffective, the 'cone' is zig-zagged up and down as Sutton imagined, and its behaviour is called looping. This is an occasion for the

use of Sutton's formulae.   The loops are contained within a wider
' cone '.

(d) Fanning

When the air is very stable the plume gases quickly reach their
equilibrium level and travel horizontally, often with very little
dilution on account of the smallness of the stirring motions in the
environment. Sometimes it may be carried into sideways
meanderings, particularly when the wind is light: this is called
fanning. A fanning plume may impinge upon a tall building or
hillside that reaches up to its level.

(e) Fumigation

This interesting phenomenon was first elicited by Hewson.
We may imagine a plume fanning in a light wind and thereby
producing a thin but concentrated layer of pollution at, say, 150 m
above the ground.   This layer may extend 50 km or more downwind if the source is operating all night.   In the morning the
sunshine warms the ground and convection begins from the ground
gradually extending to greater heights; the effect of the convection
is to stir up the layer in which it is taking place more or less
uniformly, so that when it reaches up to the pollution it spreads it
uniformly through the air up to that level.   This results in a
sudden increase in the concentration at the ground, which is
called fumigation. Thereafter the concentration gradually decreases as the pollution is spread over a greater and greater depth,
but the large concentration may endure for an hour or more if the
original fanning plume was trapped below an inversion or very
stable layer.   The convection does not penetrate this layer in some
cases until the ground temperature (and that of the convection
layer above it) has risen a further 5°–8° C.

By means of fumigation the sulphur dioxide from a smelter in
Canada was able to destroy vegetation up to as much as 80 km
away. If the ordinary processes of diffusion always operated
such damage could not occur because the concentration would
never rise above the threshold which the vegetation could tolerate.
When it was first observed, the startling thing was that the concentration tens of kilometres from the source was as great as much
nearer, and the maximum value was reached at exactly the same
time in the morning at all distances, so that it could not have been
due to a dense cloud of pollution moving away from the source.

PLATE 8. The plume from Bankside power station, London, emerges with a large velocity through a small orifice. In a crosswind the plume is, even so, quickly bent over, and the continued rise due to the upward momentum of efflux is imperceptible. In the right-hand picture the angle of the cone is less than for a jet or buoyant plume: the air into which the plume is emerging must therefore be rising (in a thermal), so that the plume is stretched vertically. (*See* page 205)

PLATE 9. The buoyant plumes from power stations emerging in a fairly smooth crosswind and passing along well-defined cones. The right-hand one is passing overhead, the left-hand one is from three adjacent stacks. (*See* page 207)

PLATE 10. Colliery smoke plumes with little buoyancy being carried passively by the eddies of the air. In the upper one there are large eddies present while in the lower the smaller ones predominate. (*See* page 207)

(f) Evening inversions

One of the main difficulties in the use of Sutton's or any other formulae is that the intensity of the stirring motion cannot easily be related to the strength of the wind and the stability of the air. This is particularly so in the evening of days during which there has been convection produced by sunshine warming the ground. As the sun goes down the ground cools by radiation into space and the air close to it becomes cooled by contact and radiation to the ground. When the wind is not very strong the layer of air affected is of the order of 10–100 m deep, and it becomes very stable. Plumes from low level sources are often not hot enough to emerge from this layer. This is very noticeable with bonfire smoke which begins ' fanning ' in the evening. The fanning of plumes from other sources also takes place, but bonfire plumes usually contain very dense smoke and are at a very low level where the stability of the air is greatest, and so the plume is clearly visible because fanning takes place very near to the source. The fanning of plumes from almost all the sources in a town can often be seen from a high vantage point, and some quite small towns in valleys produce a low level pall of smoke in a stable layer when the wind is light.

While this is taking place the plumes of tall chimneys are generally changing from looping or thermalling to coning. The low level inversion of temperature reduces the stirring motions produced by flow over uneven ground at the same time as convection from the ground ceases. The air above the stable layers close to the ground therefore flows smoothly even though it does not become stably stratified, but remains in neutral equilibrium (see figure below).

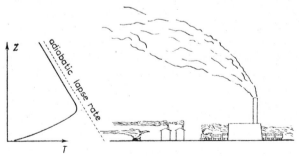

That some sources of pollution reach above the evening and night inversions is very important because the effluents from them continue to rise, often to a thousand metres or more while the smoke from low level sources is trapped near the ground.

(g) *The morning awakening*

The cooling at the ground continues all night, and the layer of air rendered stable gradually deepens, so that by morning the plumes from many of the higher sources may be fanning in it. But the stability resists downward as much as upward movement, so that even then their smoke does not reach the ground. Not until convection again stirs the air up does the accumulated filth of the night reach the ground. The duration of the period of fumigation depends on how stable the air is above the layer affected by night cooling, but it is generally less than an hour if there had been convection on the previous day and the day in question is substantially similar. One must be warned against stating rules about this because fumigation can continue for most of the day when an inversion is formed at, say, 180 m above the ground by processes more influential than simple nocturnal cooling. Dense haze may persist all day in spite of the sunshine. On the other hand the development of convection may be so rapid, because cooler air had arrived in the layers above the nocturnal inversion during the night, that fumigation may be imperceptible.

The behaviour of a plume near the orifice

In the early part of this chapter it was implied that however the effluents emerged they soon adjusted themselves to the form of a plume and behaved as if they had emerged from a point source. In so far as the behaviour close to the source represents the reaction of the effluents to the wide world into which they have been irrevocably emitted, it is worthy of the attention of the student of Natural Aerodynamics. Like human beings, the emerging gases often suffer violent experiences during this period of gaining maturity and of becoming part of Nature at large, especially if in their upbringing they have become too hot, or too wet, or have a vorticity complex, or find the cross currents too strong. We shall now describe some of the diagnoses that can be made.

(a) Bifurcation

When a plume is bent over by a crosswind there must be vorticity in it in the direction shown in the figure. The circulation is in the same direction as in a vertical section if an upward puff. The vorticity is that which exists at the edges of the orifice where the effluents are moving upwards relative to the surroundings. The bent-over plume may be imagined to consist of a series of

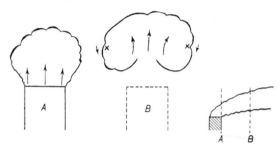

puffs, overlapping so that the vorticity at the front of one annuls the vorticity in the opposite direction at the back of the next. Only the vorticity at the sides is in the same direction in all puffs, and so the plume is gathered into two rolls. This configuration will not persist far downwind as the plume is diluted unless new vorticity is added as the mass of air in the plume grows. This is done in a hot plume. The conditions most favourable for the persistence of bifurcation far downwind are that the plume should be buoyant, that the surrounding air should not be stably stratified otherwise the buoyancy will quickly be nullified, and that the surrounding air should not possess any stirring motion which would disrupt the configuration of the plume. These are all realised, for instance, in the evening of a day when convection has occurred and the chimney top is still above the level of the stabilised layer. If the bifurcation is to be seen the plume must contain dense smoke (see Plate 11).

Bifurcation can be produced also by the cooling of the outside of the plume. This happens when the plume contains liquid water droplets. The mixing on the outside with unsaturated surrounding air evaporates some or all of the droplets and the absorption of latent heat makes the mixture cooler than the plume and the surroundings. The central part of the plume rises through this outer cool shell with a pattern of velocity as shown in the figure. This happens in the washed plume at Battersea power station (Plate 12), and in the plumes from many cement works.

(b) Downwash

If some plumes suffer the schizophrenia just described others appear reluctant to leave their mother's apron strings, and cling to the back of the chimney stack, hiding as it were from the cruel wind that is to take them away. This generally occurs when the exit velocity is small and the crosswind large. Some of the effluent enters the standing or slowly moving eddies on the lee side of the stack. They may flow up to 5–10 m down from the top before being carried away horizontally.

Although this may be due occasionally to stack design, especially where the stack has a bulging ornate top, it is mainly caused by the low exit velocity and is easily cured by increasing this. It can also be prevented by building a horizontal disc round the chimney top (Plate 13).

The term downwash is sometimes used to refer to the entrainment of a plume in the eddies produced by the building on which the chimney stands. This nearly always happens to smoke from dwelling houses. The $2\frac{1}{2}$ times rule which directs the architect to make the chimney at least $2\frac{1}{2}$ times as tall as the building has no abstruse theoretical foundation. It simply states a good practical minimum height proposed by a scientist who is also a keen observer, but circumstances under which it is either too severe or lenient a rule can easily be found. Its wide use arises from the universal desire we all have that, if we have insufficient time or inclination to understand an expert's conclusions, we ask him for a simple rule of thumb. ' What is the formula ? ' we say. If he treated us to a long dissertation (such as this chapter) on the difficulties of the subject, we might begin to suspect that he did

PLATE 11. The plumes shown in the left picture of Plate 9 seen passing overhead. The buoyancy produces a bifurcation. (*See* page 211)

PLATE 12. This plume consists mainly of water droplets (Battersea power station, London) and has little buoyancy at the orifice where the bifurcation is produced as the plume is bent over. Farther from the orifice the bifurcation is induced by the cooling of the outside as the water droplets evaporate, and the plume disappears. (*See* page 211)

PLATE 13. When there is little buoyancy and small efflux velocity smoke is carried into the wake of the chimney. This is referred to as downwash. It can be prevented by greater buoyancy or efflux velocity or by the placing of a disc around the chimney top as in the right-hand picture. (*See* page 212)

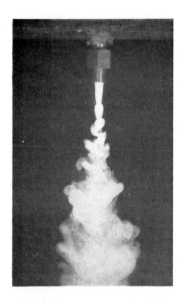

PLATE 14. These plumes are emerging from an orifice ⅜ in. in diameter, and consist of salt water made visible with white precipitate. Their density excess over the surrounding water causes a vertical stretching until the velocity appropriate to a buoyant plume is achieved. It then becomes 'turbulent', first by cumulation into thermal-like configurations. (*See* page 213)

not know the answer to our question.   In such cases it is often more prudent to examine the question itself more carefully.   It is not very sensible to ask the booking clerk, ' Which train do I take to St. Helena ? ' (Perhaps we might sometimes think a little more carefully before asking ' What will the weather be tomorrow ? ' Would not something like ' Can you tell me whether it will be cold tomorrow ? ' often be more to the point ?).

(c) Converging buoyant plume

In discussing pure plumes it was supposed that at some stage a configuration of velocity and buoyancy in conformity with the laws stated on page 190 was reached.   If the gases emerge with too great a velocity then there is a short stage in which the behaviour is more like a pure jet in which the velocity decreases more rapidly than in a pure buoyant plume (z^{-1} as against $z^{-\frac{1}{3}}$), while the buoyancy decreases less rapidly (z^{-1} as against $z^{-\frac{5}{3}}$).   But if the gases emerge with too small a velocity, Nature must devise a motion in which the mixing is reduced while the buoyancy increases the velocity to conform to it.

In the extreme case, when no mixing is required, the surroundings remain stationary.   If ρ_1 is the density inside the plume and ρ_2 that outside, the pressure inside is given by Bernoulli's equation (page 10) and

$$p_1 = p - \rho_1 g z - \tfrac{1}{2}\rho_1(w_1{}^2 - w_0{}^2)$$

in which w_0 is the value of w, the vertical velocity, at the height where $z = 0$, which is chosen as the level at which pressure both inside (p_1) and outside (p_2) is equal to p.   But in a steady state the pressure inside the plume must be equal to that outside which is given by

$$p_2 = p - \rho_2 g z$$

otherwise the walls of the plume would either shrink or swell out. Subtracting these two equations we get

$$w^2 = w_0{}^2 + 2gz\,(\rho_2 - \rho_1)/\rho_1.$$

The amount of gas travelling up the plume is the same at all levels so that if r is the radius of it

$$wr^2 = \text{constant} = w_0 r_0{}^2$$

and so eliminating w we find that

$$r = r_0 \left\{ 1 + \frac{2g(\rho_2 - \rho_1)}{\rho_1 w_0{}^2} z \right\}^{-\frac{1}{4}}.$$

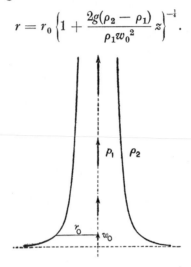

This tells us how r varies as z increases. The jet converges upwards along the shape shown in the accompanying figure. The velocity is also shown in this figure. When the velocity has reached a value such that the upward transport of buoyancy and momentum are in the same ratio as in a pure buoyant plume, mixing with the surroundings will begin and from there onwards it will behave like a pure buoyant plume. The transition is illustrated in Plate 14 which shows the same phenomenon in a water tank.

As soon as the mixing begins the velocity profile of the jet changes from nearly uniform with a thin boundary layer to one in which the mean velocity decreases gradually from a maximum in the middle to zero at the edge. It does not change by the growth of eddies in the shearing layer which surrounds the buoyant fluid but by the generation of a series of vortex ring- or isolated thermal-like structures which can be seen in Plate 14. This shows that the buoyancy is gathering the fluid together in lumps which then begin to entrain the surrounding fluid. Because of the steady acceleration of the fluid up the converging buoyant plume the boundary layer between it and the surroundings, which is produced by the viscosity, is kept thin, as in a converging channel (see page 110).   The plume also tends to begin meandering when the mixing begins, and this too can be seen in Plate 14.

The shape of the plume at the point of transition varies from one plume to another.   This is because the transition occurs when the flux of buoyancy and momentum are in the correct ratio, i.e. when $w \div g(\rho_2 - \rho_1)/\rho_1$ takes the required value.   This is not a non-dimensional number which means, among other things, that the condition cannot be determined by the non-dimensional ratio r/h alone, where h is the value of z for which r is infinite (represented by the horizontal dotted line in the figure on page 214).   This means that we could halve the value of r all the way up the plume without altering the transition point provided that the velocity were kept the same.   Thus, if the transition took place at the top of the figure, it would do likewise for the plume with half the width but the same upward velocity, and this would have a different shape to the eye because it would be reduced in only one direction.   Mathematically the form would be the same.

Converging buoyant plumes are sometimes seen emerging from household chimneys on very calm days.   They are also often seen above hot bonfires.

(d) Cumulation

Cumulation means the gathering together of the effluent emerging during several seconds into a compact mass which then travels away as an isolated thermal or puff heedless of the rest of the plume (see Plate 15).   It occurs either when the strength of the source varies so that it is in effect intermittent or when there are variations in the strength of a crosswind.

It is said that some aborigines in Australia send signals of joyous or ominous events by controlling the behaviour of the plumes from great bonfires of brushwood.   Around the fires stand men skilled in the use of long poles.   By inserting these radially into the base of the fire they can lift the whole burning mass of brushwood off the ground to let an increased draught pass through.   Other less elevated members of the tribe stand round with brushwood, ready to throw it upon the fire at a given command.   By controlling the temperature of the fire with the draught and the smokiness by the freshness of the brush thrown on, intermittent smoky thermals can be sent up by increasing the heat output over a short period just after the smokiness has been increased.

If the surrounding air is stably stratified, as it often is of a morning or evening, by controlling the amount of heat the smoky thermal can be made to flatten out at any chosen height. Some say that a skilled tribal leader can send up six successive thermals, each reaching higher than its predecessor to form a magnificent pagoda of smoke signifying at least the birth of a prince—a sophisticated camp fire activity indeed! No doubt if the matter were seriously engaged upon, Texans could send up a majestic signal to the county around more than appropriate to the discovery of a new oil well.

More common than the cumulation by variations in the source is cumulation by variations in crosswind. The plume is then gathered together into lumps (see Plate 15) and the behaviour is then according to that of isolated thermals rather than of conical plumes. This is different from thermalling (page 207) in that the buoyancy is from the source and not largely from the instability of the environment, and it depends upon the conditions at the orifice rather than far from it.

(e) Puffing

Sometimes smoke appears to come out of a chimney in a series of little puffs (Plate 16). This could be due to the pulsations of a fan or engine, but it occurs most often when there is appreciable buoyancy with a rather small output of volume from a large diameter chimney in a crosswind. On account of the buoyancy of the effluent the surrounding air tends to sink into the upwind side of the chimney causing surges of the effluent, rather like the blop-blop produced when liquid is poured out of a bottle. This analogy is not complete because air *must* flow into the bottle, in order that the liquid shall emerge.

Casual observation indicates that chimneys which puff are also liable to downwash in strong winds. This is probably because they are built with too large an orifice for the amount of effluent produced.

Plumes as natural phenomena

Clearly the problems of plume behaviour are far from solved, those of pollution included. If we must be burdened for many more years with obnoxious effluents, while we fight to rid our civilisation of them let us be philosophical. To the town sparrow Nature consists of houses, trees, houses, trees: let us think of it as chimneys, streets, chimneys, streets; and from time to time forget the bronchitis and rotting of curtains by pollution, and think while we can of the delightful mechanisms of dispersion employed by Nature. In perhaps another generation plumes will be invisible, but with their radioactivity possibly as dangerous as our smoke.

CHAPTER 9

AIR WAVES

ANY movable medium in which there is a force tending to restore displaced particles to their original position can propagate waves. We are most familiar with waves on the surface of water, in which the restoring force is gravity tending to make the surface level, and with sound waves, which are propagated as pressure waves in a compressible fluid. These two mechanisms—gravity and compressibility—are responsible for most of the properties of waves in the atmosphere, but the deviating force due to the earth's rotation also plays its part when the period of the waves is comparable with the length of a day.

Explosion waves

(a) Sound and shock waves; little bangs

An explosion may be produced either by the creation of gas out of solid or liquid or by the generation of a large amount of heat which produces an expansion. In any case an expansion wave is produced, and as it passes away from the source it displaces the air outwards, making room for the increased volume which is the explosion. If the explosion is produced mainly by the generation of heat there may be a contraction later on: this is usually slower and therefore less violent, and produces a subsonic contraction wave. When the particles are thrust outwards from the explosion at a speed greater than the speed of sound a shock wave is produced. In a shock wave the air is moved forwards in the direction of propagation with a jerk—perhaps only a few millimetres—and the air is slightly warmed and the pressure slightly increased. It is the suddenness of the increase rather than the increase itself which we perceive with our ears.

After a shock wave has spread out, either spherically from an explosion, or conically from a supersonic aircraft or projectile, its intensity decreases both on account of this spreading and on account of the loss of energy into heat which occurs when it passes. It then degenerates into a sound wave pulse which travels at, not faster than, the speed of sound, and which becomes gradually dispersed into a series of oscillations. At large distances from the explosion these oscillations are heard as a rumble instead of the single crack of the shock wave heard close to the source.

When the explosion is produced by a sudden release of heat the main effect is to reduce the density of the gas that is heated, and this decrease in density is effected by the outward displacement of mass as the shock or sound waves pass. This redistribution of density takes place at sonic speed, and has become past history before gravity produces any appreciable convective motion. Because the velocity of sound is so much greater than the vertical velocities produced by buoyancy the two dynamical phenomena are separate for practical purposes. When we see an explosion we see a puff formed suddenly; it then begins to rise gradually and its subsequent motion as a thermal may last for several minutes.

An explosion is called a *little bang* when the expansion wave becomes imperceptible in among the fluctuations of pressure that continually occur in the atmosphere at a distance of the order of 100 km from the source. A little bang's expansion wave just reaches up into the stratosphere. The depth of the atmosphere may be regarded as being of the order of 10–20 km for these purposes because most of the mass of the atmosphere is below that height.

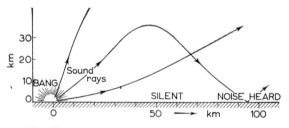

The rumbles from explosions can often be heard at distances of 4 or 5 atmosphere depths from the source, because the waves are reflected downwards from the warm layers above 30 km. Between this distance and the source there is often a silent zone which is not reached by any sound waves of audible intensity. Waves travelling almost horizontally are refracted upwards on account of the decrease of temperature with height, the velocity of sound waves being proportional to $T^{\frac{1}{2}}$. Waves travelling upwards at a steep angle are not reflected by the warm layers above 30 km but, on account of the large angle of incidence, pass into them.

Little bangs are, by definition, too feeble to be heard after being reflected from the ground and down again from the upper air a second or third time.

(b) Big bangs

Bangs which are big enough to be detected above the continual pressure fluctuations in the air at distances of 1000 km or more from the source are called *big*. The sound waves they emit have travelled in a ' wave guide ' 10–20 km deep. Instead of thinking of rays of sound we now have to think of gravity waves in which the whole atmosphere is heaved up and down as they pass. Gravity is not involved in the propagation over short distances because the sound is propagated by simple elastic oscillations of the air; but these oscillations are possible only because the air is under pressure due to its own weight and gravity becomes involved if the whole depth of the atmosphere is heaved simultaneously. For gravity to be important the *wave fronts must be vertical surfaces* and the oscillations are in phase or antiphase at all levels. It can be seen that, at points several atmosphere depths from the source, there can be no silent zones. It does not matter whether the source is at the bottom or the top of the atmosphere. The wave passes as if it had come from a very distant source, and is *propagated horizontally*, all trace of up and down reflections being obliterated by the interference of the multitude of rays passing up and down between the ground and the upper air.

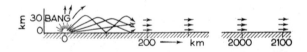

Gravity waves of this kind travel with a horizontal velocity which is an average velocity of sound over the whole depth of air involved. Thus they travel more slowly than sound at the ground (about 345 m/sec) and faster than sound in the stratosphere (about 310 m/sec); 320 m/sec is a typical speed, relative to the air, but speed over the ground may differ from this by the speed of the wind which may easily be 20 or 30 m/sec. Their horizontal speed is greater than that of waves from little bangs whose trajectory is lengthened by the passage up to heights of 30 km or more, and back.

(c) Aeroclysms

The waves from big bangs, examples of which are given below, are not usually detectable above the normal fluctuations of .pressure at the antipodes of the source. Explosions which rock the whole atmosphere to and fro deserve the grander name of *aeroclysm* (a flooding of air). The period of the waves radiating from an aeroclysm may be half an hour or more. As we shall see below, the period increases with distance from the source. With big bangs a period of a few minutes is not exceeded before the wave becomes too small to observe. The eruption of Krakatoa in 1883 is the only aeroclysm in recorded history.

(d) The energy of bangs

Explosions of atom bombs are little bangs. Their total energy is equivalent to a few thousand tons of T.N.T. Of this only a small part passes into the energy of the air wave. In CGS units an atom bomb has an energy of the order of 10^{21} ergs. If all the energy went into producing an expansion by heating the air the volume of the expansion would be 1 km³ for $3 \cdot 8 \times 10^{21}$ ergs. At a distance of 1000 km the pressure pulse would have an amplitude of the order of a microbar, which is too small to be detected.

The Great Meteorite which fell in June 1908, in an unexplored part of Siberia, produced pressure oscillations in England, nearly 6000 km away, of the order of 100 microbars, which corresponds with an original expansion of the order of 1000 km³. The total energy of the meteorite must have been several times the energy put into air waves and so we can estimate it at around 10^{26} ergs. If it fell to the earth from rest at infinity its mass must have been about 10^8 tons and its radius about 150 m. But it almost certainly had a considerable orbital velocity so that its radius may have been only 50 m or less. When it fell a forest was desolated, and the flash outshone the morning sun several hundred kilometres away. An earthquake was recorded by seismographs in distant parts of the world and it was from their records that it was possible to discover where it had fallen. By the time an expedition sent by the Russian government found the place fourteen years later the details of the event were enshrined only in the memories of a few hunters and woodcutters who had no idea what had really happened.

Hydrogen bombs produce waves of from about a tenth to half the size of that produced by the Great Meteorite, but the earthquake is much smaller. In Japan the waves from hydrogen bombs have often been recorded, and the approximate position of the explosion can often be found by comparing the times at which the waves reach various stations. They are usually big bangs, their energy being of the order of a thousand times that of an atom bomb, and having an explosion volume of several hundred cubic kilometres.

The eruption of Krakatoa produced barographic oscillations of the order of a millibar or two a few thousand kilometres away. The wave was traced to the antipodes near Bogota and back to Krakatoa, whence it was radiated again back to the antipodes. By studying barographs throughout the world the wave was seen to travel to and fro across the world at least twice before becoming too small to be detected. The original explosion created a volume of the order of ten thousand cubic kilometres.

(e) The nature of bangs and aeroclysms

In order to calculate the magnitudes given here some assumption is necessary about how the explosion occurs. The easiest assumption to make is that the sudden creation of a mountain would produce the same effect. Mathematically this is expressed by saying that the ground has a large upward velocity for a short time. A portion of the atmosphere is suddenly accelerated upwards and a wave travels out horizontally as a mixture of a pressure wave produced by the compression of the lower layers of air and a gravity wave produced by lifting a portion of the atmosphere so that it drains away outwards off the mountain that has been created.

Meteorites and bombs presumably produce single explosions but Krakatoa continued to produce a series of terrific bangs culminating after about seven hours in a paroxysmal contusion which pushed the barometer of the Batavia gas holder off its scale.

After an explosion a rarefaction is induced at the source because the air has been given an outward momentum all round. The pressure therefore continues to oscillate with rapidly decreasing amplitude for a few seconds or minutes. The same phenomenon can be seen when a stone is thrown into a pond and the water at the point of impact continues to oscillate up and down after the splash has settled and the stone has sunk. The computations referred to in the next article do not make proper allowance for this phenomenon, and therefore predict a very much simpler pulse form at points whose distance from the source is such that the time taken for the pressure pulse to reach them is the same order of magnitude as the time for which oscillations continue at the source.

(f) *Dispersion of pulses*

A train of waves consisting of many repeated identical oscillations can be propagated without change of form, but if there are only a few oscillations the end ones spread into the air beyond the ends of the train. A train of waves cannot begin abruptly but there must be a gradual surge which starts when waves travelling with the greatest possible speed for any waves first arrive from the source at the point of observation. The ' pulse ' finishes when the waves travelling at the slowest possible speed for any waves pass the point after leaving the source when the explosion ended.

A pulse of finite length can be regarded, according to Fourier's theorem, as compounded of waves of a variety of lengths superimposed in such a way that they are in ordered phase in the neighbourhood of the pulse but outside its limits their phase is such that they annul one another and produce nothing. Each component train may be thought of as extending to infinity in both directions beyond the limits of the pulse. As the various components travel with their different speeds their phase relationship alters and this leads to the appearance of oscillations outside the original limit of the pulse where they had previously cancelled out. This extension of a solitary pulse into a series of waves is called dispersion.

In most media waves of long period or great length travel faster than waves of short period or small length so that a pulse which began as a disturbance lasting perhaps a fraction of a second may, by the time it had travelled several thousand kilometres, be spread out into a series of oscillations lasting several minutes.

In some media waves have a minimum speed, regardless of their length, and then the pulse terminates when these waves have passed by. In the atmosphere the longest waves produced by big bangs travel about $1\frac{1}{2}$ per cent faster than the shortest so that the duration of the pulse is about $1\frac{1}{2}$ per cent of the time taken for the pulse to get from the source to the point of observation.

These waves travel in a kind of wave guide formed by the lower atmosphere—in this case the troposphere, with the stratosphere acting as a lid. Waves of length less than about 40 km (and period 2 minutes) are not trapped in this layer but escape into the upper atmosphere. Some of these are reflected at heights above 30 km, and it is these which can be *heard* beyond the silent zone round an explosion (see page 219). It is a very complicated business to take account of these, wherefore they have so far been ignored in computations of the form of pulses at various distances. Most of the energy goes not into audible waves, but into the gravity waves of long period. In the records

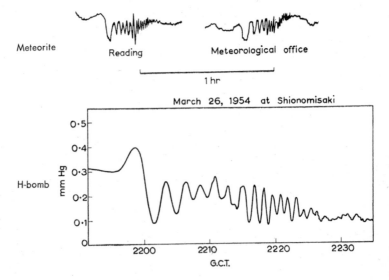

of the oscillations produced by the Great Meteorite and nuclear bomb shown here some of the higher frequency waves can be seen towards the end of the pulses. The wave observed is a combination of a whole spectrum in which the phase relationship of one component to another is continually changing, producing new crests within the pulse all the time.

The figure below shows the changes to be expected in an aeroclysmic pulse which traversed the globe, assuming that it started as a single outward surge. The amplitude decreases as the

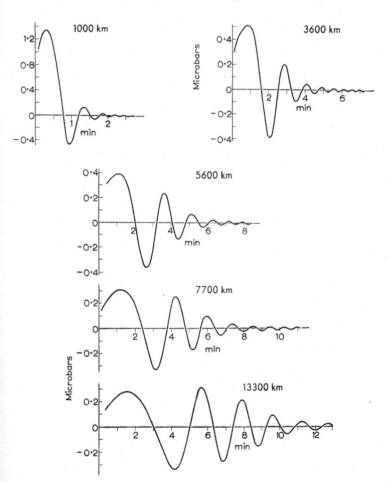

energy of the pulse is spread over an increasing distance, and over a wider wave front. After the ' equator ' has been passed and the antipodes is approached, the amplitude increases a little because the radius of the ring on which the wave lies is contracting although the pulse is still extending in the direction of propagation. It was assumed that there was no dissipation of the energy of the wave and that it was not distorted in any way by the wind. Since the wind speeds are greater than the difference in speed between the long and the short waves they could alter the dispersion considerably. Since the amplitude of the wave varies with height in a different way for different wavelengths, if there is a considerable wind shear the dispersive character of the airstream will be altered. Waves whose maximum amplitude is at the level of strongest wind will be propagated more rapidly than those whose maximum amplitude is at a level of light wind.

The wave from Charlie's pop gun must be propagated in the same way as those from an aeroclysm, but we differentiate between them only according to how far away the amplitude of the waves is important, detectable, or significant. When Johnny does the high jump in England, the weight of everyone in New Zealand is momentarily increased as he leaps into the air, and everyone in the Americas is caused to lean over sideways a little. But we do not bother about these things for rather obvious reasons. In all discussions of natural phenomena we have to decide what is important and worth considering and what can be ignored, and when we do this we find that Krakatoa's debut as an aeroclysm is essentially different from Charlie's pop gun. Mathematically the difference is that although we could start discussing the two phenomena by means of the same equations, different terms would be dominant. As soon as we have simplified them to make solution of them possible they become different.

Tidal waves; the theory of resonance

The periods of the oscillations discussed so far have been of the order of a few minutes. Atmospheric tides have a period of 12 hours, so that during one oscillation there is time for the earth's rotation to have significant effect, which is not true of explosion waves. The tidal wave is interesting because its period is *exactly* 12 hours. Oceanic tides have a period of half a *lunar* day, and they are mainly due to the gravitational field of the moon. It has been shown, first by Pekeris, and later by Wilkes and Weekes, that a tidal wave, with its two crests on diametrically opposed lines of longitude, travels round the earth in exactly 24 hours, which means that its position on the earth relative to the sun is always the same. The wave is therefore amplified by resonance and is much greater than the ' equilibrium tide ' which is what would be produced if the speed of travel of waves bore no simple relationship to the speed of travel of the force producing the tide.

It is not our present purpose to discuss the nature of the phenomenon of resonance, but to note how remarkable it is that the length of the solar day should be equal to the natural period of tides travelling round the earth with their crests on lines of longitude. This tidal period is determined solely by the dimensions of the atmosphere which can only by chance have been ' created ' in an exact relationship with the period of rotation. In no other way is there any *exact* simple connection between the amount of gas in the atmosphere and a dimension of the solid earth. The question arises, therefore, whether resonance should be regarded as a gigantic fluke of creation, or whether Nature has contrived this coincidence.

A clue to the answer is provided by the moon, for she rotates so as to keep the same side always turned towards the earth. This is because the gravitational field of the earth produced tides in the solid moon and in the oceans of dust which cover its surface. There was such great friction in these tides that they were dragged ahead of the gravitational forces producing them by the moon's rotation, and the rotation was thereby slowed down. Consequently today high tide is always in the same places on the moon, namely at the point where the earth is in the zenith and at the antipodes of that point.

The tide in the earth's atmosphere (as is argued on page 278) is almost certainly produced by the diurnal variations in the heating by the sun, but the tide itself is subjected to gravitational forces. Therefore if there were no resonance the frictional drag would cause the tide to be carried ahead of the sun by the rotating earth and the gravitational forces would slow the earth down. Holmberg suggested that this did in fact happen until the speed of rotation was exactly equal to the speed of travel of the tide in the opposite direction relative to the sun. The amplitude would then build up on account of resonance and the gravitational force would then only apply a turning moment on the atmosphere if the rotation began to decrease, and then it would be so as to speed up the rotation. According to his theory, then, the earth's rotation decreased slowly under tidal friction, mainly in the ocean, but that now a large tide, produced thermally and by resonance, exists in the atmosphere. The energy of rotation dissipated in the oceans is replenished in the atmosphere, and the winds keep the solid earth rotating at a constant speed by dragging it round.

This attractive, indeed irresistible, theory implies some interesting consequences. It may be that a planet is only habitable if there exists a sufficiently short day for intolerable extremes of temperature not to be produced, and that because of tidal friction in the ocean it can only be kept rotating at a great enough speed if tidal resonance exists in the atmosphere. Perhaps we have been spared through tidal resonance the fate of Venus who, it is thought, always turns the same face to the sun and suffers storms so queer as to be beyond our imagination. Mars rotates at very nearly the same speed as the earth. If we assume that there also there is tidal resonance some important features of the atmosphere may be deduced. The same theme might be applied to other planets.

We could only argue thiswise through a firm belief that Nature does not do things by fluke and that inexplicable coincidences do not happen. Immediately the question arises whether, on experiencing a strange coincidence in our own lives, we should seek to explain it by supposing the existence of some influence outside the ken of ordinary science, whether it be supernatural or telepathic in form. Surely we must be consistent in our approach to strange things! Yet to seek an explanation is not the same as to decide to have one at all costs, and we must be ready to leave coincidences unexplained if necessary. At the same time we must not suppose that a coincidence of inanimate Nature is of the same kind as a coincidence in individual human lives. Problems of precognition and the like involve subjective judgements as to what is a coincidence, and it is often easier for us to laugh off other people's experiences than our own because we are the centres of our own universes. Therefore having found

PLATE 15. The upper left picture shows the plume seen in Plate 7 (upper) when the air is unstable and convection cloud is present. The plume initiates its own thermals which form cumulus clouds, one of which can be seen. The picture on the right shows how wind variations across a cement works chimney can cause part of the plume to be disposed nearly vertically. This vertical part then becomes a thermal. In the lower pictures are two views of a pottery kiln plume breaking up into thermals which grow in proportion to their height as they pass downwind. (*See* page 215)

PLATE 16. When the emission veloc
is low puffing may occur at the orif
when cool air sinks periodically i
the mouth of the chimney on the w
wind side, and the smoke emerges
puffs. (*See* page 216) (*Courtesy
Hulton Picture Library*)

PLATE 17. The air above these growing cumulus clouds is made to rise enough to produce a
smooth cloud which the cumulus thermals can be seen to be penetrating. (*See* page 253)

an explanation for tidal resonance on the earth we must assume that the mechanism has operated upon our earth not by fluke but because something very like it often happens on other planets.

We need not believe that the rest of the universe is made in the image of our earth, but we must not believe that our earth has been constructed in any special way. If God did not create man in his own image, in whose image did he choose to create him and the beings which may inhabit other planets? This question is different from our scientific one because scientists are concerned only with Creation, not with the Creator.

Mountain waves

We saw on page 66 that when air flowed down the lee slope of a mountain it could be expected to undergo several oscillations over the flat ground before resuming horizontal flow.

The theory of waves in airstreams flowing over mountains is outside the scope of this book: it will be necessary, as in the earlier part of this chapter, simply to state many of the proven results.

Stationary clouds through which the air appears to pass have long been noticed, and they have often been attributed to the existence of waves in the streamlines induced by mountains below. Some doubt had been expressed about mother of pearl clouds which are at a height of the order of 30 km because, although they often looked very like clouds over mountains it was not understood how the effect of a mountain only 2 or 3 km high could extend to such a height when experiments in wind tunnels and over buildings were thought to indicate that the presence of an obstacle would scarcely be noticeable at more than 2 or 3 times its height.

(a) Lee waves

Exploration by glider pilots in the late 1930's showed that there were large areas in the neighbourhood of mountains where the flow was inclined at between 10° and 20° to the horizontal, providing, where the flow was up, places where they could soar to the neighbourhood of 10,000 m above the ground. It was also noticed that often there was a very marked inversion of temperature (a shallow layer in which the temperature increases upwards) just above the clouds and that the strongest upcurrents

were not over the wind-facing slope of the mountain but often a
few kilometres downwind of the lee slope. An analogy was
therefore drawn by Küttner with the phenomenon of lee waves
on a stream of water which had been explained by Kelvin and
Rayleigh. A train of waves is often found in the lee of any
constriction in a stream such as a submerged weir or a board
dipped in the surface. The length of the waves is such that their
speed in the upstream direction relative to the water is equal to
the speed of the water in the downstream direction. They are
therefore stationary relative to the constriction. A case is
illustrated in the figure below, in which the obstacle extends
across the width of the stream. A similar system of waves is to
be seen behind a barge which occupies a substantial fraction of
the width of a canal: in that case the waves are stationary relative
to the barge and the water ahead of the barge is moving towards
the barge relative to the bank.

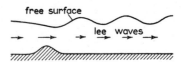

When a boat moves over the surface of water the system of
lee waves is confined within a V-shaped region with the boat at
the apex, and the amplitude of the waves decreases with distance
from the boat. A similar pattern of waves is formed in the
atmosphere over an isolated mountain peak. But most of this
discussion will be about the two-dimensional case of flow over
long mountain ridges which lie, possibly at an angle, across the
airstream, because the lee waves decrease more slowly in amplitude
downwind, and the amplitude of the waves in the upper air is
much greater than over isolated hills so that the phenomena are
more important and striking.

In 1943 Lyra put forward a theory for waves in an airstream
which had a uniform stability and velocity up to infinity. It was
demonstrated that there could be waves of the form similar to
those shown in the figure below. The notable characteristics are
that there is more than one wave crest on each streamline although
there is only one on the ground, that they have an amplitude which
increases upwards, and that they decrease in amplitude downstream. Similar patterns were computed four years later by Queney

making slight modifications for the effect of the earth's rotation. (This has little effect except over wide mountain ranges which it takes the air a substantial fraction of a day to traverse.) But Queney also showed that for ordinary sized mountains which did not have steep sides the second and subsequent waves had a very small amplitude and that a pattern more like that shown in the right hand diagram was more likely.

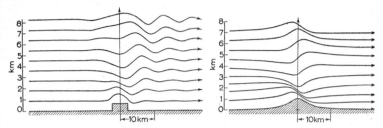

The main difference between Lyra's solution and the lee waves observed was that those observed appeared to have a maximum amplitude at a height of 2 or 3 km above which they died away. There was thus on most occasions a very marked upper limit to the height which gliders could reach in the upsloping side of a wave. This limit appeared to be not far above the level of the inversion, when an inversion was present. Küttner's analogy therefore still seemed to be the best explanation of the most remarkable instances yet observed.

(b) The conditions for lee waves

The problem then posed was to specify *all* the possible conditions under which trains of lee waves could be found in an airstream, and what kind of mountains would set them up. *The wave length is a characteristic of the airstream* because it is simply the length of those waves which remain stationary in a moving stream: in general longer waves would move upstream and shorter ones, whose velocity relative to the fluid was less, would be carried away downstream. The amplitude of the waves results from the properties of the airstream combined with the mountain shape.

The essence of the next step was to regard the waves of the type discovered by Lyra as unrealistic and to seek for waves which had a maximum amplitude in the troposphere at a height between 1 and 6 km, above which their amplitude decreased gradually towards zero at great heights.

The *static stability* may be defined as the restoring force to which unit mass is subjected when displaced unit distance vertically in the surroundings. If the displacement is adiabatic, which almost all theories have assumed to be the case, the potential temperature θ is unchanged in the displacement (see page 171), and the density is proportional to $1/\theta$. The force per unit mass whose temperature differs by $\Delta\theta$ from the surroundings, on being displaced a distance Δz is

$$\theta g \Delta(1/\theta)$$

or

$$-\frac{1}{\theta} g \frac{\Delta\theta}{\Delta z}$$

for unit distance. This is negative because it is in the opposite direction to Δz. This quantity, $g \partial\theta/\theta \partial z$, is denoted by $g\beta$. The quantity β is usually referred to as the static stability, though it is always multiplied by g when it appears in the context of a stability force.

In addition to the static stability the only other quantity which could influence the lee wave length is the wind speed, U, in the direction across the mountain. The wavelength must therefore be determined solely by $g\beta$ and U and their variations with height. Thus, if the wavelength is $2\pi/k$,

$$k = F\left(g\beta,\ U,\ \frac{\partial\beta}{\partial z},\ \frac{\partial U}{\partial z},\ \frac{\partial^2\beta}{\partial z},\ \frac{\partial^2 U}{\partial z^2}, \ldots \ldots\right)$$

where F is a function to be discovered.

It is possible that the wavelength might be influenced by the amplitude of the waves. This problem has not been more than superficially investigated on account of its complexity, but it seems that unless the amplitude is such that the streamlines are very steeply inclined to the horizontal it has only a small effect on the wavelength.

When there are inversions present $\partial\beta/\partial z$ is very large at levels where the lapse rate changes sharply, and β is very large at the same or neighbouring levels. The problem is then best treated on the assumption that there is a discontinuity of temperature at the level of the inversion, and the amount of the discontinuity is represented by ϵ, or $\Delta\theta/\theta$, where $\Delta\theta$ is the discontinuity of temperature. ϵ is the fractional change in the density, and when $\epsilon = 1$ per cent the discontinuity is about $3°$ C. If we replace gradients by discontinuities then the depths of the layers between discontinuities also serve, in part, to determine the wavelength, and

$$k = F(g\beta, U, \epsilon_1, h_1, \epsilon_2, h_2, \ldots \ldots)$$

according to how many discontinuities $\epsilon_1, \epsilon_2, \ldots$ there are with layers of depth $h_1, h_2, \ldots$ between them. In addition we might have a series of different values of β for the different layers.

Evidently there is a great variety of possible conditions under which there might be waves because so many factors can be varied. Therefore setting aside the possibility of inversions for the moment, for they are known often to make waves possible, we may examine the simplest other possible case.

We have required that there shall be certain conditions upon the amplitude of the wave as a function of height. If we set up an equation for the variation with height of the amplitude, the wavelength can be expected to occur in coefficients in this equation allied with other terms of similar dimensions composed from the features of the airstream. These other terms must be the quantities we need to study. The simplest quantities whose dimensions are the same as k are $(g\beta)^{\frac{1}{2}}/U$ and $(\partial^2 U/U\partial z^2)^{\frac{1}{2}}$ which we usually denote by $(U''/U)^{\frac{1}{2}}$. Thus we can say that in the simplest airstreams k is determined by the distribution of these quantities with height. The equation (which we shall not derive) in this simplest case is

$$\frac{\partial^2 w}{\partial z^2} + \left(\frac{g\beta}{U^2} - \frac{U''}{U} - k^2\right) w = 0$$

This gives the variation with z of the vertical velocity w, assuming that it varies sinusoidally, i.e. like $\sin kx$, in the horizontal direction.

Because k depends on the variation with height of the quantity $g\beta/U^2 - U''/U$, which we denote by l^2 (l being next after k in the alphabet), there must be an infinite variety of profiles of l^2 which make waves possible. We shall have to be content here, therefore, to deduce one fundamental result which indicates the magnitude of the wavelength.

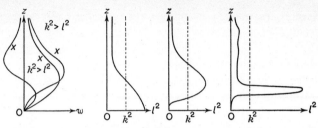

In the equation above $\partial^2 w/\partial z^2$ is a measure of the curvature of the profile of w as a function of height, as shown in the figure. We know that w is zero at the ground because the ground is horizontal. If it is zero at any other height also the following argument applies equally to the layers above the uppermost level at which w is zero. If we suppose that there are no discontinuities in l or w as functions of height then there will be none in $\partial^2 w/\partial z^2$. In all the cases illustrated in the figure $\partial^2 w/\partial z^2$ has the same sign as w on the part of the curve above X (the point of inflexion) where it approaches zero as z increases. Below X there must be a layer in which the curvature is in the opposite direction and so $\partial^2 w/\partial z^2$ has the opposite sign to w. *Therefore from the equation we see that above X, $k^2 > l^2$; below X, $k^2 < l^2$.* In order for there to be waves there must be a deep layer at the top in which $k^2 > l^2$, and below this there must be a layer, of sufficient depth for the curve to turn back to the origin, in which $k^2 < l^2$. The profile of l^2 could therefore be like one of those in the right hand diagrams. The corresponding values of k are also approximately shown. Obviously there exists a great variety of l^2 profiles which will give waves.

It has been found useful in practice to inspect the l^2 profile obtained from radio soundings in estimating the likelihood of waves.

The amplitude of the waves depends on the mountain shape. If it conforms to the shape of a wave the amplitude is much greater than if the mountain is several wavelengths wide or only a fraction of a wavelength in width. This is akin to the phenomenon of resonance, for if the different parts of the mountain make contributions which are in phase with one another the total effect is greater.

(c) Model airstreams and mountains

The chief difficulty in calculating the form of the airflow over and in the lee of actual mountains is the complexity of the problem. Neither the mountain shape nor the profile of the velocity or stability of the airstream is readily represented by simple mathematical functions. We may alternatively regard the problem as follows: it is possible to construct a number of non-dimensional numbers from the data of the problem and the solutions must vary as each one of these numbers varies. If there were only one such number we could express the answer by saying how the form of the flow varied as this number varied. If there are three such numbers the variations have to be represented in three dimensions. Such possible numbers are $g\beta/k^2U^2$, $g\beta h^2/U^2$ (where h is the depth of a layer or the depth of air below the point X in the figure opposite), H/h (where H is the height of the mountain), for very simple airstreams. If we allow inversions to be included we have many more possible numbers. We therefore try to describe the different kinds of flow and effects that can occur by making complete calculations in several simple, but different, cases. We have to be sure that the characteristics displayed are not due to the simplicity of the case chosen and are still present in the most complicated cases, and that the important characteristics which can be found in the complicated cases are present in one or more of the simple cases. Some aspects of the complicated cases can be calculated with the aid of a modern computing machine, and it may be very useful as part of a weather forecasting procedure to determine some of the properties of each day's airstream: but these properties are not essentially new and their nature can generally be illustrated by much simpler cases which can be worked out without such modern aids.

The diagrams which follow are of particular cases devised to illustrate the points mentioned. General cases *cannot* be displayed in this way, but the features of these particular cases are very common. In hilly country, not necessarily mountainous, waves can be seen in the cloud forms in temperate latitudes in about one day in three, and probably exist, but can only be detected in special ways, such as by gliders or radiosonde balloons, on two days in three. The airstreams in the neighbourhood of frontal depressions are, more often than not, suitable for the formation of trains of waves in the lee of hills, such as are shown in the diagrams.

(i) In this model the airstream is supposed to consist of two layers in each of which l^2 is constant. The bottom layer is contrived so that there are nevertheless variations in U and β and there are no discontinuities of U or of T at any level.

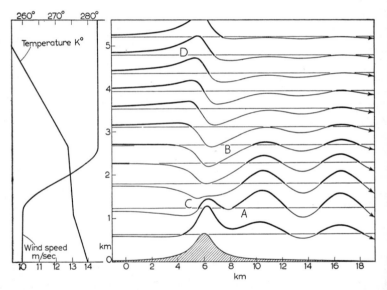

When the air has reached the second lee wave the disturbance which can be seen at higher levels immediately above the mountain ridge has died out. The lee waves have a maximum amplitude in the bottom layer at a height of about $1\frac{1}{2}$ km. The streamlines shown in the diagram are thickened where the air is above its original level in the undisturbed stream far upwind, which is shown by the thin horizontal line. Clouds can be expected where the air is displaced upwards and holes in cloud layers where it is displaced downwards. At a height of 5 km, therefore, it would be possible for an extensive layer of cloud to have a *lee* edge over the mountain crest, and for the sky to be clear downwind of the mountain at that altitude. At $1\frac{1}{2}$ km there would probably be a wave cloud over the mountain and another in each succeeding lee wave crest.

It would be possible for a glider towed into a position in the upsloping side of the first lee wave (A) to soar to B and then to C without entering a downcurrent on the way. But a pilot could not soar from C into the upslope side of the wave at D.

(ii) This case is a three layer model, the bottom layer being $\frac{1}{2}$ km thick and having no stability (adiabatic lapse rate), but the characteristics to be described which differ from the previous case cannot be ascribed to the presence of this layer. The layer is included in order to present a more realistic case. The airstream has the same natural wavelength (2π km) as in the previous instance.

There is a very strong wind down the lee slope of the mountain. A glider pilot towed to position A could soar up to position D in upcurrent all the way, but could not

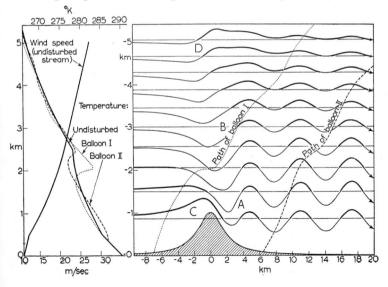

get to position C without passing through a downcurrent. At a height of 5 km there could be an extensive sheet of cloud with its *front* edge over the mountain crest, the cloud extending several kilometres downwind.   At $1\frac{1}{2}$ km a sheet of cloud would have its lee edge over the mountain and its thickest portion in front of the mountain.   There would again possibly be wave clouds in the crests of the waves.

We have imagined that two radiosonde balloons are released into this airstream in such a way that they pass through the waves.   In the wave troughs the air has been displaced downwards and so, on account of its stability, is warmer than in the crests where it has been displaced upwards.   According to the position of the balloon the temperature recorded at a given height may vary.   The tracks of the balloons are shown, assuming that they have a constant rate of ascent relative to the air, and in the left part of the diagram are shown the temperature soundings that would be obtained from them.   Both soundings show fictitious inversions which are not present in the undis-turbed airstream, and which would not appear in a sounding made vertically over any point.

Where the balloons are in downcurrents they travel along more nearly horizontal tracks: in upcurrents they ascend more steeply.   Such variations in vertical velocity are commonly observed in the records of radiosonde balloons.

(iii) The effect of inversions is illustrated by comparing air-streams which all have the same top layer and the same natural lee wave length as in the previous two cases.   It is assumed that they all pass over the same ridge, and the diagram shows the variation with height of the amplitude of the lee waves.   It is similar to the left hand diagram on page 234.   In all cases the value of l^2 in the upper layer is $0{\cdot}75$ km^{-2}.   The value of l^2 in the lowest 2 km is written against the various curves.   In case 2 the lowest 2 km have the same value of l^2 throughout ($2{\cdot}04$ km^{-2}).   If we now go to case 3 (in which the vertical axis has been shifted to the right so as to separate the curves which are all zero at the ground) we see that if there is a 1 per cent discontinuity of density (an inversion of $2\frac{1}{2}$–3° C) at a height of 2 km, it is not necessary to have so much stability in the lowest 2 km in order to have the same natural lee wavelength. Accordingly the value of l^2 in the lower layer is only 1·79 km^{-2}, and the curvature of the line is reduced. The altitude at which the wave amplitude is a maximum is displaced upwards from about 1·6 km to 2 km.

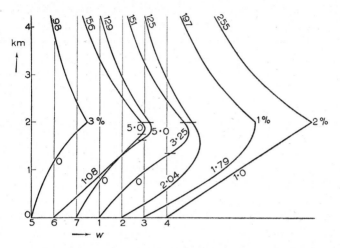

In case 4 we have a 2 per cent inversion (corresponding to a discontinuity of temperature of around 5–6° C) and now l^2 is reduced to 1 km^{-2} in the lowest layer and is equal to k^2. Accordingly the curvature of the w profile is reduced to zero and there is a sharp maximum in the wave amplitude at the inversion.

When the inversion is 3 per cent, as in case 5, it is not necessary to have any stability in the lower layer at all ($l^2 = 0$) in order to have waves of the same length, and the amplitude has a very sharp maximum at the inversion.

A sharp inversion is somewhat of a mathematical fiction and we can see what its effect really is by replacing the infinitesimally thin layer of infinite stability by a shallow one of large stability as in case 6. Here there is a layer $\frac{1}{4}$ km deep in which $l^2 = 5$ km^{-2}, which is an inversion layer of finite thickness, not a discontinuity of temperature. We then find that there is a sharp maximum of wave amplitude in this thin layer. In the lowest $1\frac{3}{4}$ km $l^2 = 1\cdot08$ km^{-2} and so this layer of finite thickness is equivalent roughly to the 2 per cent inversion of case 3, below which $l^2 = 1$ km^{-2}.

To discover what is approximately equivalent to a 3 per cent inversion cases 7 and 1 have been chosen for comparison with the other cases. In case 7 we have a layer $0\cdot37$ km deep in which $l^2 = 5\cdot0$ km^{-2} with a layer in which $l^2 = 0$ below, and in case 1 a deeper layer $0\cdot65$ km thick in which $l^2 = 3\cdot25$ km^{-2} only. Case 2 is then the next in the series having a still deeper layer 2 km in depth in which l^2 is reduced now to $2\cdot04$ km^{-2}, and the layer below has vanished.

In all these cases the maximum amplitude is in (or at) the layer of largest stability because it is in this layer that the curvature of the amplitude profile (shown in the last figure) has the sign required at the maximum ($l^2 > k^2$). We see that inversions, which may be convenient for computation purposes, produce effects similar to shallow layers of large stability.

The amplitude is inscribed (in arbitrary units) against the top of each curve in the figure. This makes a comparison between the seven different airstreams, which all have the same natural lee wavelength, when they pass over the same mountain. There is a variation by a factor of about $2\cdot5$ between the extreme cases 4 and 5, but because we have been able to deal only with particular cases we cannot draw any general conclusion, from these cases at any rate, about what kind of airstream will have the largest amplitude waves excited in it.

It is important to note that we have arbitrarily chosen to compare airstreams which all have the same lee wavelength of 2π km, and which have the same upper layer. We could make an infinite variety of other comparisons between different airstreams; indeed there is infinite scope for a research student who likes computing to exercise his skill in working out the characteristics of more airstreams. If he is short of a problem he can safely rely on finding something interesting in such work.

(d) Waves produced by isolated hills

Because each hill produces its own lee wave train, which is added to or nullified by other hills which the air passes over, it is useful to have some idea of what region is affected by an isolated hill. A long ridge lying across the airstream may in suitable airstreams produce waves at all heights up to which the airstream has a component of velocity across the ridge. The greatest height for which we have evidence of waves is around 30 km, where mother of pearl clouds are occasionally seen. (Noctilucent clouds at 80 km do not look like wave clouds.) Cloud forms at 8–10 km very commonly show evidence of waves at that level due to quite modest mountains only a few hundred metres high. But isolated almost circular hills produce disturbances which tend to decrease like $z^{-\frac{1}{2}}$ above heights of 2 or 3 km, whereas the disturbance over a long ridge contains no such factor.

In the direction directly downstream from the crest of an isolated hill the amplitude of the lee waves decreases like $r^{-\frac{1}{2}}$, where r is the distance downstream. Behind a long ridge there is no decrease in amplitude of the lee waves, and they may extend for as many as 100 wavelengths over the sea where there are no other mountains to interfere.

Finally, the lee wave system of an isolated hill is confined within a wedge shaped region with the sharp edge of the wedge placed vertically through the hill crest. This is rather like the wash of a ship on water which is confined within a region subtending an angle* of $19\frac{1}{2}°$ at the ship on deep water. The angle varies with the depth of the water, and in the atmosphere the angle of the wedge containing the lee wave system also varies. It is of the order of 12–15° for typical airstreams, but when there are sharp inversions at a low level, or very stable shallow layers near the ground the angle may be as much as 35–40°.

The figure shows the streamlines in a particularly simple two layer airstream behind the crest of an isolated circular hill whose cross section is also shown. The dashed lines indicate for comparison the outline of the section of a long ridge and of the waves which it produces. Also shown in dotted lines are two per-

---

* The angles given here are *half* the total angles at the apex. It is most convenient to define the angle of a cone or wedge as the angle between the line of symmetry and a line on the boundary.

pendicular sections of an oval hill which produces the same waves in the central plane downwind of its crest as the circular one. The steeper sided section of this oval hill lies in the plane of the wind, the other in a vertical plane at right angles.

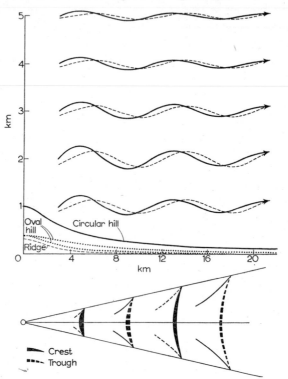

For both the isolated hills the lee wave system lies within the wedge indicated in plan below, and the wave amplitude falls off to zero at the edge of the wedge. This is indicated for the circular hill by the width of the lines, which is proportional to the amplitude of the crest or trough. Out of the central plane the waves produced by the oval hill are of smaller amplitude than those produced by the circular one. The waves that do not lie across the central vertical plane downwind from the hill crest are of very small amplitude. In the case of a boat these may be the largest amplitude part of the disturbance, but a mountain produces nothing analogous to the bow wave of a boat.

(e) Production of shearing layers

If the wave amplitude varies from one altitude to another the horizontal wind is subjected also to variations and these vary with height over a point on the ground if the amplitude profile is curved. This is shown in the figure below. Shear may be produced over a mountain in an airstream that did not possess any on the plain. If the undisturbed airstream possesses shear, the shear due to the waves is added vectorially. Consequently the direction of shear over mountains may vary right round the compass if the mountains are complicated in shape. Billow clouds, which are normally formed lying across the direction of shear (see page 154) may be oriented in almost any direction. Often the billows are produced when cloud is formed in the crest of a wave, the formation of cloud making the air unstable (see page 259), and the direction of the shear they indicate may be different from the direction of the shear in the undisturbed stream. Two directions may sometimes be indicated in one patch of cloud which has passed through a wave over a mountain and been subjected to shear in two different directions on the two sides of the wave.

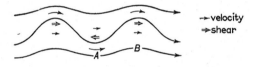

Occasionally glider pilots have encountered turbulent layers in clear air in waves over mountains. In some cases they have been able to observe large shear as they have passed up or down through the layer, because if the glider is facing into the wind it may be almost motionless relative to the ground and changes in wind produce changing motion of the glider relative to conspicuous objects on the ground. In those cases in which there is no cloud the air cannot have been statically unstable and so one seeks for a mechanism which would produce a smaller, though positive, Richardson number in the wave than in the undisturbed airstream.

It can be shown that in shallow layers in which the shear is very large, if the motion in a wave is adiabatic, the magnitude of the shear produced by the wave is inversely proportional to the velocity. Thus where the velocity is reduced on account of the wave motion the shear is increased because the slower moving air is retarded more than the faster moving air above it (or below it, as the case may be). Where the velocity is increased in the wave the shear is decreased. Thus if in the figure above there were a sharp shear along the lowest streamline shown, that shear would be reduced at A and increased at B.

At sharp inversions also large shear is generated, and it is proportional to the magnitude of the temperature ' discontinuity ', and to the amplitude of the wave. Since $Ri \propto (\text{shear})^{-2}$, the Richardson number will be changed most where it is large on account of large β. The smallest values will be found in the waves where the most stable inversions were present in the undisturbed airstream, if the waves are of sufficiently large amplitude. Such an argument, used to predict the occurrence of turbulence at inversions in waves of large amplitude is necessarily very tentative because we have no satisfactory criterion for predicting the onset turbulence from the Richardson number. The observation that inversions have been found in the neighbourhood of clear air turbulence may simply mean that there is present a mechanism, such as an indirect circulation induced by the large scale motion (or even the turbulence itself), which reduces the static stability in the layer below the inversion and that it is in the less stable layer that the turbulence is (or has been) produced.

By the simple theory of gravity waves the shear is easily computed, but any subsequent consequences of the shear are at present a matter of guesswork and mainly qualitative argument. But it must be noted that if turbulence occurs then automatically ' discontinuities ' of temperature and velocity will be produced at the top and bottom of the stirred layer if the original airstream is stably stratified and shearing.

(f) Separation

When the flow separates from the ground the upper layers of air move as if the ground had the shape of the streamline which leaves the ground. Since an airstream in wave motion possesses more kinetic energy than if there were no wave disturbance, the streamline leaving the ground will be induced to assume a shape which does not produce waves aloft. On this account waves often disappear by day because the flow up a lee slope heated in the sunshine produces separation near the top of the slope (see page 109). By night the *katabatic* flow down the cold slope often prevents separation and produces lee waves as a result. Lee waves are induced in such a way that they increase the velocity down the lee slope (dotted lines in the figure below), and so what begins as, and appears to be, an ordinary *katabatic* wind may develop into a gale down the lee slope as the waves grow in amplitude. It is then transformed from a shallow effect close to the surface into a dynamical property of the whole airstream.

When there are no lee waves the flow opens out over the lee slope and there may be an eddy formed there (continuous lines in figure below), but when lee waves form the eddy is removed and may reappear under the crest of the first lee wave (dotted lines) where the flow is being retarded.

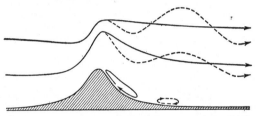

Conversely we may argue that airstreams in which lee waves can occur are less liable to separation on a given mountain lee slope than those in which they cannot occur.

When separation occurs the question arises of where the flow returns to the surface, as of course it must do at some point. In steep sided valleys the separation may occur at a salient edge and the flow may either rejoin a few metres away or may extend across the valley. The former is more likely if the airstream can

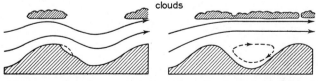

clouds

contain waves for the causes just described, and if there is any cloud the shape of the flow may be made visible by thickening of cloud in wave crests and clear holes in the wave troughs. If the

separation fills the valley there will be no evidence for the valley
in the clouds. If there is no salient edge the point of separation
may vary over a distance of 1–200 m in the course of a few minutes,
particularly if it is being induced by heating of the lee slope in
sunshine: as thermals ascend the slope the point of separation is
temporarily pushed up the hillside.

When the valley shape is complicated the flow may be very
unsteady. At one moment the eddy may fill the valley, at another
the flow may rejoin near the foot of the wind facing slope, gusting
from time to time so as to make itself visible in the movement of
trees, bracken, grass, or corn blown in the wind. When the
wind separates at a coastal cliff top the point at which it rejoins
can be seen by a ruffling of the sea similar in pattern to that
produced by downdraughts in storms on cornfields. Sir David
Brunt has offered a meteorological explanation of the Loch Ness
Monster in terms of the gusts at the point of rejoining.

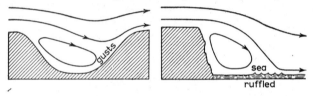

If the flow is strictly two-dimensional the air in the eddy is
never replaced and smoke in it remains there. Generally,
however, there is some motion into or out of an eddy from the
sides so that smoke generated in it does not accumulate. In
particular there may be separation from the surface of an isolated
hill without any closed eddies: the air flows round the sides,
separating at the dotted line in the figure, and up the lee slope,
the flow rejoining the surface again at the point X in the central
plane.

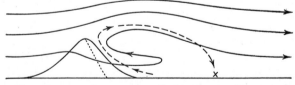

The point of separation may easily be detected by smoke or by
walking over the hillside to observe the surface wind. Besides

the form of the clouds and the motion of smoke the size of the eddy can be deduced from the sounds which can be heard. Sounds heard very clearly are generally transmitted under an inversion (as across a lake by day or across a valley in the evening) or in the direction of the wind. The reduction of the wind at the surface bends the sound rays towards the surface and increases the audibility there. If one stands just downwind of the point of separation and can hear very clearly without intermission the sounds of traffic, animals, streams, etc., in the valley bottom it is almost certain the wind is blowing all the way up the slope. But if the sounds are not much better heard on the downwind than on the upwind side of the point of separation the eddy must be small and cannot extend far towards the source of the sound.

The motion of the air far from the surface in a valley can often be deduced from the behaviour of birds who avoid the down-draughts and exploit the updraughts. Seagulls are particularly useful in this respect because they behave differently according to the configuration of the upcurrent. A group will circle in a cluster in a thermal rising from a warm patch on the valley bottom or hillside, but will soar in straight lines and more widely separated from each other when exploiting the steady upslope flow in an eddy. The two forms of behaviour may be combined in a

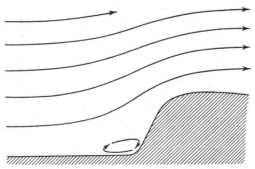

curious manner when there are thermals passing up a lee slope from the top of which separation is taking place. Having ascended to the top of the eddy they may even glide upwind and use the upslope wind on the windward side of the mountain. The rarity with which they have to flap is an indication of their success in exploiting the updraughts.

In addition to eddies on the lee sides of hills there may be eddies at the foot of windward facing slopes. These are called ' bolsters '. They may make the lower ledges on a cliff unsuitable for habitation by gannets because it would be difficult to land on and take off from the nests if there were a prevailing downdraught over them.

(g) Rotors

A rotor is the name given to an eddy of large dimensions which is produced in a stably stratified airstream independently of any effects of viscosity (molecular or eddy) and friction at the surface. If there is a cloud in a rotor it appears to rotate. Such eddies were first observed in the 1930's notably in the lee of some long mountain ridges in central Europe and under the Helm Bar clouds in Cumberland. Under the crests of the lee waves the surface wind was seen to be reversed, and apparently the air passed almost vertically upwards from the point of separation. In the Helm wave a glider piloted by Maclean was able to soar after being launched by winch to about 200 m in this upcurrent, which is a very unusual experience over level ground when there are no thermals. A superlative example of a rotor has been explored in the Owens valley in California: the Sierra Nevada reach to about 2500 m above the valley floor and in their lee a rotor is sometimes formed in which the air from the ground at the point of separation is carried up to about 6 km above the ground in a distance of 2 or 3 km. On one now classic occasion dust was blown up in the strong winds just upwind of the rotor and was carried in an almost vertical wall into clouds at the top of the rotor at about 5 km above the ground.

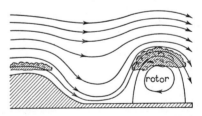

The correct explanation was first given by Long who gave a theoretical treatment of the same phenomenon in a stably stratified stream of water in the laboratory. The water was confined between two horizontal surfaces, the bottom of the tank and the free surface, and was stratified internally by increasing the concentration of salt solution towards the bottom. A model ' mountain ' was drawn along the bottom to produce the effect of a stream flowing over it.

In the theory of wave motions it is generally assumed that the surfaces in the fluid are not tilted to a very steep angle and that the wave amplitude is small. If the amplitude is increased the wave form is steepened until at one or more points the amplitude of the vertical displacement ζ satisfies the conditions

$$\frac{\partial \zeta}{\partial z} > 1 \;\; ; \;\; \zeta \frac{\partial \zeta}{\partial z} > 0$$

When this happens it means that a particle has been displaced upwards to a point *above* that to which a particle originally above it has been displaced: consequently either the wave has overturned as in the left hand figure so that the particles A and B are turned over relative to one another, or a portion of the fluid has become separated from the main stream as in the right hand figure. If we number the streamlines as shown we see that the fluid inside the rotor has been turned upside down as well as being separated from the main body. The rotor remains fixed relative to the mountain producing the wave and the rest of the airstream passes round it.

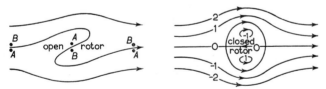

The rotor may be regarded simply as a phenomenon of large amplitude waves. The figure below shows the form taken by the lee waves in the same airstream behind three mountains whose widths are the same but whose heights are such as to produce waves with amplitudes in the ratio $\frac{1}{2} : 1 : 1\frac{1}{2}$. After passing over the smallest mountain the airstream executes waves which are almost sinusoidal, as in the simplest theory. In the middle case the rotor has just begun to appear, and the air is motionless at one point. If the amplitude is still further increased a rotor appears.   The surface wind is reversed and the air rises vertically from the point of separation.

It is particularly interesting that the most favourable conditions for rotors are those which prevent separation from the lee slope of the mountain.   The air should be very stable, with an increase

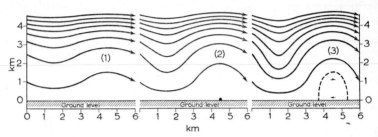

in velocity across the mountain with height, so that l^2 decreases upwards, and lee waves are possible.   Flow round the sides or ends of the mountain must be prevented otherwise the air will not flow down the steep lee slope into the valley.   It is also required, in addition to having a large steep mountain, that the wave amplitude shall increase rapidly with height.   It will be seen by inspection of the figure on page 239 that of the seven airstreams considered in that article Nos. 2 and 3 will produce rotors at the ground first, while Nos. 1, 5 and 7, will first produce them just below the inversion (or stable layer) as the amplitude is increased.   In these cases the flow might appear in the form shown in the figure below, with a rotor isolated in the wave crest,

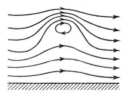

if the amplitude was not large anough to induce reversed flow at the ground.   There might be reversed flow at the ground under such a rotor in a shallow layer in which separation occurred because of friction.   The region of separation would, of course, be displaced towards the upstream side of the wave crest and rotor.

If the airstream were such that there were a nodal surface in the flow at some upper level the flow might appear as in the right hand half of the figure on page 249. Alternatively there might be rotors with their direction reversed, in the levels of an airstream in which the amplitude decreased rapidly with height, for example in wave troughs as shown in the figure below. There would then probably be no clouds visible in them to make the rotation visible. Rotors in the free air rotating in both forward and backward directions have been reported by Förchtgott in Czechoslovakia.

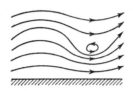

(h) Forest blowdowns

It is not surprising that, in view of the complicated nature of the flow over a hill, that forest trees are laid low by the wind, not most frequently on wind facing slopes but on the lee slopes. The great variety of actual airstreams that can exist makes the prediction of where on a particular hill a blowdown is most likely almost impossible. One must generally be guided by experience; but weather and climate are continually changing and catastrophes are by their very nature unexpected and unprepared for.

The mechanism whereby a strong local wind can be intensified on a lee slope can be understood in terms of the vorticity. If the existence of lee wave produces a strong wind which decreases upwards, a fanning out of the airflow sideways, into a widening valley for example, would stretch the vortex lines and increase the wind shear and the wind at the surface.

However, we know that the flow pattern is not always steady, and the stretching of vortex lines is likely to be most violent in unsteady conditions, and these we have been least able to discuss.

Travelling waves

Disturbances in the atmosphere are usually fixed relative to a ground feature (e.g. lee waves, heat lows) or travel with the air (e.g. depressions, cumulus clouds, billow clouds). Exceptionally waves travel through the air over the ground. We have described the waves produced by bangs and tides; these are due to influences outside the atmosphere: we are concerned now with those which can be produced within the atmosphere.

The most common mechanism is for a sudden link to be created between two airstreams moving with different velocities; the jerk applied to them is then transmitted through each as a travelling wave of the same kind as lee waves. Conditions favourable for the transmission of such waves are also present when one stream flows over the top of the other, and there is an inversion of temperature or stable layer separating them. (If there is a change in wind speed at the inversion we know from the theory of the thermal wind that it must be tilted, perhaps a few metres per kilometre.) To establish a link between them we must either have convection upwards from the lower layer into the upper by means of thermals, which is rather ineffective because the thermals grow slowly and do not apply a jerk to the upper layer, or we must have downdraughts from the upper layer into the lower.

In the case which produced the waves whose records at Abingdon are shown in the figure below, and which was studied by Pothecary, there was an outbreak of thunderstorms over the English Channel at night in the upper layer. The downdraught produced by the fallout (see page 274) applied a horizontal impulse to the lower layer which was moving with a different velocity.

If we note that waves of the lee wave type can only exist if l^2 decreases with height, and that in calculating l^2 in this case we have to measure the velocity of the air particle relative to the wave, we can see that generally the waves can only be propagated in one direction which, in this instance, was towards England. They were propagated in a kind of wave-guide, the top of which was provided by the layer with low values of l^2 (relative to the wave). In the opposite direction the waves would be dispersed upwards and would soon become of negligible intensity at the ground.

The waves that can be propagated in such a wave-guide have their wave number k within the limits of the extreme values of l^2 of the airstream, so that only a small band of wavelengths of the whole spectrum which compose the original pulse are propagated within the wave-guide. In a typical example the extreme values of the wavelengths which are thus propagated may be as close as 3 and 4 km, the waves outside those lengths being dispersed upwards and therefore decreasing in intensity away from the source. In many airstreams no such propagation is possible at

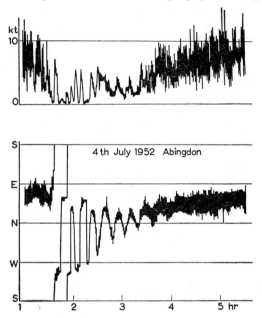

all; but unless there is a difference in velocity between two layers no pulse will be generated, and it is this difference which also serves partly to make the propagation possible.

Waves produced by thermals

The surroundings of cumulus clouds are stably stratified and are therefore set in wave motions by the thermals penetrating up through them. Clouds similar in appearance to wave clouds often appear above rising cumulus cloud towers, and sometimes they are displaced to one side by wind shear. They are called pileus (cap) clouds, and are produced in the air that is displaced upwards above the thermal. Often the thermal penetrates into them (see Plate 17) and mixes with them. When thermals and downdraughts are widespread and strong as when violent showers are occurring, clouds similar in form to pileus clouds often appear for 2 or 3 minutes when the wave motions combine, as in a choppy confused sea, to lift the air here and there enough to produce condensation.   These clouds are most often seen when the convection has carried up enough water vapour nearly to saturate the surroundings in which the cumulonimbus clouds are growing.

The heating of land surrounded by sea, or of a mountainous region in among plains also produces wave motions which are dispersed as they spread from the source region; and when cooling occurs at night, particularly on account of the evaporation of large volumes of cloud (the cooling of the ground cannot produce motion at higher levels) wave motions in the opposite sense are produced.   The sinking which occurs over mountain regions spreads out as the clouds disperse and produces up-motions over valleys which often cause clouds to appear there during the night.

Noise in nature

The rustling of the leaves on the ground or as they impinge upon one another in the trees, the thump of horses' hooves, and the splashing noise of waterfalls is due to the sudden motion of a solid or liquid surface sending out sound waves in a manner which is more efficiently displayed by the big bass drum.   A more interesting question is why do leaves on trees dance, flags flap, swans' wings whine, hedges hiss, and wires sing in the wind, when there is no impact of solid surfaces.   It is outside the scope of this book to discuss how we say ' hiss ', but we can note simply that in the unsteady motion in which eddies are released from the rear of a solid the pressure forces on the surface vary.   The effect of the changes in motion is propagated outwards from the source region with the velocity of sound and the motion of the fluid at a distance is determined by the passage of a pressure wave from the source.   The audible noise is greater when the body can move under the influence of the variations in pressure on its lee surface. Sound waves are then transmitted from the rest of its surface.

We saw in Chapter 6 that small eddies resist being stretched by larger eddies or by the mean motion.   This means that while they are being stretched the pressure within them is being reduced: this is because their rotation is being increased.   The effect of these changing pressure fields in the small eddies spreads out as pressure (sound) waves because the air is compressible. If an eddy is stretched with sufficient violence the pressure wave, which is an expansion wave associated with the increase in volume of the gas in the eddy as its pressure is lowered, may be of audible intensity, and noise is produced if the number of eddies being stretched is large. Lighthill has shown that this mechanism is largely responsible for the noise produced by a jet, in particular from the jet engine of an aircraft. On the edge of the jet the shear is very large close to the orifice and the small eddies are stretched so violently as to produce explosive pulses. To reduce the noise one has to prevent, as far as possible, the presence of the eddies, and to reduce the magnitude of the shear at the edge of the jet. This can be done by corrugating the jet pipe along the direction of motion so as to spread the shearing over a layer at least as thick as the depth of the corrugations.

We can see that the amplitude of the pressure fluctuations will be proportional to a high power of the velocity, v, of efflux of the jet in the following way. Assuming that the shearing layer and the eddies have the same linear dimensions at all efflux velocities, the time t taken to stretch an eddy will be inversely proportional to v. The volume affected by the fluctuations is proportional to c^3t^3 because ct is the radius of the sphere into which sound waves expand from a source in time t. The expansion due to the pressure decrease in the eddy is spread over this volume so that the pressure fluctuation, being inversely proportional to this volume, is proportional to v^3. The pressure gradient is the fluctuation divided by the length over which it is spread, namely ct, and so for a given initial disturbance is proportional to v^4. The velocities in the eddies are proportional to v and the pressure differences within them are therefore proportional to v^2, and the gradient of pressure experienced at a point is proportional to v^6, and the frequency of the oscillations is proportional to v. As the velocity rises the noise therefore increases in intensity and pitch. Noise becomes more unpleasant as both the intensity and frequency of reversal (pitch) of the pressure gradients to which the ear is subjected are increased. Since these are proportional to v^6 and v, the noise quickly becomes painful as the jet velocity is increased.

CHAPTER 10

CLOUDS AND FALLOUT

THERE are two ways in which water can produce motion in the atmosphere—by the exchange of latent heat when water particles are condensed or evaporated, and by the drag of water particles falling through the air.

Although water vapour constitutes less than one hundredth of the mass of an average sample of the atmosphere, the heat released by condensation of only part of the water vapour present is enough to produce temperature changes in the whole mass of the order of a few degrees. Buoyancy forces are thereby produced which are of the same order as those which can be produced in other ways. The appearance and disappearance of cloud is therefore a major cause of motion in the atmosphere.

Clouds often serve to concentrate the vapour condensed from a large volume of air into a small volume in the form of rain, hail, snow, or sleet. This adds significantly to the total weight within a given volume and produces significant motions. The particles which do this are collectively called *fallout*,* in contrast with the ordinary cloud particles whose terminal fall speeds are small compared with the motion of the air, whose total mass is comparable only with the vapour in the volume containing them, and which for our purposes can be said to move with the air.

The energy of water

(*a*) *The tephigram.* (A complete tephigram is printed inside the jacket of this book.)

---

* Meteorologists are in the habit of using the word *precipitation* for fallout. This is a confusing divergence from the usage of chemists which is well established. By its form *precipitation* suggests a process or act rather than a substance. Clouds are sometimes described as *precipitating*. This is an unnecessary use of a complicated word, for *raining* will do. If the fallout happens to be hail the cloud can be said to be ' raining hail '. It is also in accordance with existing usage to say that ' hail is raining ' from a cloud. The additional word ' fallout ' is required because ' rain ' means only one kind of fallout, not because there is not a word for the processes of falling out.

256

This diagram was devised by Sir Napier Shaw to represent conditions and transformations of the air. It has several advantages over alternative diagrams devised for the same purpose, and is the most widely used in meteorological services throughout the world. Height is not a convenient coordinate because it has no direct relevance to the condition of the air; but the adiabatic lapse rate (see page 169) is a property of the air that is independent of temperature and pressure. The changes undergone by air ascending adiabatically are therefore represented by horizontal straight lines. Temperature is measured on a linear scale along a horizontal axis. The pressure is defined by a logarithmic scale *down* a vertical axis. This fixes the pressure at one point of each adiabatic line, and since in an adiabatic change pressure and temperature are uniquely related the pressure at all points of the adiabatic lines is defined, and so the isobars can be drawn. The isobars all have the same shape, having corresponding points at the same temperature. They are slightly curved, and it is customary to choose the scales of T and $\log p$ so that the isobars are inclined at about 45° for ordinary atmospheric conditions.

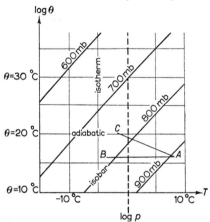

The adiabatics are drawn horizontally through the points where the 1000 mb isobar intersects the isotherms (vertical lines) at equal intervals of T; (these points of intersection are mostly off the right-hand edge of the figure shown above). They are lines of constant potential temperature and they intersect the vertical axis on a logarithmic scale of θ. The entropy Φ of the air is proportional to log θ and so the vertical scale is linear in Φ. The diagram is therefore called a *T-Φgram*. The three sets of lines, isobars, isotherms, and adiabatics, are for dry air and are related by the physical properties of air expressed in the well-known gas laws.

A sounding of the atmosphere made by balloon or aircraft would determine T as a function of p. The isotherms and isobars are therefore used as coordinate lines when a sounding is plotted.

In dry air a sounding such as AB would indicate that the lapse rate was adiabatic, the potential temperature independent of height, and that the air was approximately dynamically equivalent to an incompressible fluid of uniform density. A sounding such as AC would mean that the air was stably stratified, and equivalent to an incompressible fluid whose density decreased upwards.

(b) *Saturation mixing ratio; condensation level*

Air is said to be *saturated for water* with water vapour when there is no net flux of vapour by condensation or evaporation across a plane liquid water surface at the same temperature. It is said to be *saturated for ice* when there is no net flux across an ice surface at the same temperature. The *mixing ratio* is the ratio of the mass of the water vapour in the air to the mass of the other components, which we call *dry air*. This ratio is measured in grams of water vapour per kilogram of dry air. The *saturation mixing ratio* is the value of the mixing ratio when the air is saturated.

In the atmosphere there is always an abundance of condensation nuclei so that for our purposes it can be assumed that the air cannot become perceptibly supersaturated for water, but that if it is cooled below its *dew point* condensation occurs in the form of a water cloud.

The vapour pressure over water at various temperatures has been measured experimentally. From this the saturation mixing ratio as a function of temperature and pressure has been computed and is indicated on the tephigram by the dashed sloping lines. One such line is shown in the accompanying figure. For the sake of example we suppose that this represents a ratio of 3 g/kg and that this is the actual mixing ratio of a sample of air at the point A.

A represents the present temperature and pressure of the air. If it is lifted and cools adiabatically its changes are represented by the horizontal line *AB*. When the pressure level represented by the point *B* is reached the air will be saturated. Provided that the air remains in a condition represented by a point to the right of the water vapour saturation line it may be treated as dry for most purposes.

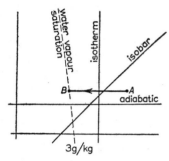

The altitude represented by the pressure at the point *B* is called the *condensation level* of the sample.

(c) The wet-adiabatic lapse rate

If the air is carried by the motion above the pressure level of *B* to that of *C* where the saturation mixing ratio is 2 g/kg, 1 g of

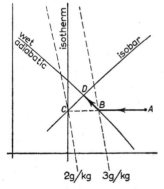

water must have been condensed out as cloud in each kilogram of air. The significant fact now is that the latent heat of condensation of the amount of water condensed in this way in the atmosphere warms the air enough to produce important buoyancy forces.

The air does not cool to the isotherm through C but only to that through D, and so less than 1 g of water vapour is condensed out. From a knowledge of the latent heat of condensation and the saturation mixing ratio at various temperatures and pressures it is in principle straightforward, but in fact very tedious, to compute the curves such as BD, which represent the cooling undergone by air ascending adiabatically but with condensation taking place. These have been computed and are inscribed upon tephigrams in current routine use, so that the changes can be readily deduced.

These curves are called *wet adiabatic* lines. They have been computed on the assumption that the condensed water is removed, otherwise the amount of liquid water present as cloud would have to be known in order to determine the rate of cooling of the whole mass because the specific heat of water is not zero. For our present purposes this does not introduce significant errors.

If air is made to descend the wet adiabatic lines represent the changes in air that is kept saturated as it descends but no finite amount of liquid water is brought down from the cooler levels above.

Strictly, allowance should be made, when using the tephigram, for the water vapour present in the air. Its density is about two-thirds of the density of dry air so that saturated air has a lower density than dry air at the same temperature. ' Thermals ' can therefore be produced at a wet surface from which evaporation is taking place. The higher humidity of thermals rising from a wet surface is important at altitudes of 1–2000 m where they may have risen into very dry surroundings. No new dynamical principle is involved in considering this effect, and we shall not pursue it further. The heat released progressively during the ascent of saturated air is, however, of great importance.

(d) Heat lost by evaporation: erosion of thermals

Let it be supposed that a thermal rises to the condensation level B and ascends farther wet adiabatically to a height represented by the point D in the figure, by when about $3 \cdot 2$ g of water will have condensed into each kilogram of air. Its rise has been possible because the surroundings, whose temperature is indicated by the sounding QR, were colder. If at the level of D the thermal now emerges from the top of a cloud and begins to mix with the

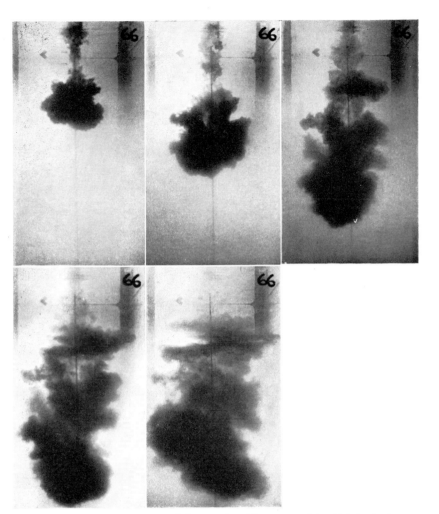

PLATE 18. In this experiment a dark solution was released in a water tank in which the density was uniform in the top quarter but which increased downwards in the lowest three-quarters. At first the cloud behaves like the thermals in Plates 4 and 5. In the stably stratified part of the tank it does not grow but leaves a trail behind. This process is called erosion. (*See* page 265)

PLATE 19.   A complex system of wave clouds over rugged hills.   The central cloud is composed of layers which appear to shift within it and which are indications of patchy sheets of variable humidity probably formed from regions made damp by large cumulus stretched by shearing motion.   (*See* page 268)

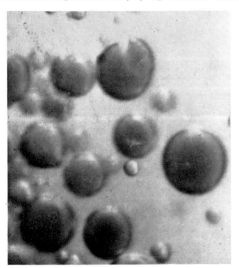

PLATE 20.   On the left are seen water drops of about 50 μ diameter supported between fluids at about $-35°$ C.   One, near the top of the picture, has frozen on the outside first; the expansion when the interior subsequently freezes bursts the shell like a hatching egg.   On the right the path of such a drop falling through air in which the temperature decreases downwards, is seen in alternating light of 100 flashes per second.   The dashes are about 2 mm apart.   The drop was at about $-5°$ C when it froze in air at about $-60°$ C and on bursting ejected a particle whose curved path can be seen.   These photographs were taken by E. J. Langham.   (*See* page 272)

clear air around it which has a mixing ratio of only 1 g/kg, the condensed water will gradually evaporate as the thermal air is mixed with an ever growing amount of clear air.

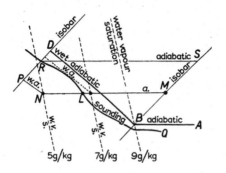

We may compute the temperature of the mixture by assuming the air to be taken adiabatically to the level of B. The thermal will be represented by the point B and the surroundings by the point S. According to the ratio of the mixture the temperature of the mixture will be at point on the isobar between S and B. If the thermal is mixed with an equal quantity of environment, since its mixing ratio is 9 g/kg, the mixing ratio of the mixture will be 10 g/2kg, or 5 g/kg, and the condition will be represented by the point M, midway between S and B. In order to get the mixture back to its original level we follow the adiabatic from M to N on the 5 g/kg water vapour line, and the wet adiabatic from there to the isobar through R and D to P.

Although the thermal at D was 1° C warmer than the surroundings at R, after mixing with an equal quantity of surroundings the mixture at P is 2° C colder than the surroundings, and unless further mixing occurs will come to rest at the level of L where the path from M to P crosses the sounding.

Since the temperature deficits produced by the evaporation of cloud can be greater than the excesses in the thermals we can expect downdraughts on the outsides of convection clouds to be comparable in strength with the updraughts within, when the surroundings are very dry. This accords with the experience of glider pilots. If the surroundings had been nearly saturated and had a mixing ratio of 5 g/kg the mixture at M would have had

7 g/kg and at the level of D would have had a temperature between that of D and R.

The consequence of this is that cloudy thermals rising into surroundings which are very dry are continuously eroded on the outside, where their buoyancy is destroyed and often reversed in sign. In order that a large cloud shall grow and the thermals reach up to the greatest height possible for an unmixed parcel of air, a region of air must be made damp and the supply of new thermals through the base of the cloud must exceed the loss by evaporation.

A cumulus cloud is composed of the thermals which have ascended through its base diluted by the air into which the thermals have risen. Very roughly it is composed of the air that occupied the region before the thermals rose into it, mixed with the thermals. There is some outflow (and upward flow above the top while it is ascending) to make room for the thermals just as there is motion ahead of an isolated thermal in model experiments (see Chapter 7), but there is no observational evidence of inflow at the sides of a cloud. The shrinkage at the sides is largely due to evaporation which is hastened by the mixing induced by the downward buoyancy forces produced by the evaporation itself.

Clouds occasionally appear to have inflow at one side, but this is almost certainly because the cloud is growing upwards on that side and is mixing into the clear air there. Any ordered inflow would cause the cloud to shrink.

If there is no wind and thermals are sent up continuously into the same volume of air from good thermal sources, that air rapidly becomes dampened and a large cumulus cloud may grow. If there is a wind, the thermals must rise into the region of the cloud as it passes over the countryside if they are to continue building it, and generally there is no mechanism which makes them rise preferentially into existing clouds as long as the clouds are small. It is therefore a matter too complicated to comprehend to predict where and when the clouds will grow. That our minds boggle at the problem is shown by our habit of describing the process of cloud building as a ' matter of chance '. Maybe it is, in some sense; but so long as we wish to understand the processes ' chance ' must be studiously excluded from our considerations. Perhaps Nature has not bothered to make things simple, just as she does not plant her forest trees in rows; but the idea of chance is an attribute of our thinking, and only in order to pretend that the limit of our present powers has not been reached do we sometimes ascribe to Nature an element of arbitrary caprice.

When there is wind shear the regions of dampened air are tilted over into almost horizontal sheets, and so the upward growth of cumulus is very slow. The whole extent of the lower layers of air has to be made much damper before thermals can rise into the upper layers.

Isolated cloud thermals rising into very dry surroundings do not necessarily grow as they rise in the manner described in Chapter 7, but are often diminished in size by erosion. When a thermal has been diluted throughout, by one complete turning inside out, its buoyancy is often completely destroyed. Typically a cloud thermal might rise once or twice its width in clear air before its buoyancy vanishes. The distance it rises is determined less by the humidity of the surroundings than by the rate at which the dilution penetrates throughout its volume. Only when the surroundings are nearly saturated can it rise more than about 2 diameters because such a rise would require that a portion of the thermal should withstand dilution by surroundings and still retain enough buoyancy to pass down the outside and up the centre of the thermal a second time.

(e) *Saturation for ice; frost point; ice evaporation level*

The vapour pressure over ice is less than over supercooled water at the same temperature. The magnitude of this difference is shown in the accompanying table which gives the differences between the frost point T_f and the dew point T_d at various dew points. If the air is saturated for water at temperature T_d then it must be warmed by an amount $T_f - T_d$, at constant pressure, before condensation would cease on to any ice surface which might be present.

T_d, °C	−9	−19	−32	−41
$T_f - T_d$, °C	1	2	3	3·5
Δh, m	100	200	300	350

The height Δh, in metres, in the table indicates the distance below the condensation level at which the frost point would be reached by a sample of air ascending adiabatically. Condensation to ice cloud does not occur in clear air cooled to the frost point. Brewer and others have shown experimentally that it is necessary to cool the air beyond the point at which it is saturated for water in order to produce cloud. The cloud is then composed of super-cooled water droplets if the temperature is below 0° C. The larger the drops are, and the colder they are, the greater is the fraction of them which turns into ice in a given time. Under natural conditions droplets at a temperature below — 40° C freeze in a fraction of a second, that is instantaneously for practical purposes. At — 35° C a substantial fraction may freeze in a few minutes, according to their size; at —15° a cloud that has existed for a few hours may be composed almost entirely of ice particles; clouds that have been formed for only a few minutes do not contain many ice crystals unless they reach up to levels where their temperature is near to or below — 40° C.

If a cloud of supercooled water is formed and some of the droplets turn into ice, since the air is supersaturated for ice the crystals will grow. If the air is descending, and contains a cloud of ice crystals, the evaporation of the cloud will not be complete until the air has reached the level at which there is only just enough water substance present to saturate the air for ice. The level at which the frost point is reached during an ascent is therefore called the *ice evaporation level*. It is not the ice condensation level because condensation does not normally occur there. If a water cloud is formed at the condensation level, and is turned to ice, it will only be completely evaporated by descending motion on reaching the ice evaporation level.

When water freezes 80 calories of latent heat are released by one gram. Though large, this is small compared with the 540 calories released when a gram of water condenses. One of the most important results of the particles turning to ice is the reduction in the rate of evaporation at a cumulus cloud top. At a temperature of around — 30° C the air can hold about 30 per cent more vapour when no ice is present than when it is. The clouds which first glaciate therefore grow rapidly above the others because the evaporation at their tops is virtually stopped.

Convection in a stable environment

(a) Erosion of thermals: their lack of similarity

Cloud thermals can remain buoyant as they ascend into clear stable surroundings on account of the heat liberated by condensation. The motion differs fundamentally from the rise of thermals in neutral surroundings on two accounts.

The first has already been mentioned, namely that negative buoyancy may be produced when cloud particles evaporate. This negative buoyancy produces vorticity in the opposite direction to that required to make the mixture flow in at the rear end of the centre of the thermal, and in consequence the thermal is eroded and leaves a trail below it.

The second effect is similar but arises because every parcel of buoyant air loses its buoyancy after rising a finite distance into stable surroundings. The exterior parts of the thermal are more dilute than the core and therefore reach their level of no buoyancy earlier. Any further upward displacement produces negative buoyancy and erosion of the thermal. A series of pictures of a ' thermal ' *descending* into stable surroundings in a water tank is shown in plate 18.

When there is shearing motion, with the horizontal wind decreasing, increasing, or simply changing direction with height, the most diluted parts of the cloud will be found displaced down the direction of the shear because they will also have acquired more momentum in the direction of the upper wind than the less diluted parts.

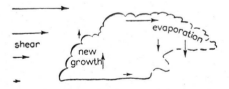

The downdraughts will therefore be found on the down-shear side of the cloud. There may even be updraughts above the newly growing part on the other side. This is well borne out by the experience of glider pilots.

The nature of the motion in an eroded thermal has not yet been investigated in detail. All isolated thermals in neutral surroundings behave similarly except in so far as they are complicated by details peculiar to the creation of each thermal. But the behaviour of thermals rising into stable surroundings differs according to the stability of the surroundings quite apart from any peculiarity of the thermal itself. This fact can be expressed by saying that in addition to the quantities $g\overline{B}$ (the buoyancy) and r (the size) which determine the velocities in an isolated thermal (see page 161) there is an additional buoyancy force represented by $g\beta$ (the static stability, see page 232). In addition to the Froude number relating the inertia forces to the buoyancy forces, namely

$$C = \frac{w^2}{g\overline{B}r}$$

we can form the number

$$C' = \frac{w^2}{g\beta r^2}$$

which is a ratio of inertia forces to static stability forces. Alternatively we could note that βr is a non-dimensional number which can be derived from the conditions of the problem in addition to C. This means that experiments would have to be used to determine the relationship between C and C'. A fuller discussion of this idea is given in Chapter 11.

Even if experiments were performed to discover this relationship the possibilities would not be exhausted because in realistic problems β may vary with height. The behaviour of a thermal at any particular level in stable surroundings depends not only on its buoyancy and size and the stability of the surroundings, but also upon its present velocity which depends upon its history up to the moment in question, and therefore upon the stability, buoyancy, and size of the thermal at all levels below. Investigations into the phenomenon of erosion in stable surroundings must therefore be limited in some way by special objectives, because the problem is too vast to be tackled as a whole.

A thermal rising into stable surroundings is not similar at successive stages in its growth except in very special cases.

(b) Thermals in unstable surroundings: vortical thermals

In neutral surroundings a thermal elongated vertically ultimately assumes the shape common to all isolated thermals, because the top, by advancing into and mixing with the surroundings, becomes more dilute than the lower part which therefore rises up into it. But in rising through unstable surroundings the total buoyancy of a rising portion of air increases and the upward velocity may therefore be increased during the ascent, in spite of the dilution. Vertical columns of air are then stretched, not flattened, vertically and if they possess any vorticity it is intensified. In this way dust devils are initiated in the very unstable air over desert ground by day. They are not a normal phenomenon because ordinary cultivated or well covered ground generates thermals which prevent the establishment of a lapse rate sufficiently in excess of the adiabatic (see page 175).

The lapse rate above the condensation level of the surface air may often be greatly in excess of the wet adiabatic before clouds are formed, but as soon as clouds begin to appear heat is carried upwards and the lapse rate is made to approach the wet adiabatic. If, however, a sufficiently large cloud can be produced before the lapse rate has been significantly altered, a lapse rate within the cloud much in excess of the wet adiabatic can be produced because the upper part of the cloud is more dilute than the lower part and therefore more cooled by evaporation. If there exists vorticity about a vertical axis a motion similar to that in a dust devil can be produced by the vertical stretching in the region that is unstable for cloud thermals.

Such a thermal must then extend downwards because the rotating air cannot enter the vortex at the sides. If the air below is also possessed of vorticity the vortex extends downwards until it reaches the ground. The funnel cloud which is produced in this way in a *tornado* or *water spout* indicates that the pressure at its surface is approximately the same as at the cloud base, where it is low enough to produce condensation in the air below cloud.

If the funnel is fed by air not possessed of vorticity it will collapse into the cloud. If it reaches the ground it may continue to feed on air with vorticity induced in it by friction at the ground in the manner of a dust devil. Once a tornado extends down to the ground it becomes more likely to persist. The friction over the sea is less than over the land so that the same phenomenon, then called a water spout, is less persistent and dangerous.

(c) Motion in the environment of cloud thermals: the subcloud layer

If there is a net upward transport of mass in cloud thermals there may be a slow settling motion in the surroundings. The downdraughts around the thermals due to the evaporation cannot reach down to the cloud base; and by considering likely cases it can be seen that with mixing in the proportions favourable to the greatest downward displacement the downdraughts do not usually extend more than one half to one third of the way down to the original condensation level of the air of the thermal. On a typical day thermals only occupy less than a tenth of the sky, and often very much less, so that the sinking motion between them is generally too small to be observed directly.

Since the clear air is stably stratified the sinking motion warms it. The cloud thermals therefore warm the whole mass into which they penetrate, *without being mixed into it*. The parts made more moist by the evaporation of clouds may be limited to a small fraction of the total.

If after several hours a slow shearing motion has distorted these damp patches into almost horizontal sheets, a vertical sounding of the humidity would reveal alternate dry and damp layers. This is one mechanism which can produce laminations of humidity such as would explain the ' plywood ' appearance of some wave clouds (see plate 19).

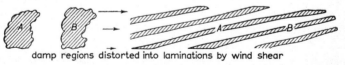

damp regions distorted into laminations by wind shear

It is possible that cloud thermals could cool the uppermost levels of the layers into which they penetrate. There may be a transport upwards of cloud which all evaporates in the upper levels. The latent heat for evaporation must be extracted from the air, and if this exceeds the heat transported up on account of the excess temperature of the thermals and deficit of the down-draughts, there must be a net cooling of the layer. This is particularly likely if the environment is very dry because the buoyancy of the water *vapour* in the thermals may be sufficient to carry them into the layer with no excess heat. Since the air above the cooled layer is unaffected a very stable layer is often produced just above the uppermost level reached by convection. The sounding may thus be changed in the way indicated in the figure.

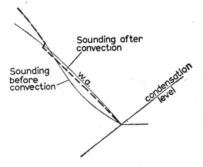

Another way of thinking about this process is as follows: cloudy thermals rise up into a stable layer and evaporate therein. If the surroundings are dry enough the mixture will be cooler than the surroundings and will sink. In effect, therefore, the thermals serve to snatch volumes of air downwards, and spread them out below their original surroundings. These surroundings, being stable, are cooled by the lifting of them which results.

There must be a net flux of air upwards through the cloud bases otherwise the clouds would not be where they are. There may also be a downflow in the surroundings through this level, and since the air is stable this means that in between the clouds the stability extends below the condensation level. This stable layer below the cloud base is called the *subcloud layer*. Thermals rising into growing clouds do not mix with the warmer drier air of the subcloud layer because the layer does not exist below growing clouds, but only around them. Thermals rising else-where often have not enough buoyancy to penetrate the subcloud

layer; and because it is much drier, even if they do penetrate it
and reach the cloud base level, they may ascend no farther because
no condensation occurs.

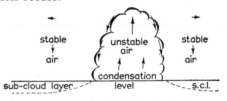

This means that the latent heat of condensation of the vapour
in the thermals is released preferentially in the cloudy areas,
which therefore remain cloudy. This process is particularly
important when convection occurs over large areas of ocean or
continent, because then the compensating downward motions
must occur in among the thermals. The subcloud layer then
often reaches one or two hundred metres below the cloud base
level. In oceanic trade-wind areas, where convection occurs
continuously for days, the clouds appear often to gather themselves into groups perhaps 10 miles across, with clear spaces in
between. There must be a slow inflow into the cloudy regions
below cloud base and a slow outflow near the cloud tops.

Over smaller land (or sea) regions, such as are found around
Western Europe and the Mediterranean, the down motion may
occur over the neighbouring sea (or land) so that there is no subcloud layer between the clouds to perpetuate the growth of
clouds in particular places. However, mountain ranges may
produce thermals which cause sinking motions over the valleys,
and so cumulus clouds may be absent over the low ground all
day. In the evening when thermals from the ground cease, the
evaporation of the clouds over the mountains may cause enough
cooling and sinking to produce lifting of the air over the low
ground and a removal of the subcloud layer. Clouds may then
appear over the valleys, or over narrow seas such as the English
Channel.

The reality of these mechanisms is revealed in the diurnal
variations of cumulus cloud over valleys, mountains, and narrow
seas; but it has not been possible to put the theory on a satisfactory quantitative basis because, although there is some analogy

with cellular convection, the turbulent motions which restrict the larger scale velocities are very complicated and confined to the cloudy regions and the region of thermals below cloud base.

The transformation of thin layer clouds

(a) By elevation

If a layer of cloud is gradually lifted together with the air above and below it, the cloud will ascend at the wet adiabatic lapse rate and the air above and below at the adiabatic rate, assuming that the air above and below it is not saturated in the course of this lifting, and so that the layer is therefore not made deeper. The top of the cloud will ultimately become unstable because the cloudy air will become warmer than the air above.

The nature of the buoyant convection which then occurs depends on a variety of factors. If the lapse rate within the layer is stable the cloud will tend to sprout cumulus towers into the air above, from an ever greater depth of itself as the lifting continues until elements at the base are warm enough to rise into the air above. The distance which the thermals penetrate into the air above will depend on the lapse rate and humidity in that air. The base of the layer will become gradually more wrinkled until holes appear in it when air from above sinks to the base of the layer, and the cumulus tops can be seen from below.

Sometimes air from above can penetrate down to the base of the layer. The layer will then quickly be transformed into cloudlets, which will assume the form of parallel rolls across the shear if any shear exists (see page 153). Sometimes the downward motion of the air above makes holes in the cloud which then assumes a net-like form.

(b) By subsidence

Provided that the cloud is not evaporated by sinking motion it will cool at a greater rate than the air below and the base will become unstable. Again, if the layer is not stable it will quickly break up into cloudlets; but if it is stable the downward penetration of it into the air below will cause the base to assume a pouched or pocked appearance. This will only happen if the air below is not saturated and the air at the base of the cloud has an appreciable liquid water content, otherwise the vertical motion of air at the base will not move the base up and down, but condensation or evaporation will occur as air moves up and down through the base level. A discontinuity of water content at the base can be produced either by the ascent of air up a sloping frontal surface where there is a discontinuity of velocity also, or by the spreading out of the tops of cumulus, at a stable layer, over the top of the drier air.

(c) By glaciation

If a water droplet layer cloud is partly converted into ice the fragmentation of the crystals formed infects an ever growing volume of the cloud with ice. In 20 minutes or so the width of the area affected may be half a kilometre.

The infection is brought about partly by the stirring motions within the cloud but also by two mechanisms which multiply the number of ice particles. First, when a drop freezes the latent heat released may be enough to bring the temperature of the drop momentarily up to $0°$ C, and the interior may remain unfrozen. As heat then escapes into the surrounding air the interior freezes, and because it expands it shatters its ice shell and ejects tiny ice particles into the surrounding air (see Plate 20). These make contact with other water droplets and the process is repeated. Secondly, when ice crystals are first formed they are in supersaturated air and so they grow rapidly by condensation. They grow branches (see page 103) and some of the delicate 'twigs' break off either under the stress of air through which the crystal is falling or on contact with others. These tiny particles either grow on their own or make contact with a water droplet and make it begin to freeze.

Soon, because of the condensation on to the crystals and evaporation from the water droplets which quickly (in 10 minutes or so) disappear, the whole cloud is turned to ice. The total amount of water in solid form is more than was formerly in liquid form because additional vapour has been condensed on to the ice. The total number of particles is less than before because many, perhaps most, of the droplets evaporate before they freeze. The particles are therefore bigger, and often fall out as fibrous trails from the cloud leaving clear holes. Usually the trail of ice crystals evaporates before reaching the ground but occasionally a few drops of rain are observed.

The first glaciation might occur in one of several ways—spontaneously, through the agency of some rare particle which nucleates a crystal in a droplet; through the seeding by ice falling from a cloud above; by crystallisation due to the passage of an aircraft (either by cooling in the wing-tip vortices or by nucleation by an exhaust particle or by frost particles blown off the aircraft surface where supercooled water could not remain unfrozen); or through the deliberate arrogant or inquisitive action of a man seeding the cloud with ice neuclei of some sort.

(d) By radiation

The absorption of sunshine by clouds is only significant in amount in great depths of cloud of a kilometre or more, and then it is usually not comparable with other influences determining the life of the cloud. This absorption is partly by the droplets themselves but mainly by the water vapour between them as the light is scattered to and fro along a path large compared with the depth of the cloud.

Thin clouds, in which small influences can have an observable effect on the cloud form, absorb so little sunshine that other influences are still dominant.

Long wave black body radiation is both absorbed and emitted by clouds, in wavelengths to which the clear air is largely transparent. Therefore, although much of the long wave radiation emitted by the ground and clouds is absorbed and re-emitted by the water vapour and other minor constituents of the air, a substantial fraction passes unabsorbed through depths of the air great compared with the height of cloud layers above the ground.

We can be conscious of the magnitude of this effect when we note that ground frosts at night can be prevented sometimes by layers of cloud, whose temperature is below freezing, moving overhead. The radiation downwards from the base of the cloud which is absorbed by the ground, is sufficient to reduce the rate of cooling of the ground due to radiation upwards and to prevent frost occurring in a night's cooling.

Cloud layers, therefore, receive a substantial amount of heat by long wave radiation from the ground. Thin patches and layers of altocumulus are sometimes warmed to evaporation in the morning in this way when the ground temperature rises in the sunshine, and the clouds appear to be 'burned up by the sun'. At the same time the cloud radiates into space from its top even in bright sunshine. The loss of heat at the top and gain at the base will make a layer cloud a few hundred metres thick unstable in an hour or less, so that thin layer clouds cannot remain amorphous layers for long but soon break up into cloudlets. Again, these cloudlets are in rows or rolls if there is a shear in the wind.

Measurements by aircraft and balloons frequently show an increase of temperature of a degree or two on rising out of the top of a layer cloud. This is often due to the loss by radiation of heat from the cloud top. It can be nullified by ascending motion, or intensified by subsidence.

These radiative processes are too slow to be of importance inside deep layer or convective clouds: other processes are then dominant.

When cumulus cloud reaches up to a stable layer and spreads out horizontally it often shades the ground so much that thermals become very much feebler, as experienced glider pilots know. Nevertheless, convection sufficient to maintain this 'parasol' layer in existence may be produced by the scattered sunshine which penetrates the layer and is absorbed by the ground.

The loss by radiation from cloud tops is thought to be responsible on some occasions for keeping the air in a state of instability, even when convection is vigorous and rainfall so copious that the loss of heat by evaporation of the clouds is substantially reduced. In this case the loss occurs mainly from the glaciated 'anvil' tops of cumulonimbus.

Fallout

(a) The production of downdraughts

If the temperature of air in the lower layers of the atmosphere is decreased by about $1°$ C the density is increased by about 0.3 per cent. To produce a comparable increase in density by means of water particles sinking at their terminal velocities the amount of water present would have to be about 3 g in a kilogram (about a cubic metre) of air. If this were falling at speeds typical of raindrops, say 3 m/sec, the rate of rainfall would be about 9 g/sec m² or about 3 cm/hr. Larger drops may fall at 5–8 m/sec.

Since this rate of rainfall is not uncommon in showers in temperate latitudes, is greatly exceeded in tropical showers, and is approached even in more continuous rains in the tropics, it is evident that downward convection currents must be produced by fallout, and that their strength must be comparable with the up-draughts in thermals whose excess temperature is commonly of the order of $\frac{1}{2}$° C below clouds. Downdraughts are often experienced in rain by glider pilots, and under heavy shower clouds they may reach 10 m/sec in strength.

The downdraught is the accumulated wakes of the particles, and was described on page 123. The significant difference between it and the vertical current in a thermal is that it is comparable in magnitude with the fall speed of the particles, so that the leading particles fall out of it into slower moving air below. The negative buoyancy producing the motion is thus infused into the air ahead of the current without a mixing of the air of the current with the air ahead of it in the manner of a thermal. The particles tend to accumulate at the bottom of the downdraught where the foremost particles are retarded by the slower moving air into which they sink, and they often arrive at the ground as a ' gush ' of rain.

Of comparable importance is the cooling of the air by the evaporation of rain into it. If the air below cloud base is almost uniformly mixed, as it generally is when showers are being produced by thermals, it cannot be cooled to a temperature below that on the wet-adiabatic through the condensation level, because if it were kept saturated on being brought down from the cloud base it would have this temperature. It cannot be made cooler than this by evaporation of water into it because evaporation ceases as soon as the air becomes saturated. This minimum temperature is the *wet bulb* temperature and is reached when the air is saturated at a water surface and all the heat to effect the evaporation is taken from the air, as it is in the case of a thermometer wet bulb. It can be seen on the tephigram that at a level 50 mb below cloud base the cooling could easily amount to 2° C. Without any experimental or theoretical knowledge about the rate of evaporation from falling rain we can notice that after rain has fallen fragments of cloud appear as much as 300 m below the main cloud base and this proves that evaporation has occurred. We can also notice, using wet and dry bulb thermometers on the ground, that the air in the downdraughts has a higher mixing ratio of water vapour to dry air than the air it displaces. Typically the condensation level of the downdraught air is of the order of 200 m below the general level, but it varies greatly. Cooling by evaporation of rain can therefore contribute substantially to the production of downdraughts. The fact that rain is colder than the air through which it is falling contributes negligibly to the cooling in comparison with the effects of evaporation; and though it may possibly be of some significance within clouds where evaporation from fallout has no effect, the weight of the particles is then the dominant force.

(b) The production of updraughts

The idea that fallout could produce updraughts was first put forward by Marshall and co-workers in Canada and has since been applied by Ludlam to explain one type of behaviour of fall-streak clouds. If ice crystals fall through air that is between its condensation level and ice evaporation level they will grow by condensation and the latent heat will be released. If the air at pressures around 300 mb (10,000 m a.s.l.) and temperatures around $- 35°$ C is almost at water saturation and is reduced to ice saturation, the heat liberated is sufficient to warm it through about $\frac{1}{3}°$ C. This is sufficient to produce thermals which will rise up to the condensation level and produce a water cloud. The water cloud then freezes and more ice particles fall out into the air below producing new thermals in the same manner. Lines of fall-streak clouds with transient cumulus tops can be formed in this way. An example is shown in Plate 21.

(c) The spreading out of downdraughts

If the air is neutral or unstable downdraughts reach down to the ground, where they must spread out horizontally beneath. Over flat land where there is no wind shear they spread out radially unless interfered with by others spreading out below other shower clouds. On mountain sides they descend the slopes into the adjacent plains, often in the form of very strong shallow winds, with speeds of 30 kt or more at the ground with a depth

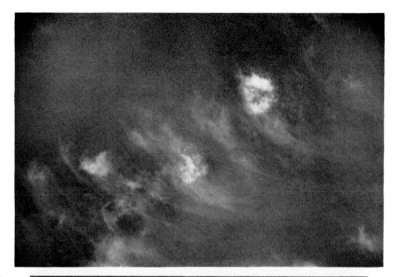

PLATE 21. In the upper picture are seen trails of ice crystals falling through air in shearing motion. The condensation on the crystals releases heat which produces thermals which become visible as cloud on reaching the condensation level. One such thermal is seen from beneath to be ring-shaped like that in Plate 4. In the lower picture the condensation and growth of cumulus towers on the left is probably due to a slow rising motion of the air over a large area. These cumulus glaciate and trails of ice crystals fall out. These are drawn aside by the shear, and when they fall into unsaturated air the larger ones which remain longest produce downdraughts, which can be seen as mamma on the trails, by their weight and by the cooling produced as they evaporate. (*See* page 276)

PLATE 22.   The upper picture shows mamma after a thunderstorm.   The outline is in some places trans
parent where the boundary of the cloud which is evaporating in the downdraughts can be seen inside th
front of the larger fallout particles.   The cloud was illuminated from below by a setting sun.   The lowe
picture taken by F. H. Ludlam is of the fallout front of a snow shower seen looking towards the bright sk
from beneath the shower cloud.   (*See* page 278)

of only 50–100 m. Above these strong winds the air may be moving in a quite different direction, with a sharp discontinuity of around 50 kt in speed and about 4° C in temperature at the top of the layer.

When the upper wind is stronger than the wind near the ground the downdraught arrives at the ground with a velocity more nearly equal to that of the upper wind, and therefore tends to spread in the direction of the shear which is usually nearly the same as the direction of movement of the storm cloud producing the fallout. The rain of the storm is then preceded by gusts of cold air at the ground, which tend to lift the air on the front of the storm and produce new growth there. This shovelling effect of down-draughts which have spread horizontally is most noticeable when the storms are in lines and when they are advancing into plains over ground sloping downwards. In tropical or desert countries soaring birds can be seen to fly fast and freely without flapping in the lifted air. The storms appear to advance faster than the upper wind because of rapid growth of new cumulus cloud on the front of them.

When the downdraught air arrives convection from the ground is effectively stopped because the layer of cold air is cooler than the air above it. Consequently there is often a period of clear sky after the passage of a shower which lasts until the sunshine has warmed the cold air up to the temperature of the air it has replaced. Frequently a downdraught produces gusts of wind but no rain is subsequently observed, either because the rain shower has ceased or because it has passed to one side of the observer.

Sometimes puffs of cold air can be observed on calm evenings after a day of well developed convection. These may be very shallow, rustling only on the lower leaves of a tall tree. They may occur under cloudless skies and are not due to fallout. They consist of air descending to replace thermals rising from places which have remained hotter than their surroundings in the cooling evening.

Pressure surges of a millibar or two often occur when a squall is produced by the arrival of the cold downdraught air: and centres of high pressure are built up under the centres of cumulo-nimbus storms. The new growth of cloud is on the edges where the air below cloud base is lifted above the condensation level by the shovelling effect of the squalls. This is a mechanism whereby raining clouds can perpetuate themselves when the ground is too cold for thermals to rise from it spontaneously.

(d) Mamma

Thermals growing downwards from a cloud base are called *mamma* on account of their breastlike appearance (see Plate 22). They may be produced when a cloud layer is subjected to subsidence (page 271) or when the cloud is dragged down by fallout or when fallout itself is dense enough to be seen and produces a downdraught by its weight or by cooling the air by evaporation into it.

The folded cauliflower-like surface seen on a cumulus cloud is not seen on mamma for a variety of possible causes. First, if the downward mixing motions on the front of such a negative thermal exist they tend to produce evaporation and are therefore not visible. Secondly, unlike the mixing on the surface of an ordinary thermal, the evaporation may increase the buoyancy force in the direction of motion of the thermal. Thirdly, the downward motion of the thermal as a whole tends to cause evaporation of the whole cloud and of the most dilute part first. Finally, if there is a substantial amount of fallout the thermal will have a smooth surface as described on page 124.

Tides in the atmosphere

There exists a tide in the atmosphere which is clearly shown by the barometric oscillations which occur in the tropics. It has a period of exactly 12 hours. The tide cannot be a simple gravitational tide like those in the ocean because the lunar component is not detectable on an ordinary weekly barograph trace. Two possible explanations have been offered: Kelvin suggested that it was induced by the semidiurnal component of the temperature changes, and not by gravity, but Pekeris, and later Wilkes and Weekes showed that 24 hours was almost exactly the time taken for a tidal wave with two crests on lines of longitude 180° apart to pass round the earth, and so they suggested that the solar gravitational tide was amplified by resonance which the lunar tide was not.

Both explanations are probably correct in a sense, and it seems that the force producing the tide is mainly thermal in origin, but that the tide is greatly amplified by resonance.

In Chapter 9 we have discussed the question of why there is resonance. Here we shall suggest an answer to the question, how is the tide induced thermally? It is required that there should be temperature variations with a period of 12 hours; and since the diurnal (24 hour) variations are not strictly sinusoidal there is inevitably a fairly large semidiurnal component. The most obvious diurnal variations occur near to the ground, and these are conducted upwards with a time lag by convection. Unfortunately most radio-sonde stations send up balloons only at 12 hourly intervals so that the amplitude and phase of the temperature variations in the upper air are not known with any assurance, particularly in the tropics where observations are most important in this connection. However there are two observations which can easily be, and have in places already been, observed, which are very relevant—cloud amount and rainfall.

If there is a large variation in cloud amount with time of day, there is a corresponding variation in the heat content of the air as the latent heat is released when cloud forms and absorbed when cloud evaporates. ' Cloud amount ' in the ordinary sense of ' fraction of the sky covered ' is not a good measure of the amount of water condensed because early morning clouds tend to be shallow while afternoon ones are more often several kilometres deep, and therefore contain more water for a given amount of blue sky obscured.

Rainfall tends to occur at particular times of day, in the tropics in particular. Whether there is any evaporation into air below cloud or not, the rain deposited on the ground represents its latent heat given to the atmosphere in the hour or two before it fell, and so diurnal variations of rainfall can be a source of energy for the tidal wave.

These two sources of energy are probably the most important in producing the tide because the air above the condensation level, which is about 85 per cent of the mass of the atmosphere, can only be heated by the action of clouds, or by wind systems and radiative exchanges which have no dominant diurnal variations.

Thunderstorms

Lightning and thunder are certainly spectacular but the energy exchanges are only a small fraction of the total kinetic energy produced by the buoyancy forces or of the latent heat released by the fallout. They are therefore an interesting by-product of the dynamical properties of cumulonimbus clouds but do not shape the storms. Recently, Reynolds, in the United States, has discovered a probable mechanism whereby the fallout separates the electric charges which are subsequently neutralised by lightning flashes. We shall not discuss the growth of fallout, nor the details of how the discharge occurs.

Reynolds has demonstrated experimentally that when two pieces of ice at different temperatures make contact with one another the warmer piece acquires a positive and the colder a negative charge. It has long been known that hailstones often have alternate concentric clear and frosty layers inside and it used to be thought that somehow they were carried up and down to and from the upper frozen and lower unfrozen parts of the cloud. From what we now know about the motion it seems very unlikely that they do ascend and descend in this way, but that the different layers are produced as they fall through thermals rising inside the cloud. Ludlam showed how a hailstone could collect supercooled water droplets as it fell through the cloud so rapidly that the latent heat released as they began to freeze on contact with the hailstone raised its temperature by several degrees centigrade. Accordingly, hailstones can even be warmed up to near 0° C, and instead of freezing on impact and forming a frosty accumulation the supercooled droplets splash over the surface producing a layer of clear ice as they freeze. The clear layers therefore represent the falling of the hailstone through the least diluted thermals within the cloud where the greatest concentrations of supercooled droplets are to be found. The frosty layers are the accretion which takes place in regions where the latent heat released by freezing does not exceed the loss to the cooler air around, and the droplets freeze on impact. Hailstones can therefore be warmer than the cloud through which they are falling, often by several degrees centigrade, but only if the cloud contains supercooled droplets.

If the cloud also contains small ice particles they will not stick to a hailstone which makes contact with them but will acquire a negative charge, and will tend to be carried upwards in the cloud by the up-draughts.   The hail acquires a positive charge which it carries towards the base of the cloud.

It is interesting that although the hail is falling from the cooler part of the cloud it is warmer than the air surrounding it.

We cannot exclude the possibility that, once the major charge separation has occurred, charged particles falling differentially may continue to separate charges by other mechanisms; but the one just described is probably responsible for the existence of electrical phenomena in the first place, and if there were no other mechanisms thunderstorms would not generally be noticeably different from what they are.

From this it is concluded that lightning will not be produced in clouds composed only or predominantly of ice particles, wherefore thunderstorms do not occur in polar regions.   Nor is lightning observed in all tropical showers because many of them do not reach high enough to contain a significant amount of ice.

Because glaciation is infectious (see page 272) the charge separation only occurs in new thermals in cumulonimbus clouds because when ice has begun to appear the supercooled water particles either freeze or evaporate in a few minutes.   Indeed thunder may sometimes be heard only in the early stages of a thunderstorm because when the cloud is mostly glaciated snow, rather than hail, is the dominant form of fallout, and this sinks too slowly to collect enough supercooled water (if any is present) to be appreciably warmed by its freezing.

CHAPTER 11

PHILOSOPHY OF METHOD

NATURE is so complex that we are often satisfied by very rough solutions to problems. Our solutions do not correspond with reality but with hypothetical mechanical systems which are much simpler than Nature. It is worth while, therefore, examining more closely what we do when we 'solve' a problem, in order that we shall know what kind of solution we have got and under what circumstances it may be applied.

Some of the more practically minded readers may consider a discussion of the philosophical aspects of our methods rather unnecessary, but if we are to be wise as well as clever, to know how clever or how foolish we are, to know our limitations in the face of Nature of which we are only a part, then before setting out again to conquer the physical world it is as well to take stock of our powers so that we may not delude ourselves that we have understood Nature when perhaps we have only classified a few events.

In this chapter our main theme will be how to approach the problems of Natural Aerodynamics. What is said about mathematicians, physicists and geographers is therefore only a simplified summary of how they proceed. We do not attempt to go deeply into their mode of thought. Least of all shall we discuss how it is that words have meaning even if man has never troubled to define them formally; how definitions can be satisfactory if the words or symbols used in the definitions have not themselves been defined; whether an idea can exist apart from the physical world; and, even if almost all our ideas are derived from our experience of the physical world, whether we can have ideas which are not derivable from our *own* experience. Thus if our conception of God's purpose is derived from our physical experience is it not simply a part of this world? And if not, how can we understand it in terms of its relevance to this life?

It is hoped that as these pages are turned the reader's mind will digress into all the avenues and cul-de-sacs suggested by the argument. Let it be assumed that there exists one world only, in which the methods to be discussed are the only methods: then what are the consequences ?   If they are not, then what methods, which might be applied to other enigmas of the universe, could equally be applied to Natural Aerodynamics ? My own view is at present quite definite on this matter: it is that there is only one world, and that if a method is not valid in Natural Aerodynamics it is because it is not valid: if it is valid, then it may be appropriately applied in Natural Aerodynamics.

In Natural Aerodynamics we study the liquid and gaseous part of what we live in.   The solid part requires no basically different methods.   But in this book we have not used all possible methods and have discussed only a tiny part of what is included in the title. The point is, however, that the person cannot be separated from his work and thoughts: this is typically expressed in the fact that we read and write books like this because we *want* to, because we *enjoy* it, and because *we* think it worth while.   Our whole scale of values is operating when we select material, when we evaluate the work of others, when we choose a naughty word here and a safe one there.

But if the reader thinks otherwise he will presumably have a place of some sort for everything that is said.   He is invited to analyse his own methods and systems, in the way we are now about to tear apart our methods in Natural Aerodynamics.

The mathematician's method

However complicated the argument may be the principle is the same in all mathematical problems.   A certain collection of data are provided and it is required to deduce their logical consequences. The answer is always contained in the data; mathematical skill is in extracting it.   The wisdom of the natural philosopher is in choosing worth-while problems.

Mathematicians aim at two things; conciseness of argument— never use a more complicated method of argument when a brief one will do—and perfect efficiency.   This last may seem a tall order, but what is required is that no more data or more powerful principle than is absolutely necessary should be used.

The mathematical analyst seeks to formulate the simplest possible definitions of all his ideas, and to use as few axioms as possible. It is considered a great achievement if one of the axioms hitherto used can be dispensed with, or shown to be contained in the others, or if the set of axioms can be simplified. In simplification of this kind we achieve a deeper understanding of what we are discussing.

Whether or not the ideas contained in the axioms are derived from the physical world, or the solutions of the problems posed are of any use, the mathematician as such is not concerned; but in fact those branches of mathematics which are pursued are those which have uses or are delightful in themselves. It could be argued that to every mathematical problem we could create a physical analogy, or at least imagine it, so that all mathematical theorems have some practical relevance, to the engineer for instance.

When we use mathematics we make our assumptions approximate to what we conceive to be the controlling conditions under which the natural process we are studying is taking place. Our training in pure mathematics then enables us to discover whether we have sensibly conceived the conditions. Have we, for instance, not supposed enough conditions for the answer to be determined, or have we thought of too many? The mathematics will tell us what outcome we can compute from the conditions. Often the problem is too difficult for us, and we have to make a cruder approximation to what we thought were the conditions in Nature.

Eddington used to say that if we were clever enough we could solve all problems by mathematical methods. It would, he argued, never be necessary to perform an experiment because we could always predict the result. But in this thesis he assumed that we were also able to state correctly the conditions of the experiment, while in fact many experiments are performed simply to discover whether our assumptions about the conditions were correct. There is trouble here because the experiment does not tell us for certain whether or not we were right, because we might have predicted the right answer for the wrong reason. At this point we have to return to the mathematical method and examine whether all our conditions are necessary in order that the answer shall be what it is observed to be; and so Eddington had to assume that we were clever enough not only at applied mathematics to formulate and solve the problem, but also at pure mathematics to examine the deductions that could legitimately be made from an experiment that confirmed our predictions. (The question of experiments not confirming predictions did not arise with his all-clever mathematician.)

Mathematics, therefore, is a form of logic, of the exercise of our power of reason.

Physics: the method of dimensional coefficients

Nature is too complex for even ordinary physical problems to be expressed in terms which the mathematician can conveniently deal with. The physicist therefore has to invent concepts which arise out of his problem. This can conveniently be called the *method of coefficients*. We can imagine that theoretically (i.e. possibly for Eddington's all-clever mathematician) a problem in heat flow could be expressed in terms of the dynamics of the molecules, but it is more convenient to use such concepts as specific heat and thermal conductivity. These are statistical quantities which represent the effect of a complicated process, in this case involving a very large number of molecules. We call them coefficients, and we assume that if we measure them once their value will be the same on the next occasion.

The trouble begins when we wish to extrapolate to inaccessible situations and use the coefficient for conditions very different from those under which it was measured. What is the specific heat or thermal conductivity or coefficient of expansion of a substance in the centre of the earth under great pressure, or on the sun at high temperature ? To solve this problem the physicist has to gain a deeper understanding of the meaning of the coefficient, and either derive its value from more elementary properties of matter or deduce theoretically how it would vary as a function of pressure and temperature, and extrapolate the measured value to the conditions in question.

Once a coefficient has been defined mathematical methods can be used upon it.

The physicist seeks to discover the fundamental properties of Nature. He assumes that matter behaves in the same way everywhere in the universe, the only differences being due to differences in local conditions which are not fundamental. Sometimes he attempts to discover the properties of matter by observing its behaviour under many different circumstances and noting what is common to all cases.   This method is mainly suggestive and he is not satisfied, even if he has discovered a ' law ' in this way, until he can devise a theory which predicts the observed behaviour from the basic principles he already has set up.

A good example is offered by Kepler's laws for the motion of the planets round the sun.   The laws were a great discovery from the observations, but not until Newton had formulated his principle of gravitation did they make sense, for only then could they be derived from some more deep-seated principle.

From time to time it is necessary to formulate a new principle to explain phenomena in this way; but, like the pure mathematician, the physicist always hopes that the number of principles can be kept small in number, and it is his aim to devise fewer simpler principles from which those in current use can be derived or by which they can be replaced.

We have to recognise, however, that many of the things we wish to understand are too complicated.   In particular, every locality in the universe, every person, every situation, is different in some recognisable respect from every other.   Eddington used to distinguish, in astronomy, for instance, between the principles of astronomy which his all-clever mathematician could work out on paper and know all about without ever doing an experiment, and the actual ' geography ' of the observed universe and the solar system in particular.   He, sensibly, said that you could not, theoretically, predict the actual universe and its behaviour but only its general properties.   Only God could predict John Smith : but having observed him and his circumstances presumably we could predict his behaviour from knowledge of the basic laws, if we were clever enough.   The scientist's objective is to become cleverer, and to attain not only physical control over Nature but also spiritual control, that is understanding.   To some this seems a blasphemous heresy.   But as part of Nature we also become spiritually humbled by the understanding.   We do not seek to predict John Smith or even ask why he exists.

The geographer's method

There is a necessity therefore for observations of creation (as distinct from experiments) before we can relate our science to our own circumstances and environment. We need cartographers to map the earth and sky, to analyse the relative abundance of the various chemical elements, to catalogue the live inhabitants of our planet.

We have, indeed, in our own individual lives to strike a balance between controlling and accepting our surroundings. In science we have so little time that there too we have to apportion our effort between informing ourselves of the circumstances in which we shall have to operate and equipping ourselves with understanding of how to operate.

We should not confuse this process of mapping, as geographers often do, with the process of critical observation. We map or explore for curiosity or to give ourselves scope. But we may also observe Nature, not because we wish to know about a region or an event but in order to obtain inspiration for our theoretical ideas. This kind of alert observation has to be made with a purpose and with a theory. We may observe smoke or clouds for inspiration, but we cannot expect the inspiration to flow in like material for maps—simply by observing. We have to try all the time to fit what we see into a theory, or pattern, and the inspiration comes when we notice something which will not fit, or which suggests a simplification. It is therefore necessary to have a theory, even if it is a ludicrous one, if anything significant is to be observed.

A geographer, on the other hand, is not taught to be analytical in this way but to be a commentator or guide to the map he is making; and to this extent he is not a scientist but more like an art critic. He uses the results of scientific research as idioms in which to express his appreciation of the bit of the human habitat he is describing. He does not aim at discovering a process of Nature, only features of a piece of territory. He delights in observing the interplay of various influences; but he never attempts to deal with them quantitatively (as the mathematician deals with ' forces ') for he has no principles or equations to relate them in the abstract: in fact he has no general theory about them.

This absence of the search for a general theory in the geographer's method, and his concern always with the particular, is a handicap which is in part self-imposed, probably because he thinks it unlikely, in the complex nature of his subject, that any can be found. This may, however, deprive him of that key to alertness in field work which zoologists, meteorologists and others possess.

A cruel comparison is with the man searching for religious relevation by performing the prescribed routines of an orthodox church. The scientist is a St. Paul who tries hard to fit Nature into his own pattern: he achieves revelation by ' kicking against the pricks '.

No doubt a form of emotional appreciation of environment, comparable in intensity with what is evoked by scientific analysis, can be gained by the geographer's form of criticism; my point here is that it is not scientific and is open to the dreadful consequences of error if rigorously applied in life. By it one does not come to know Nature's ways, but only becomes familiar with a bit of Nature.

In this connection the consequences of error must not be confused with the consequences of having to make decisions in ignorance. Often, indeed most of the time, we have to make decisions—that is to say, arrive at conclusions—without enough data to do it scientifically. The geographer's method might be described as the application of the methods of daily life—getting to know things, situations and people—to the material of geophysics and social science. But in this book we are concerned to discuss methods of formulating and treating problems which we can hope to solve in the scientific sense. Our aim is to develop our scientific knowledge of Nature's general properties so as to rely as little as possible on intuition or guessing when facing real problems and unfamiliar regions. We do not, like the geographers, begin by asking questions to which there may at present be no scientific answer.

But we all have to deal with the world through our own selves, in our own age and environment. Engineers can choose to tackle only problems they can hope to solve; weather forecasters have to solve problems formulated in fairly definite way but beyond their certain powers. They always try to make their methods more scientific, but have to rely upon indefinable skills, art, and experience. In practice the geographer's method has often served them well in the past. In natural aerodynamics we are in many ways at the mercy of Nature for we cannot completely choose our problems: it is desirable therefore that we should seek to know how far our difficulties are due to lack of mathematical skill, and how far to the essential nature of the problems. In the latter case it may often be a question of deciding how many coefficients we need to know before we can give a scientific, that is quantitative, answer. Each coefficient represents a process which we call physical, and which we think of as additional to the basic concepts of mechanics.

Dimensional analysis: numerical coefficients

In a mathematical problem we deduce the answer as a logical consequence, already hidden in the data. In a physical problem the procedure is the same but we use, where necessary, coefficients, which we measure. These coefficients possess dimensions. Viscosity, specific heat, various conductivities, are examples of such coefficients. Quantities such as density (volume coefficient of mass) with which we are more familiar in purely mathematical problems, are also physical coefficients. They are all expressible in terms of the ' basic ' units of *mass*, *length* and *time*; but any of these units can be replaced by another such as force, or energy, which at present is expressed in terms of the original three. As soon as a coefficient representing a physical process is brought into the argument it is possible that additional basic dimensions may be required. Heat is a form of energy; but if there is no interchange between the mechanical and thermal forms of energy, although they are composed from the same basic units, they remain distinct. It may then be necessary to express the conditions of our problem in terms of more than the basic three dimensions, *amount of heat* being a fourth.

At other times one of the basic dimensions may not be involved. Thus time is not involved in problems of statics such as bridge construction. Nature may force us to introduce it later when metal fatigue occurs but we can easily exclude it from discussion. If we can, largely by physical intuition, state what quantities determine the outcome of the problem, by a dimensional analysis we can say how they are combined in that outcome. This is because the dimensions of mass, length, and time are independent in these problems. Even if heat, or some other quantity with dimensions, is independent in a particular problem, we know that it is not actually independent. It may even be that mass, length, and time are not really independent and that it is only the nature of our particular problems that keeps them separate. So long as they remain separate we can proceed as in the following simple illustration.

If we have a simple pendulum we can set ourselves the problem, what is its period of oscillation? We only ask questions of this nature if we are certain that the answer is contained in the data. The question only makes sense on the assumption that the data is provided. The real problem here, as we shall see, is to provide the correct data. Kelvin once said that the essence of a problem is to reduce it to the form of a Mathematical Tripos question; that is to state it. If our physical intuition suggests that the period of the pendulum depends only upon its length, l, then we discover our error by noting that a time cannot be derived from a length. On thinking again we next suppose that the acceleration due to gravity, g, is also involved. This has dimensions Lt^{-2} ($L =$ length, $t =$ time) and we note immediately that when combined as $l^{\frac{1}{2}}g^{-\frac{1}{2}}$ a quantity whose units are time is produced. By supposing that the period τ is of the form

$$\tau \propto l^{\alpha}g^{\beta}$$

and stating that the two sides of this equation have the same units we quickly find that $\alpha = \frac{1}{2}$, $\beta = -\frac{1}{2}$ is the *only* solution.

The supposition that τ can be expressed as a function of l and g is the same as the supposition that l and g are the only (and all the) quantities which determine τ. The supposition that the form is as simple as $l^{\alpha}g^{\beta}$ is not arbitrary, but founded on the mathematical theorem that any mathematical function can be expressed as the sum of a series of terms such as $l^{\alpha}g^{\beta}$. If the form were more complicated each term of the series would have to have the same physical units and the analysis would reveal that a variety of values of α and β were possible. The variety would be infinite if the series representing the form were an infinite power series. Thus we might have supposed that the horizontal amplitude of swing of the pendulum, represented by the length a, also played a part in determining the period of oscillation. In that case we would write

$$\tau = l^{\alpha}g^{\beta}a^{\gamma}$$

and would conclude by equating the dimensions that

$$\alpha + \gamma = \tfrac{1}{2}, \quad \beta = -\tfrac{1}{2}.$$

Another way of expressing this is to say that

$$\tau = l^{\frac{1}{2}} g^{-\frac{1}{2}} f\left(\frac{l}{a}\right)$$

where f is an unknown function, which a full analysis using the laws of motion would reveal. By dimensional analysis we can only discover β. Since l/a is dimensionless so is $f(l/a)$.

We note here that the attributes of the pendulum so far discussed are its period, length and amplitude, and the field of gravity in which it swings. The first equation we derived can alternatively be expressed in the form

$$\frac{\tau}{l^{\frac{1}{2}} g^{-\frac{1}{2}}} = \text{constant.}$$

A full analysis, as given in most elementary books on mechanics, shows that the constant is 2π. This is a pure number, and our original statement can be rearranged as

$$F\left(\frac{\tau}{l^{\frac{1}{2}} g^{-\frac{1}{2}}}\right) = 0$$

where in this case the function F is $\frac{\tau}{l^{\frac{1}{2}} g^{-\frac{1}{2}}} - 2\pi$. $\tau / l^{\frac{1}{2}} g^{-\frac{1}{2}}$ is the *only* non-dimensional number which can be derived from τ, l, and g.

But in the second case the amplitude was also involved, and l/a was another non-dimensional number which could be derived from the data. We then deduced an equation which is equivalent to

$$\frac{\tau}{l^{\frac{1}{2}} g^{-\frac{1}{2}}} = f\left(\frac{l}{a}\right)$$

or

$$G\left(\frac{\tau}{l^{\frac{1}{2}} g^{-\frac{1}{2}}}, \ \frac{l}{a}\right) = 0$$

in which G is an unknown function of the two numbers $\tau l^{-\frac{1}{2}} g^{\frac{1}{2}}$ and

l/a. This last formulation simply says that *there exists* a function of the two independent non-dimensional numbers derivable from the data which is zero. Experiment or a complete theoretical analysis is required to discover the form of the function. The other non-dimensional number $\tau a^{-\frac{1}{2}} g^{\frac{1}{2}}$ is not independent of the first two and so a function of the three can always be reduced to a function of the two.

The general theorem of dimensional analysis, which is fairly evident by this line of argument, but for a proper proof of which we refer the reader to a book on the subject, is that if $A, B, C, \ldots$ are the independent non-dimensional numbers derivable from the conditions of the problem, then

$$F(A, B, C, \ldots) = 0$$

where F is a function which can be determined theoretically or by experiment.

This method is most useful when there is only one non-dimensional number for then

$$F(A) = 0$$

and so $A = $ constant.

A can then be measured by experiment. It is a numerical coefficient. For example the coefficient C in the equation on page 161 was measured by experiment, and can be applied to isolated thermals on any scale provided no new physical properties of Nature are involved (such as viscosity would be if the linear dimensions were very small).

If there are two non-dimensional numbers involved then we have to perform experiments to discover the relationship between them. For instance, we could discover the relationship between the drag coefficient and Reynolds number (see page 119) for a given shape of solid body in a viscous fluid. If three non-dimensional numbers are involved the problem becomes almost impossibly complicated, and we have to limit our researches into the cases where one or two of them do not matter. Thus in the convection of a thermal (page 161) we treated the case in which variations in Reynolds number did not matter, and variations in density were reduced to a small value. R was large and B was small compared with unity. In the case of large bubbles of air in water (pages 15 and 120) R was large and B was fixed at approximately unity.

When we say ' R was large ' we simply mean that it was large enough for the function of all the non-dimensional numbers to be unaffected by variations in it in this problem.   The form of the function must express this fact by containing terms which tend to a constant value as $R \rightarrow \infty$, such as $A_1 + A_2/R^2$.

Finally, some warnings about the use of this powerful method. It is necessary to make the *correct* suppositions about the physical nature of the problem.   Thus, we could, quite logically, suppose that the period of a pendulum was determined by a and g only.   We would then conclude that

$$\tau \propto a^{\frac{1}{2}}g^{-\frac{1}{2}}.$$

Experiments to determine the constant of proportionality would then reveal no constant, because in fact τ would not be proportional to $a^{\frac{1}{2}}$.   In supposing as we did at first, that τ was independent of a we had to be prepared for some restriction in a to be put on the system.   This restriction is either that a/l is small, or that the string must wind up on a particular cycloidal curve as the pendulum swings.   If we determine a constant, either experimentally or theoretically, we must be sure when applying it that no new physical condition possessing dimensions has been introduced.

We may find, in using dimensional analysis, that we have specified too many conditions.   Thus if we supposed that the mass m of a pendulum bob was involved in determining the period of oscillation together with gravity and the length of the string we would write

$$\tau \propto l^{\alpha}g^{\beta}m^{\delta}$$

and would conclude that $\alpha = \frac{1}{2}$, $\beta = -\frac{1}{2}$, $\delta = 0$.   This would tell us that the period was independent of the mass of the bob. The question arises whether this conclusion is correct or not. If we assume that a is involved we still find that $\delta = 0$ because m is the only quantity involving the dimension of mass.   We can conclude that the mass is unimportant so long as there are no other physical factors involving mass.   One such possible factor is the viscosity of the air μ, which is expressed in terms of force ($= \text{mass} \times \text{length} \times \text{time}^{-2}$) and shear ($= \text{time}^{-1}$), and so we need further investigation to tell whether m affects the period. Clearly the period would be lengthened if the pendulum were immersed in treacle.

It is evident, therefore, that physical insight into the nature of a problem is a most important requirement if we are to use dimensional analysis. This insight is born of observation and analytical thought.

A physical assessment of the factors controlling the motion must include an appreciation of which dimensions determine the motion and which are products of it. For example, in the problem of the isolated thermal there are two linear dimensions—the distance z from the virtual point origin of the thermal and its horizontal radius r. The ratio of these, z/r, we denote by n. Here n is a non-dimensional number which we had to determine by experiment, but it is determined by the same factors as C^2 the Froude number relating the buoyancy and inertia forces. n is another aspect of the same motion, and if we were able to make a complete analysis both C and n would be revealed by the one theory. n is not expressible as the ratio of two kinds of force.

Yet we found that n varied from one thermal to another in the experiments; C was also seen to vary and we found a relationship of the form $F(C, n) = 0$ (viz. $Cn^{\frac{1}{2}} = $ constant, page 166). Neither of the numbers varied over a wide range of values and the form of the relationship cannot be regarded as established. Indeed the variation in n is probably a fault of the experiments and is determined by the mechanism for releasing the thermal and slight motions in the fluids which were assumed to be at rest. Until we know how to control the value of n experimentally, or at least have some idea of the physical processes determining it, we either have to assume that in perfect experiments it would not vary or else grope for a relationship with C or any other non-dimensional number such as m (page 161).

Likewise the size of the orifice of a chimney making a plume can be used to form independent non-dimensional numbers. If we assume that the exit velocity and buoyancy are given, the diameter of the orifice determines the amount of gas emerging per second. It thus determines the strength of the source, and the magnitude of the velocities as a consequence. If the strength of the source were given it would clearly be one of the determining factors and to give the chimney width is simply a way of expressing it. Thus chimney width ÷ chimney height is a non-dimensional number relevant in the study of pollution strength at the ground. It is generally a small ratio and is only relevant because it is a measure of source strength; but it is also part of the geometry of the system if we are concerned with downwash (page 212) or if the chimney is very short and wide.

Dimensional analysis is a process of relating the physical quantities and dimensional coefficients by non-dimensional numerical coefficients. These have to be obtained either by a complete theory or by experiment, or a mixture of both, but we are most concerned to use this approach when we do experiments because it tells us how to arrange our results.

The method of small perturbations

Natural problems may be difficult to solve either because the motion is so complicated that we cannot specify it completely and cannot therefore use the ordinary equations, or because it is easy to specify but the equations, though simple to express, are too difficult to solve. The turbulent motions of thermals and plumes are of the first kind, and a complete description of them has not yet been attempted. Wave motions or oscillations are of the second kind (the pendulum being a special example). The equations describing the dynamical laws are fairly simple, but they are non-linear and usually have no known formal solutions. If the amplitude of the oscillations is assumed to be sufficiently small the terms in the equation involving the square of it are negligible in comparison with the linear terms, and if they are omitted the equations can often be formally solved. These solutions correspond with the case of small amplitude oscillations and are called *perturbation* solutions but they may happen to tell us many of the features of large oscillations.

From the point of view of dimensional analysis they are derived not simply from the assumption that the amplitude is small but that the amplitude does not affect the relationship between the other quantities involved. Thus we may study a particular form of airstream in which the static stability is represented by $g\beta$ and the undisturbed velocity by U (β has dimensions of length^{-1}). We find that, if the length of stationary waves, $2\pi/k$, can be correctly assumed to depend only on these two quantities, it must be given by

$$k^2 \propto g\beta/U^2$$

or

$$2\pi/k \propto U/(g\beta)^{\frac{1}{2}}.$$

This is confirmed by the complete analysis of the theory of small perturbations, but it is equally true for any amplitude, either for a fixed amplitude or if conditions are such that the wavelength does not depend upon amplitude. For instance, under these wider conditions the wavelength is proportional to wind speed. Many of the conclusions of small perturbation theory are thus applicable for special cases of large perturbations, but the value of the constants of proportionality may depend upon the amplitude, or upon any other quantity which might be varied.

Formulae for plume dispersion: the dangers of extrapolation

It is necessary to proceed with great care in using arguments such as these. For instance, if the concentration of pollution σ in a plume is to be computed, it may depend, if one type of force such as the buoyancy forces are dominant, only on the concentration σ_0 at height z_0 and the distance above the source z. We found (page 190) that for this case

$$\sigma \propto z^{-\frac{5}{3}}.$$

If we measure σ for two values of z, then the origin from which z is measured and the constant of proportionality can be determined, and we could compute σ for any other value of z. By analogy with the last section we might then argue that this relationship holds for any velocity of efflux of the plume, provided it is kept constant. But this would only be true if this velocity had the correct relationship to the buoyancy: if it were much too large then the plume would begin as a momentum jet (page 186) or if it were much too small it would behave at first as a converging non-turbulent jet (page 213) and neither of these obeys the above relationship between σ and z.

The buoyancy and velocity had to come into the computation of this relationship because of the physical nature of the motion in the plume under the influence of buoyancy, and the argument in effect said that if K is the Froude number relating the buoyancy forces to the inertia forces then

$$F(K) = 0$$

because no other non-dimensional number existed. In this case

$$K = \frac{W^2}{gBz}$$

The other condition used was that buoyancy was indestructible.

In all the simple cases we discussed in Chapter 8 we found that the inflow velocity, or the widening velocity, was proportional to the vertical velocity so that, even in a horizontal wind, the width was proportional to the height. (In the case of a plume widened by the stirring motions of the surrounding air Sutton argued that it would again widen along a cone, this time horizontal.) Bosanquet has derived formulae for the concentration in a plume making as one of his assumptions that the inflow velocity is proportional to the velocity of the plume relative to the surroundings. A difficulty then arises because the constant of proportionality may vary from one part of the plume to another, as it must if buoyancy gradually becomes more important and is later swamped by the motion of the environment.

If these problems are propounded in simple enough form so that only one Froude number is involved, we find that the concentration (or any other property of the plume) takes the form

$$\frac{\sigma}{\sigma_0} = \left(\frac{z}{z_0}\right)^{\alpha}$$

that is, as a power of a distance. It is tempting therefore to use similar expressions in more complicated problems in which there are more non-dimensional numbers involved, and to find by experiment not only the coefficient C but also the power α in the equation

$$\sigma = Cz^{\alpha}$$

If the problem is determinate then we must be able to compute α. It is interesting therefore to see what is involved in measuring α in a more complex problem.

If the effluent emerges with a large vertical velocity the concentration is given by (page 188)

$$\sigma^{-1} \propto z.$$

But higher up the buoyancy may be dominant, and so (page 190)

$$\sigma^{-1} \propto z^{\frac{5}{3}}$$

the origin of z being different in the two cases.   In the transition zone the plume would change from one form to the other and so by measurements we might obtain the points indicated in the diagram by the crosses.   The measured points might lie very close to a third curve represented by a different power law with a different origin of z, as indicated by the dotted line.   Beyond the limit of the measurements the curve $\sigma^{-1} \propto z^{\alpha}$ diverges from the true curve $\sigma^{-1} \propto z^{\frac{5}{3}}$.   It is therefore erroneous to *extrapolate* from observations using an empirical law if the relationship between the different forces is changing along the plume.   Extrapolation is only valid if the law has theoretical justification, and this one (represented by the dotted line) has none.   A theory would determine α without experiment.

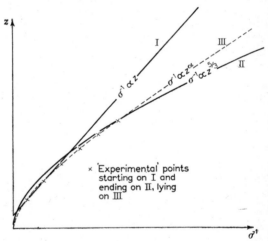

× 'Experimental' points starting on I and ending on II, lying on III

The sense in a question

Many problems we set ourselves are too difficult to solve by using our understanding of the processes at work to obtain a mathematical representation of the answer we seek.   We may wish to obtain a quantitative relationship between the yield of wheat and the application of a fertiliser. For problems of this kind a highly developed theory of mathematical statistics has been constructed. The philosophy behind this theory is both delightful and penetrating but, like dimensional analysis, it must be used with caution. It deals with uncertainties and propounds criteria for evaluating probabilities and the formulae and methods should not be used indiscriminately. It does not deal with questions of cause and effect except by inference, and it is in making the inference that the wisdom is required. The obvious source of error is in attributing a high degree of correlation to a cause and effect process. It is obvious that a correlation between the numbers of motor cars and television sets cannot be taken to imply that cars and television sets have any direct causal connection with one another. A more careful investigation would reveal this.

The presence of an inversion of temperature when mountain wave clouds are seen cannot be used to deduce that waves can *only* occur when there is an inversion even if no exceptions had yet been observed. The two phenomena—the inversion and the lenticular cloud—may be independently associated with one another in the absence of waves, and the waves may be an agency drawing the observer's attention to both simultaneously. Yet argument by correlation in observations—a kind of ' guilt by association '— is freely used the world over. It is not uncommon for a meteorologist to be asked ' What does that kind of cloud mean ? ' (meaning ' What does it tell us about tomorrow's weather ? '). And the behaviour of the flora and fauna, which is known to be influenced by the weather, is widely, but erroneously, supposed to have some significance for the future. A fact associated with the weather does not necessarily signify anything about another aspect of weather, such as its future.

In approaching problems of natural aerodynamics, therefore, we must be wary of ascribing causes, even if they seem reasonable, and highly correlated with the phenomena in question. In this book we have tried to foster the analytical approach whereby we first understand the physical processes at work and construct in our minds from them the behaviour we see in Nature. We have to be aware of all the forces and processes which might be at work if we are to be sure our explanations are correct, and we must beware of the temptation to try to explain everything. This means that we must not ask ourselves silly questions: and by ' silly ' is not meant ' easy ' or ' trivial ', but ' impossible '. There will always be an infinity of phenomena which we do not understand. Our task is to select from the complexity of Nature problems which we can solve.

Generally the procedure is not to pose problems, but to construct an ever-growing edifice of theory and knowledge which we call science, and as it grows we find that phenomena we have observed begin to fall into place. We tend to think as if we had posed a question and found an answer, whereas the question is seldom formulated properly until the answer is known. Seldom, because occasionally it is possible to see a sure way to an answer when it is simply a question of performing tedious and lengthy calculation: but in such cases the answer is logically contained in our knowledge at the time the question is framed. However, even then, there are usually interesting surprises waiting for us when the calculation is finished, and the answers to other questions which we did not pose may often be found.

Scientists investigate phenomena; they are ever curious, but that is not the same as proceeding by asking questions. It is a common fallacy that scientists are people who go about solving problems posed to them: engineers and technologists perform tasks, which is different. Scientists never know what they themselves are going to meet next, yet their work tends to make more certain and secure the ordinary events in the daily lives of others.

It is odd that this ignorance of the future should be the supreme experience of one whose success is derived from a belief in causation. Through the scientists man attains dominance over Nature; the scientist must await the caprice of her being. His experience of discovery is what we call relevation, and if he has a sense of mystery his emotion is what we call religious.

Problems and experiments for discussion

1. A bubble of air rising through water has a spherical cap. How would the cap of an oil bubble differ in shape if there were circulations within the oil? What would happen to a bubble of mercury released in water? (In what ways would it differ from a bucket of water emptied out of the window?)
2. If a glider can circle at a maximum rate of one turn in 30 sec and has a rate of sink of 1·5 m/sec, what would be the least magnitude of a discontinuity of wind velocity at which a pilot of perfect skill could maintain height by dynamic soaring? Would it be easier if the discontinuity were in a vertical plane than if it were horizontal?
3. According to Bernoulli's theorem the wind is greater where the pressure is less, therefore the wind increases with height. Comment.
4. Where can confluence and divergence occur simultaneously in the same place?
5. Why is a balloon filled with hydrogen less likely to be carried into contact with a very tall building than one filled with air at the same height? (The results of vertical motion to be ignored.)
6. In what circumstances could a ridge of high pressure move backwards against the wind at all heights? (In view of your answer, why is it often asserted (a) that pressure systems move with the wind at an upper level, (b) that they move with the thermal wind?)
7. Why do depressions form on the slow moving parts of cold fronts but on the fast moving parts of warm fronts? (R. C. Sutcliffe.)
8. Show that at a jet stream exit there is surface cyclogenesis on the left but on the right at a jet entrance. (R. C. Sutcliffe.) What does this second conclusion really mean when the jet entrance is *behind* a moving depression?
9. Under what circumstances would there be divergence at the ground from a centre of low pressure in the atmosphere?
10. Why is a tilted inversion also a wind discontinuity?
11. The geostrophic wind is along the isobars. Wind in circles round a centre of low pressure may or may not be geostrophic. Suggest circumstances for each case.
12. Show that at the point of intersection the sum of the rates of rotation of any two mutually perpendicular lines of fluid particles is the same for any such pair of lines through that point in the same plane.
13. Design a gramophone turntable which rotates at a constant angular velocity, which draws energy from the sinking of weights under gravity, and which has no moving parts other than the weights which can slide down grooves, and the turntable to which the grooves are fixed.

14. If silt were deposited where the flow in a river were slowest would it always accumulate on the outside of a river bend?

15. Where does blown sand collect behind a tree or post? Why is it scoured out on some corners?

16. Devise a method of turning about while standing on a frictionless horizontal turntable, without moving your feet from the turntable, and without making use of air resistance. Hence show how a cat can turn rightway up in mid-air if dropped from an upside down position (again no air resistance).

17. When the four condensation trails from a four-engined aircraft are observed from a distance at the ground why do the two most distant ones appear to merge with one another sooner than the two nearer ones? If the aircraft banked so that you viewed it directly (a) from underneath, (b) from the side, what would the trails appear to do?

18. Can an eternal universe in which hydrogen is continually created without velocity relative to its surroundings have any angular velocity?

19. A bowl of water is set in solid rotation. Show that, neglecting air resistance, a ping pong ball floating on the surface will move towards the centre. If it is now weighted so that it just does not float show that it will move away from the centre. (Sir Geoffrey Taylor.)

20. In 19, can you imagine a method of making a sphere which just does not float (a) not move outwards, (b) move inwards. (No forces may be applied in a direction towards the axis of rotation except those due to the fluid pressure.)

21. How many vortices can dance on the head of a pin?

22. If you were a tree desiring to catch cloud water droplets on your leaves, what kind of leaves would you try to grow? Does any tree grow the kind of leaves you imagine?

23. When a flag begins to flap in the wind is the pull on the rope supporting it increased? Has this any bearing on the swimming of (a) tadpoles, (b) plaice on the sea bed?

24. Try dropping large ball bearings into treacle or glycerine so as to make contact with (a) small ones previously dropped in, (b) air bubbles rising from the bottom. Is it theoretically possible to do either of these; if so what are the practical difficulties?

25. Why are there generally two vortices with horizontal axes to be seen in exhaust smoke behind a car? Under what circumstances could the circulations behind a moving car be (a) in the same direction as, (b) in the opposite direction to, those behind a stationary one?

26. If a circular basin is made to rotate with water in it initially at rest the fluid near the surface will begin to move towards the centre yet the surface will become hollowed there. If, when all the water is rotating with the basin, the basin is stopped the hollow centre begins to fill up yet the water at the surface begins to flow outwards. Why?

27. Why is accretion of tiny particles greatest but condensation of vapour not greatest near a forward stagnation point?

28. In the case of the figure on page 108 what would be the effect of placing a flat plate, extending beyond the edge of the table, above the air jet ?   What would be the force on the plate ?

29. In order to increase the velocity on the outside of the bend in the case of the air intake (into a gas turbine engine) which turns flow through 180°, the velocity on the inside could be reduced by making the air flow over pegs sticking out from the surface on the inside of the bend.   Would this provide a satisfactory answer to the snow accretion problem discussed on page 113 ?

30. How is the vorticity of a smoke ring induced in the air when the ring is made by a puff from an orifice ?   Could an orifice that would never produce rings be made ?

31. According to a well-known theorem, vorticity cannot be produced by moving the boundaries of an inviscid fluid.   Now take a circular vessel containing some water and place it on a horizontal surface: move it round in circles by holding it in your hand and sliding it on the surface, so that the vessel itself is neither rotated nor tipped, and so that a wave travels round it on the water surface.   Cause the waves to be kept going for a few seconds.   Now bring the vessel to rest and in some cases the water will be seen to be rotating as a whole. How has vorticity been imparted to it ?   And is not the vorticity in the opposite direction to that which would be produced by friction at the walls ?   (Try rolling a ball round the vessel: see which way it rotates.)   Why is it easier to impart vorticity to the water if the vessel has overhanging sides, as in a jug which tapers upwards or in a conical flask, than in a wide topped cup or bowl ?

32. What are the vortex lines near the walls of a stirred tea cup ?

33. Why should there be standing eddies at the edge of a wedge pointed into the wind only if a solid surface is placed in the plane of symmetry upwind of the edge of the wedge ?

34. Separation occurs when the boundary layer is thickening.   Why then does the point of separation move forward if the boundary layer is made thinner by an increased velocity ?

35. How does the Karman vortex street produce forward momentum in the wake of a cylinder and why does it make wires oscillate ?

36. Prove that if the eddies are small enough momentum is a strictly transferable quantity like heat.

37. How can condensation result in water transported by air not being a transferable quantity ?   Under what circumstances could the water evaporated from a large area of ocean be mostly accumulated in a small region ?

38. What is wrong with this argument ? In turbulent motion the eddies are oriented in a chaotic random manner.   Therefore for every one that is stretched there is another which is compressed, and for every smaller eddy that is produced a larger one is also created from the eddies of a given size.   There is on the average, therefore, no

transfer of kinetic energy from the large to the small eddies. If this argument is wrong can we deduce anything analogous to the second law of thermodynamics for inviscid fluids, composed of continuous indefinitely divisible matter, in turbulent motion?

39. Can there be any eddying motion not possessed of vorticity? If you think so does your definition of an eddy differ from the ordinary idea of one?

40. Why can eddies only extract energy from the mean motion when there exists mean shear? Is there an analogous theorem in the study of heat?

41. Express the Richardson number as the ratio of two types of force. Show that in a viscous boundary layer, where viscous forces are important, the Richardson number cannot be the only non-dimensional number involved in a criterion for the growth or onset of turbulence.

42. Prove that turbulence in a fluid without mean shear tends towards being isotropic.

43. Show that turbulence can produce layers of greater static stability in a stable air mass and regions of greater shear in a shearing air stream than existed before. How does this affect an assessment, from observations of the existence or non-existence of turbulence, of a critical value of the Richardson number for the occurrence of turbulence in the free air?

44. Why do trees withered by the wind assume an 'aerofoil' shape?

45. Why should separation at the top of a wind-facing cliff be less likely if convection is occurring than when it is not? Is it more likely if the cliff faces the sea than if it faces a plain?

46. For a given cross section area how could a shape which produces large viscous drag be efficient at catching airborne particles in the wind while when the form drag is large the efficiency may be small? Under what circumstances can large form drag go with large efficiency of catch?

47. A glider pilot finds that he can soar up a sunwarmed mountain side provided that he keeps within 30 or 40 m of the mountain. At greater distances he can find no updraught. Deduce that the air over the valley is stably stratified and getting warmer.

48. How does the subcloud layer affect the amount of (a) sunshine, (b) moonshine, in the plains of Spain?

49. If a plume is in the form of a vertical cone of angle 5° deduce that it must be in an upcurrent.

50. If convection on a sunny day reached up to 5000 m and apart from the convection there was no wind, what fraction of the solar energy could be extracted from some imaginary machines capable of extracting energy from the motion of the air within 100 m of the ground? Would they be less efficient than reflectors focusing the sunshine upon boilers or thermopiles?

51. Show that the mean streamlines up a vertical pure jet follow the curves $r \propto z^{\frac{1}{3}}$. Can the *mean* be plausibly defined so as to give a different result?

52. In heating a room how does the effect of the following apparatus with the same heat output differ? (*a*) a fan heater blowing warm air across the floor, (*b*) a convection heater with a small area high temperature source, (*c*) a convection heater with a large area low temperature source, (*d*) a system which blows warm air in near the ceiling and extracts it from floor level. Which would you avoid if you were allergic to (i) cold feet, (ii) draughts, (iii) hot head?

53. How many non-dimensional numbers can be constructed from the following factors controlling the velocity of sonic gravity waves: $g\beta$ in the stratosphere, $g\beta$ in the troposphere, c (velocity of sound) at the ground, c_w (velocity of the waves)?

54. Why are wave clouds more common in Greenland and South Georgia than in Venezuela?

55. Why does the wind blow uphill by day more often than downhill? (A. J. Whiten, from cycling experience.)

56. A radio sonde balloon ascends through waves: why will the period of oscillation of its vertical velocity generally decrease as it rises?

57. Why do condensation trails which enter the cores of the wingtip vortices last longer than trails which do not, on an occasion when none persists for more than a minute or two?

58. Why does rain generally fall in vertical streaks and not in horizontal sheets?

59. The air over a desert has a relative humidity of 10 per cent and the air over an oasis 50 per cent at a temperature of 30° C, at which the saturation mixing ratio is 28 g/kg. Show that the air over the oasis will rise unless the surrounding desert air is at least 1·5° C warmer.

60. A thermal reaches the subcloud layer, where the relative humidity of the surroundings is 50 per cent. The temperature is 7° C. The thermal is saturated. Show that it can penetrate the layer even if it has a temperature deficit of 0·3° C.

61. Why on earth are lee waves more likely to occur than on Mars where there are no clouds of condensation?

62. Show that if non-buoyant pollution is emitted with zero velocity into a steady horizontal wind, and the rate of dilution is proportional to the velocity relative to the surroundings and the surface area of the plume, that the radius of the plume is related to the distance from the source by the equation

$$r = \text{const.} \times y^{\frac{1}{3}}$$

approximately. Show that this is not true near the source where there is a large horizontal gradient of relative velocity.

63. How many non-dimensional numbers can be composed from the following data which are known to affect the dispersion of a plume ? Chimney height, distance downwind, height above ground, wind speed, efflux velocity, buoyancy at efflux, diameter of orifice. If in addition the wind shear and vertical temperature gradient affect the dispersion, how many more non-dimensional numbers can be obtained ? What if these quantities vary with height ? Is it humanly possible to produce a general formula for the concentration in a plume ?

64. Do you believe that exceptional or special astronomical events could take place (*a*) this year, (*b*) in your lifetime, (*c*) in recorded history, (*d*) ever ? If one were apparently observed would it be profitable to investigate it as if it were special ?

65. Could the universe be rotating ? If it were what could determine its angular velocity ? If its angular velocity cannot be deduced from its other attributes is it profitable to believe that it is other than zero ?

66. " *You'll find it's already stirred.*"

Reproduced by permission of PUNCH.

Books suggested for further reading:

Meteorology: Weather forecasting and weather control
'Further Outlook,' by F. H. Ludlam and R. S. Scorer (Allan Wingate)

Cloud forms
'Cloud Study,' by F. H. Ludlam and R. S. Scorer (John Murray)

Air pollution
'Air Pollution Handbook,' ed. P. L. Magill, F. R. Holden and C. Ackley (McGraw Hill)

Turbulence
'Atmospheric Turbulence,' by O. G. Sutton (Methuen)

Advanced treatment of dynamical meteorology
'Weather Analysis and Forecasting,' Vol. I, by S. Petterssen (McGraw-Hill)

Hydrodynamics: Theory and experimental techniques, particularly boundary layers and turbulence and engineering applications.
'Modern Developments in Fluid Dynamics,' ed. S. Goldstein (Clarendon Press)

Dimensional analysis: 'Physical Similarity and Dimensional Analysis,' by W. J. Duncan (Edward Arnold)

Journals which frequently publish relevant research papers:

Quarterly Journal of the Royal Meteorological Society
Journal of Fluid Mechanics (Cambridge University Press)
International Journal of Air Pollution (Pergamon Press)
Tellus (Svenska Geofysiska Foreningen)

INDEX